BIRD OF FIRE: A Tale of St. Francis of Assisi

Novels by Helen C. White

BIRD
OF
FIRE: *A Tale of St. Francis of Assisi*

ILB *by Helen C. White,* Constance *1896-*

The Macmillan Company : New York : 1958

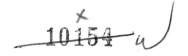
First Printing

Printed in the United States of America

Library of Congress catalog card number: 58–10473

1: A Bird Sang in a Wood

There was a burst of laughter, and a voice cried out, "That is the way all your tales begin, Francis Bernardone." But the other young noblemen bade the mocker be still and let the young cloth merchant go on with his tale. Now Francis tried to remember how it went. What happened when the young hero went into the wood after the bird? Did he go up on a mountain, following that teasing voice ever higher and higher until he came to . . . ? Or did he go into the darkness of the forest, deeper and deeper, into shadier and shadier thickets, until finally he came to a quiet clearing, and there he found . . . ?

Francis tossed on the bed. It was hard and it was hot. In that cold, bare stone room in Perugia, Francis' stories had been the light of those dark days. Indeed, it was because of the fame of his story-telling and his singing that the young nobles of the Assisian army had begged their Perugian captors to take the cloth merchant's son out of the dungeon deep below, where the commoners were held, and let him come up to their more spacious hall to brighten their captivity. How proud he had been, that far-away Francis of so many months ago! But what was the story which he had told? He could not remember it now. All he could remember was that a young man had heard a bird sing in a wood and had followed that bird.

A bird was singing now, outside his window, but this raucous sparrow chattering through the gray dawn was nothing like that bird of the tale in Perugia. This was the wakeful voice of reality, making impossible the sleep which, the doctors had told him, was his only chance. This was the fog in his throat; this was the weakness that had melted all the strength of his limbs. "Oh, noisy chatterer be still," the young man cried, starting up with a flash of his old energy. Curiously enough, the bird seemed for a moment to be silenced. Then Francis fell back weakly on his pillow—a gray little thing, no more than a ball of dust on a branch of the locust tree by his window, certainly not worth getting up to look at.

For with that curious intensity of these last weeks the things that were past and over forever were so often more vivid than the present. Francis' fevered thoughts went back to another moment in the great stronghold in Perugia. He and the other prisoners were looking out on the sunset, the only time the sun ever found the high window in their prison hall. They were grumbling that even then the light never quite reached through the battlements, and Francis guiltily remembered that in the dank dungeon underneath not even the feeble light of the setting sun ever seeped into that fetid darkness. So Francis had watched the single bird flying past the battlements, out to the hills beyond. He saw it vividly now, a drab gray creature, perhaps some sea gull that had come up the Tiber, looking for the sea among these barren hills. Francis remembered that bird now, as dreary a thing as the grumblers at his back in the hall at Perugia. He was almost ready to drop back to the stone window sill when he noticed that the bird had flown into the light. Suddenly it was a shining thing, the gray wings dazzling white. As it flew on, the flame of the sunset caught it, and it glowed, as if it were made wholly of fire and light, and Francis stepped down to ask one of the other men to take a look at the wonder. But when his companion had climbed up to his narrow perch, the bird had flown out of the light, and the man had only laughed and said, "It is your imagination, Francis, that turned the bird to flame."

There were other birds now outside his window, their flat voices pecking away at the fading darkness. There was a little breeze, too, fingering wistfully through the slim locust leaves. It would be another day soon, not a day two years back but a day in this weary spring of the year of our Lord 1204. It would not be a day of setting out to battle with the banners and the laughter, and the bright silks, and the shining of the sunlight on the shields and helms. Nor would it be a day of that strange battle madness when a fire that Francis had never known he harbored within his being had burst forth, and in the terror and the horror of the melée he had for a little exulted. It would not be that still moment, either, down by the River Tiber's edge when he had found his friend lying there half out of the bloodstained water, half on the trampled grass, and the whole world had stood still in a great calm, the calm of the dead. And, thank God, it would not be that dark thrust, that endless dragging over the old Roman bridge of St. John with the swords of the Perugians at their weary backs and their curses in their failing ears, the hunger gnawing at the fog of sleep dissolving their last strength. For that day had not been at all like the day of which one had heard so much in the tales of the old romancers. And yet even as they huddled, that sodden rabble, into the dungeon in brutal Perugia, Francis had known one thing, and that was the pride of a man who has, when the enemy beset his city, gone out and played a man's part. And this was the end of it, the end of all the old heroic dreams—this washed-out rag of a man, steaming in the stench of an invalid's straw. A bird sang in a wood, and something sharper even than the mockery of that old laughter filled the heart of the sick man.

But the birds were still now, and the gray day was sifting into the low-beamed room, picking out the familiar bulk of the old bridal chest which his mother had brought from Provence and bleaching out the tender watchfulness of the night light before the Madonna's picture. He must have slept for a moment then, for he was startled to hear the clanking of the shutters on the shop front below his window. He heard the familiar grumble of his father's voice, and then the too compliant "Yes, Father," of his brother Angelo. The rattling of the shutters ceased, and he could make out his father's voice grumbling now a little louder, "He was always frail."

And then his mother's soft voice, "No, it was that dreadful prison," and again Angelo's voice, a little warmer now, Francis noted gratefully, "But the doctor says he will be all right. You know he's letting him down today."

Francis had forgotten. Before his fears could take over, he swung his thin legs out of the bed and sat on the edge for a moment. It was true that the stitch no longer caught him in his side. He began to dress, a little feverishly. Then he heard his mother's voice behind him, "You'd better have your morning draught first. You remember what the doctor said." It was light enough now for him to see the Lady Pica's face, quiet as always, with that indefinable air of elegance about it which had long ago caught his father's eye. "You mustn't try too much," she said reproachfully, noting his hurried breathing. As he took the goblet from her hand, she stroked the dank hair from his forehead, "You've been through so much."

"Nonsense, Mother," he protested cheerfully. "Every young man in Assisi has been through no less, and some—" but he saw the old anxiety coming back into her face, and he lied gaily, "I'm as fresh as the spring breeze outside." And to prove it, he went quickly to the stairs.

But when he'd reached the shop below, he was not so sure. He caught at the nearest counter, and then, seeing the look of alarm on the face of Old Michael, the chief of his father's servants, he straightened up and defiantly let go of the support.

"You're down early," said the old man. "I'm afraid we were too noisy."

"Just enough to break into my gloomy thoughts."

"Ah, but twenty-three is no age for gloomy thoughts."

"You've forgotten, Michael," Francis laughed. "All of you old men forget how hard it is for us young blades to be as gay as you think we are."

And then at the bafflement on Old Michael's face Francis sobered. "You mustn't take sick-bed meditations as seriously as all that. You remember when the Devil was sick, the Devil a monk—" but Francis had caught sight of his face in the mirror that hung above the counter. It was startling to see those familiar features so pale. The large eyes which he got from his father looked even larger than usual, almost as large as his father's, he thought; not like his father's, bold and laughing, but with a queer shaded look about them, peering out from the cavern of his shrunken eye sockets. And the lower part of his face, the chin and the mouth with that delicacy that always embarrassed him with its look of his mother about it—he shrugged his shoulders wryly and turned to face his father.

"Well!" said Peter Bernardone, with that familiar assumption of boisterousness that was his common refuge from surprise. "So you think you can come back and help us?"

"Of course."

"But remember," said Angelo, his round face rosier than ever, "the Doctor said—"

"Nonsense, doctors are always spoiling things."

Then he turned to find his mother watching him. As briskly as he could, he went behind the counter. At that moment the door opened, and the mattress-maker, Bombarone, came in.

His solemn face lighted a little. "Oh, so you're back. I heard you were going to be laid up for a long time yet."

"No, the doctor was exaggerating as usual. But what can I do for you today?"

"It is not for me," said Bombarone proudly. "It is for my son Elias. He is being made a Master at Paris, and I am sending him the material for a new gown, a scarlet gown."

"Congratulations, neighbor," said the elder Bernardone, coming forward.

And then Francis caught the little tinge of envy in his voice. "Your Elias was always a student, with his Latin and his philosophy, not reading romances like my good-for-nothing here."

But the elder Bombarone, flattered into magnanimity, shook his head generously. "A lot of good Latin and philosophy would be here in our shops, neighbor."

The elder Bernardone smiled as he took down a piece of cloth. "Here is a handsome length of Flanders wool, with a dye that will see your son through to the doctorate."

"But," protested Francis, "that is a sober thing for a young scholar. Take a look at this piece of damask, Master Bombarone. It is fine enough for a bishop's gown. See"—as he held up the fabric—"how the pattern comes out of the shadows of the dye when the light falls on it. Candlelight or sunlight, it will be grand enough even for Elias."

The mattress-maker looked curiously at Francis as if he suspected a touch of irony, but when the latter held up the fabric for his inspection, he relaxed. "Ah, Francis, you are the best salesman I ever knew. You could persuade the birds to come down out of the trees and change their old feathers for new."

"A bird sang in a wood"—a cloth shop in Assisi was hardly adequate bourne for that magic song, and yet to Francis' convalescent eye it suddenly was fresh and wonderful. While he was ill, his father had had some new shelves put in, and the fresh smell of the wood—it was cedar—was still in the shop. And Peter had brought in some new fabrics that he had bought from the Greek merchants at the great fair in Champagne last fall. There was still a smell of camphor about them.

Now the familiar noise of the town was coming in: a cart rattling over the cobblestones, a servant sloshing water over stone steps, the cries of some peasants from the country, and presently the smell of oxen, and laughter and little squeals of excitement as a shepherd drove his flock down the narrow street. Life had gone on while he was ill. It was going on still. Francis looked back at the shelves. They were only half-full now, tier upon tier going up to the low ceiling, with the coarse canvas and the rough wool on the lower shelves, and higher up the linens and the fine wools and the silks. There would be money to spend. He could make a feast for his friends, and yet even as the thought came, he realized that there was no excitement in it.

"Here come some of your fine friends," his father's voice broke into his reflections. But for all the wonted irony in his rich voice, Francis saw the old flash of pride in his eye as the door opened, and two young men came in.

"Why it is you, Leo, and you, Martin!" he added as he caught sight of the heir of the Offreducci.

"Old Bombarone said you were about," the young nobleman hastened to explain; "I've waited all winter for you to choose me the stuff for my new robe. Now I'm in rags."

Francis looked up and caught the look of envy on his brother's face. "I will keep the shop now, Angelo," he said, "while you go in to Mother for your dinner." Then he turned to the two young men.

"Rags!" repeated the young heir of the Offreducci, lifting up his fashionable long sleeves that fell almost to the slim tips of his shoes. "Another month, and it will be falling off me."

Francis turned from the gay persiflage to look at the sober young man at Martin's side, who had not said a word. Now as Francis looked at him, he blushed a little, and then he forgot himself in his pleasure. "It is so good to have you back with us, Francis!"

"Thank you, Leo." For a moment Francis' eye lingered. How grave he was, this young Leo. Though he had been little past twenty at the time of the battle, when Francis was ill in prison, he had waited on him hand and foot; and yet it was only with the greatest difficulty that Francis could ever make him laugh. It was a curious thing, Francis thought: alone of all his friends, Leo made him feel old. The rest took what he so carelessly gave as a sharing of a common store, but Leo followed him around and looked to him almost as if he were his master. "What a queer thought," said Francis to himself, "for me, who have always laughed at all this master and student thing!" But even as he was thinking of Leo, Francis' eyes were scanning the shelves. Normally he would have known what color and texture to give to his friend as soon as he came in the door. But he was rusty now on the files of the shelves. "I think it will be this green," he said, signalling to Old Michael to reach down a folded piece of cloth. Then he opened it and held out an edge to the young Offreducci. But the latter only laughed.

"You know perfectly well, Francis, I shall take it. For if I do not, you will give it to the next man, and then at the first banquet I shall see him shining in it and kick myself for being such a fool as not to take your advice."

"What a poor merchant you make me out," laughed Francis, "to say that I'd just take the same piece of goods and palm it off on the next one who comes into the store."

"Not you," said the young Martin, and then he leaned over the counter. "But what I don't understand is the way in which you can guess how the robe will look when it is finished, so that years later a man will still be hearing his friends saying it is just the right color and the right texture for him."

"Ah, that," said Francis lightly, "is the gift of the imagination."

"Imagination!" snorted his father. And then, seeing the young nobleman draw back, he rubbed his hands. "It doesn't matter what you call it so long as our customers are satisfied." The young heir of the Offreducci laughed. Only Leo stood there with that curious solemnity in his singularly pure face. Perhaps it is because he is so young, thought Francis.

"Whatever it is," said the young Offreducci, "when the new robe is done, I shall have a feast in its honor, and you will come and make me a song, Francis, on my fine green gown."

As the young Offreducci started for the door, he hesitated. "By the way, speaking of singing, a party of us are going up the hill to sing in honor of your friend Matthew's marriage. Will you not come with us?"

But as Francis was ready to take up the merry challenge, there came a little stab in his side, and he knew he was tired. "Not just yet," he said, with a smile. "Give me a day or two more."

"We shall miss you, and the bride most of all," laughed Martin. But as Leo turned to follow his friend, he looked back anxiously, "May I come to see you this evening when the shop is closed?"

Francis' first thought was that he was too weary for his young friend's adoration, but at the look of disappointment on Leo's face, his habitual kindness rebuked him. "Of course, you can come and sit by my bed," he said.

"Imagination!" said his father when the shop was empty again. "And yet, I suppose that is what makes you the best merchant here."

"How drearily you talk, Father," said Francis, "as if I were already middle-aged."

But when the shop was shut that night and Francis had crawled back into bed, he thought "middle-aged" was right enough. His strength was coming back, but there was something else. . . . At that moment there came a rattle of laughter down the street, and the sound of many footsteps on the cobblestones—not the heavily shod feet of the shepherds or of the peasants, but lighter, finer leather. Then came a burst of song. It was his friends, he recognized with a pang. They were singing one of his own songs, too. Slowly and stiffly, he crept out of bed and looked down into the darkened street, and watched the torches guttering in the evening breeze. Somebody must have seen his shadow against the candlelight because there was a glad cry from the street. But Francis only shook his head, and after a moment's lingering, they went on. At his back he heard his father's voice grumbling, "They are noisy enough, those fine friends of yours, but they throw their money around generously, too. And I must say that normally you keep up with them." A little note of indulgence had come into the grumbling, and Francis knew he was smiling.

So he protested gaily enough, "But today, I've only been making money. I'm not spending any."

"True," said his father, "it has been better business today than any day since you were ill. But, whoa! What is this?" as he caught sight of Leo in the doorway. "Are you quite sure, Francis?" There was concern in his voice.

"Yes," said Francis. "Come in, Leo, and sit on the chest where I can see you, though I think I do you wrong to let you come and sit up here with me so drearily. You ought to be out singing with the others."

"But you know, Francis—"

"Yes, I know. But I am still too old for you to be spending the evening here with me."

"Old?" said Leo, and for the first time that day he smiled.

"Old," said Francis firmly, and then more gently, "Tell me, Leo, what have you been doing all these weeks?"

But Francis was hardly listening. It was not just that he was tired. A bird sang in the wood, and the young hero of the romance went out to look for him. It was not that he found in the wood only a cloth shop, or perhaps nothing at all. It was, rather, that he could not any longer hear the bird's song. He was like that bird in Perugia that flamed in the sunset and then flew out into nothingness. It was within himself that the singing had ceased, and the wonder, and all was empty. He made no protest when Leo took his leave, soon after, nor when his mother came and took the candles away. He was spent.

2

But there was little time for Francis to sit staring at the emptiness within. Normally, the summer was not the busiest season in the cloth shop, but this year it seemed that a never-ending stream of Francis' friends came in to visit and to buy at least one piece of cloth before they went out again. Then there were all the celebrations that followed, the feasts, and revels, and serenades in the soft evenings. There were parties along the river and out into the little country towns in the mountains, and finally there was all the bustle of making ready for his father's trip to the great silk fair in Provence at the end of the summer. All in all, there was little time for Francis to look inside.

Only when the thin fingers of the locust leaves were scuttering down the cobblestones of the street outside and the first word had come that Peter Bernardone had been seen coming with high-piled pack mules through the Saint Bernard Pass did Francis remember the weakness of his convalescence and wonder if his father would still look worried when he saw him. But when Peter came to the door with his first look, as always, for his eldest son, Francis knew from the way his father's face lighted that he was pleased with what he saw.

"How brown you are, my little Frenchman!" he exclaimed. "And even if it is thin, it is real bone there," he said, as he patted his shoulder. And then as he looked from Angelo to the cloth shelves around the shop, he cried out in admiration, "Why the shelves are empty! What a summer you've had!" And then with a mocking roughness, "That is, if you've not spent all the profit on some new folly."

"He has really spent very little," said Pica.

How like her, thought Francis, to have stood there in the doorway in the back of the shop, waiting until her husband should have greeted his sons and looked around his store. And then as her face lighted and her husband's arms came around her, Francis thought again how little justice he did his father. And yet, as Peter looked away from his wife— "How well you have done without me!"—did he a little resent the unfailing efficiency of this quiet woman, who seemed always to be watching the accomplishments of others without any thought that anybody might watch what she was doing?

The door opened, and one of the consuls of the Commune came in, a curiously wry fellow with a meagre mouth and a thin nose, who always chose the brightest and the richest of garments. Now he came ruffling in. "I've just heard you're back, and I want the first look, Bernardone," he said, putting his thin hand with its heavy agate ring on the brown bale on the counter.

"How well you know, my lord," said the cloth merchant, "that I always bring my best stuff with me. I have some brocades which the Greeks brought from Constantinople." As he deftly slit the cords around the canvas cover, Bernardone smiled proudly. "Here is one—" but there was laughter as he lifted a very soft blue damask from the roll. "Oh, this," he said, recovering quickly, "this will do for your bride, Francis. And time enough it is that you produced her for us."

But before Francis could think of some light retort, the Lady Pica had stepped into the breach. "It is just the right color for a new robe for the Madonna in Santa Maria Maggiore. Her robe is dusty enough."

Bernardone shrugged his shoulders. "Bride or Madonna, here it is," he said, throwing it into Pica's outstretched arms. "This red, here, this you may have, Francis, for your good storekeeping." This time Bernardone did not throw the folded cloth but spread it out so that it hung down over the counter; and Francis saw that deep purple tones shimmered where the pattern was raised by the light.

"It is beautiful enough for the Bishop," said Francis in awe.

The consul agreed. "It would make a fine gift."

But Bernardone shook his head and squared his broad shoulders, and for a moment he looked like the stalwart peasant that he had been before he became the richest merchant in Assisi. "It is fine enough for my son," he said. The consul laughed a dry papery laugh, and Francis, rummaging among the rich fabrics, pulled out a deep saffron-gold brocade and held it out for the older man's inspection.

not only his cloth but the horse, too. Stuffing his purse with silver and gold coins, he started to walk back to San Damiano.

But now it seemed, as it had on the day when he went down to the leper hospital of San Lazzaro, that his feet had been given wings so that they scarcely touched the muddy earth. And full of the pride of the knight who has accomplished his lord's quest, he even sang a little French song of the triumphant knight coming back from battle, which he had heard his mother sing when he was a child. For the whole way he kept on singing in a low voice to himself. Only when he was alone now and then in a wood of ilex or of hemlock did he allow his voice to rise, and then it seemed to him as if the whole creation were echoing his triumph. But not once did he think of his father.

The evening had come when he reached San Damiano again, and the old priest, Father Nicholas, had gone into his shack, and over a charcoal brazier by the guttering light of a single candle he was stirring a little mush for his evening meal. Then he took the candle, shielding it against the still sharp wind, and went into the old church. As he set his candle on the altar, Francis called to him from the doorway so as not to frighten him and came down and flung himself upon his knees and put the knotted leathern purse full of silver and gold into his hand. The old priest had greeted Francis with absent-minded surprise, but when he saw the glint of the gold and the silver in the candlelight, there was no mistaking his shock and his fear. Now there was nothing vague in the clear voice with which he challenged Francis, "Where did you get that money?"

"It is not stolen," laughed Francis. "I took some cloth from my father's shop, and I sold it in the cloth market at Foligno. It was a good day's marketing. Take it, Father, to rebuild the church."

"But it belongs to your father," said the old priest stubbornly.

"He has given me many times this for all the follies of my youth," said Francis, "and this for the service of God he can hardly deny me."

But the priest, knotting the purse again, forced it back into Francis' hands. "He will tell the Bishop I have stolen it."

Francis took the purse and contemptuously flung it into a corner of the sanctuary, and as he saw the anxiety with which the old man's eyes followed the bag into the dark, the face of his father came before him again. "He is not such a fool as the Patarin thought," said Francis ruefully. Then he turned to the priest. "I am hungry, Father. Let me stay with you tonight."

Relieved at Francis' seeming acquiescence, the old priest gave what was left of the bowl of gruel to the hungry young man and made a bed for him in the straw in a corner of his hut. As Francis fell asleep in the stale, cramped little room, he thought wistfully of the sweet-smelling mattress in his spacious bedchamber at home, and then he wondered remotely what his father would do when he heard.

In the morning, after an uncomfortable night's sleep, Francis awoke to a world out of which the light had faded. There was no music in his heart nor any song upon his lips. With scarcely a word the old priest went into the church and spread a strip of tattered linen upon the altar and, with Francis to make the responses, said Mass. Then he went over and picked up the purse, and before Francis could ask him what he was doing, he went up the road to Assisi. But Francis did not have to wait for the old priest's return to know of his father's wrath, for by noon Old Michael had come down the hill to warn Francis that his father had sworn that if he could lay hands upon that madman he would chain him in the cellar beneath the shop until he came to his senses. As the old man talked, it seemed to Francis that a great chasm opened at his feet, and however stoutly he looked across it, he could not see the other side or make out anything but the thunder of his father's wrath across that deepening abyss. So when the old priest came back, dusting his hands with relief, Francis begged him for refuge.

"I think you had better stay here," Nicholas said dryly. And so Francis had set about cleaning up the old church, chinking up the cracks with mud, and putting back stones that had fallen. It was mere puttering compared with what he had dreamed of doing, but it gave him time to collect his scattered wits. Now and then as he worked, he would look up at the figure hanging above the altar, but no voice spoke within him. Suddenly Francis thought, "How like children we are, tugging at our mother's skirts, thinking only of our need and never of the weariness that may lie behind the glance that rules our days." He thought of the great Innocent in Rome and how his eyes had seemed to grope above the heads of the praying throng, and then he began to think of Christ, and of all the centuries that had gone by since His Passion. Then he went on to think of the suffering of the human garment in which divine wisdom had garbed itself, and he wondered if the foreknowledge of all the myriads for whom this sacrifice would be in vain had not deepened the pain of that more than human suffering.

"I have thought too little of all this," he said one day, kneeling down and looking up at the sad old face. "I have thought too little of anything," he added presently, and for the first time in his life, desiring that he might enter into the mystery of that Passion, he knew that he was unworthy so much as even to think of it.

Other visitors came, too. And of these the first was Leo, who, characteristically, said little but that all of Assisi talked of the wrath of Peter Bernardone.

"And what do they say of his son?"

Leo would not answer that question, however Francis pressed him. But the younger Bernardone was not long left in doubt, for a couple of weeks after he had been hiding out at San Damiano, his brother Angelo came up to see him, and he lost no time in telling his brother roundly that the common opinion was that the elder son of Peter Bernardone had been driven mad at last by his fantasies. Indeed, there were not even wanting those who said that old Peter was right when he swore that the fool was possessed.

"And you?" asked Francis coldly.

"There is no hope," said Angelo, "if you can even ask that question." And he turned and went back.

Francis asked the priest of San Damiano if he thought he were mad, and the old man smiled and said that in a long life he had seen a great many kinds of folly, and it did not seem to him that Francis was more mad than many another. But when he asked him what he should do about his father, Nicholas shut his eyes. "He is your father"—and that was all he would say.

"It is all he can say," said Leo when he next came up with a little present of food from the Lady Pica for her son. "After all, it will go hard with him if your father tells the Bishop that he is encouraging your rebellion against his authority."

"What will my father do if I come back? Have you thought of that?" asked Francis.

"Yes," said Leo. "He has sworn that he will chain you up like a mad dog."

"I don't know about the mad dog part of it," said Francis, standing outside the church with Leo and looking up the road to the city. "But fear of him has chained me here as firmly as any iron could do. Even the lepers shrink away when I come down to see them."

"It is odd that men should think cleaning out a leper hospital saner than rebuilding a church," mused Leo.

But Francis did not hear him. Skulking in a ruined church was no way for a knight to be serving his lord, and if he could not face his father, whom should he face in this world that he had thought to take by storm? So when he had been there for some weeks, Francis took leave of the old priest Nicholas and with the promise of his prayers went back to Assisi. Characteristically he had thought of nobody but his father as he started out. But the first pair of boys he met out looking for birds' nests along the road reminded him of what he faced. They took one look at him, and then screaming, "The madman of San Damiano!" they took to their heels.

Francis only strode the faster. There was nothing winged about this return. It was on stony enough ground that he trod, and it was resolution alone that froze his face and kept his eyes straight on the way ahead so that only from time to time did he hear shocked cries of alarm, or bursts of laughter, or, once, the sharp cut of a stone. By the time he reached the quarter of his father's shop a veritable mob had gathered at his heels, and everywhere over his head shutters were rattling, and all Assisi seemed to be coming out on its balconies. But when they reached the door of his father's shop, they all fell back so that he stood alone in the doorway.

Peter Bernardone was busy with a customer, measuring out a scarlet cloth as bright as the brocade that he had given for his son's crusading. Then as the whole shop quieted, Peter looked up. He stood transfixed as he contemplated the gray, dusty little figure standing in the doorway. Francis stretched out his hands, but his father came around the counter with a shout and fell upon him, beating him with tightly clenched fists. He was not much taller than his son, but he had always been broad and stocky like the Umbrian peasant he was. Now he flung himself upon the frail figure of his son as if he would beat the center of his disappointment out of existence. Francis stood without moving. He made no protest either, when his father dragged him down into the cellar and, calling a couple of his servants to him, tied him up with a chain and stapled the chain around one of the supporting wooden pillars. It was dark, and there was the sound of water dripping, and the stench of old stone rotting and straw falling into slime. As Francis fell to his knees and tried to bring his manacled hands together, he thought, "This is what I prayed for."

4

In the middle of the night when the distracted household had at last quieted, the Lady Pica came down into the cellar, as Francis had known she would. The maid carrying the lighted taper for her brought bread and meat and fresh linen, but she herself carried the ointment and wine. As she washed away the grime and blood, she murmured soothing words as if to a child. And when she saw that the hurt was no worse, she began to hum a little tune to herself. Characteristically, she said nothing of the source of her son's trouble and nothing of the division with his father. As she sat there on the floor, watching her son eat, it was as if there were nobody else in the world but those two in the little halo of candlelight.

And then Francis saw that waiting look in her eyes, that look with which he had become so familiar of late in the eyes of Leo, and he shrugged his shoulders, and taking her hand in his, he said simply, "If I could tell you, Mother, I would; but I simply do not know what to say."

Then the Lady Pica rose and kissed her son and bade him sleep as if he were a child who had overplayed himself, and in the morning all things would be right again.

But in the morning Peter Bernardone came down to see what a night would have done to his mad son, and finding it all tidy about him, and the mad son kneeling praying, Peter Bernardone stumbled up the stairs in his wrath and went to find the Lady Pica, quietly sorting linen with her maid.

"No wonder my son scoffs at my authority when my wife has no respect!"

"I would not have left a dog untended in that dungeon of yours." She drew herself up to her still slim height. And as Peter began to storm about being master in his own house, she coolly reminded him that only he who could master himself could hope to claim the respect of others. As his face whitened with anger, she turned calmly back to her work, and the unanswerable defiance sent Peter stumbling sputtering to the door. At first he found some relief in cursing his lot and calling down the wrath of heaven on all ungrateful sons and fools of wives who put romantic nonsense into their heads. But when toward noon he suddenly noticed that the shop was filled with open mouths and bulging eyes, he flung a bolt of cloth at them, shouting, "Go to hell, the pack of you!"

It was at that moment that the Lady Pica came in to remind him that he had an engagement now of some weeks' standing to go over and look at a barn full of prize fleeces beyond Foligno.

"Foligno!" he snorted, but he went and made ready just the same.

That evening when there was no possibility of any absent-minded return, and the darkness was falling over a curious world, the Lady Pica went down to the cellar and released her son.

"I suppose you don't want a horse," she said.

"No."

"Then," said she, "here is a basket of bread and wine. And you may tell the old priest that the linen is of my weaving, and he may wear it without fear." And she blessed him.

"I am still at the end of my father's chain," said Francis to himself as he walked slowly through the city streets. But the night air was cool and sweet. "It is a longer rope, anyway," he said to himself, and he hurried before any late revellers should discover the madman.

It was well that Francis was taking the way down the hill to San Damiano, for that night there was not much sympathy for him in Assisi. The solid merchants of the town shook their heads over their night draughts, "A thief for a son! A poor end of all Peter's boastings." This was what came of marrying above one's class, and romantic dreams were a poor substitute for grandchildren creeping under the counter. But in some of the high towers Francis' old friends laughed over a heavier draught. "What mudheads these merchants are!" said the young heir of the Offreducci. "The brightest spirit in Assisi, mad or sane, and nothing better to do with him than chain him in his cellar!" Only Leo knelt with hot eyes, looking at an old crucifix in the family chapel. His father was dead and his mother, too, and his uncle the Canon always dismissed him with a little sermon on the temptations of youth. And the Lady Clare, too, who had heard of Francis' madness from her brother, knelt before a picture of Our Lady and weeping bade her have mercy on all of them. So Assisi laughed or wept or mused over Francis that night as he trudged thoughtfully down the road to San Damiano.

Only in a little room in the Benedictine abbey high on the western slopes of Monte Subasio was anything like a calm consideration of the day's happenings attempted. There in the Abbot Simon's lodging,

Guido, the Bishop of Assisi, was having a little late supper with the Abbot, and an old friend of the latter, Ugolino del Conti, the Cardinal of Ostia, who had come for a couple of days of rest before he should report to the Pope on his last mission to Germany. After the great issues he saw no way of solving, it was restful to the great diplomat to toy for a moment with this village tempest in a teapot. Such a fuss over a mad son stashed in his father's cellar!

"He really isn't mad," said the Abbot, a tall man with a kind of hoarfrost freshness about him and an easy firmness in mouth and gesture.

"No, there is nothing that you, my Lord Abbot, could not soon put right up here." Bishop Guido was obviously blaming himself for this disorder in his vineyard, and with his simple practicality he had spent the day alternately praying and trying to think of some solution for what was growing into a scandal.

"Well, then, that is settled," said the Cardinal of Ostia lightly, the delicate shadows on his face blurring a little with amusement. "If only one could send the Emperor to a Benedictine monastery!"

But his friend the Abbot seemed less sure. "I really don't know," he said holding up the clear glass between his fingers to look at the pale golden wine of the abbey, gleaming in the candlelight. The brothers who attended his table sometimes laughed that that was all the good he ever got of the wine they poured into his cup for supper. Then he remembered his duty as a host. "Your glass is empty, my lord."

"No more," said the Cardinal, putting his hand with its heavy ring over the top of the glass. "My head is fuzzy enough already." It was his profession to make the wise laugh and then snap back their minds to the business at hand; so now when the laughter quieted, he asked, "What makes you so doubtful of your prospects with this young man?"

"It's just," said the Abbot thoughtfully, "that I don't think he belongs here."

"The Benedictine Order is losing its grip," smiled the Cardinal, "if it admits there is any man whom it cannot save."

"It isn't a matter of saving; it's rather a matter of not spoiling. There is a fire in that young man."

"But fires banked—" began the Cardinal of Ostia.

"It is not that," said the Abbot. "What I am afraid of is putting it out."

The Bishop stared open-mouthed, but the Cardinal of Ostia nodded. "Would to God more abbots remembered that."

"But he does need guidance and direction," said the Bishop firmly. "He's all imagination and impulse. There's nothing wrong with imagination—for a young man," the Bishop qualified his admission, and added justly, "and the impulses are all generous."

"He lacks direction, then," said the Cardinal.

"No," said the Bishop. "I don't think he knows himself at all. From the time he was a small child he has had the most winning way, and I don't think he's ever been at all conscious of it."

"That is remarkable," said the Cardinal.

"He is a remarkable man," said the Abbot.

"To everybody but his father, I take it." There was a smile at the Cardinal's exception.

"Oh," said Guido, obviously striving to be just, "his father is a good enough man, no greedier than most of his class, and generous enough. He never made any real difficulty with what his son spent for all a young man's follies."

The Cardinal raised his brows half-seriously, "All?"

"No," said the Bishop, suddenly looking a little surprised. "It was clothes and song, but I never heard of anything arrogant or vicious about him. Only"—the Bishop groped for the word, and the Cardinal of Ostia, whose level glance had made many a much greater doctor back up and weigh his words, waited. "I don't think that Francis knows yet quite what is in him. Take this talking crucifix down at San Damiano—"

It was the Abbot's turn now to look concerned. "You know how it is, my Lord Cardinal; the old superstitions die hard in these hills, and the peasants make a miracle of anything."

"Tell me about it," said Ugolino. "I hear a lot of talk in my days, and some talk from a crucifix would be a welcome change."

"Oh, it isn't much—" the Bishop shook his head. "They say that the Christ on the crucifix leaned down over Francis and said to him, 'Rebuild my Church.' "

In an instant the benign indulgence in the Cardinal's majestic figure sharpened. "That sounds like what the Patarins are saying."

The Bishop hastened to reassure him, "He's no heretic."

"No," said the Abbot. "The things the heretics talk about don't interest him. He was never much of a student, though his schoolmaster still says that he had the quickest mind of any boy he ever taught."

"No," said the Bishop, his gaze relaxing a little as if a distant figure described in a mountain pass were coming into reach of identification. "He did not take it in any such big way. He thought all it meant was to rebuild the little chapel down there. It's a very little chapel, my lord, really nothing more than an oratory," he added, as if apologizing for the time they had taken of the great Cardinal of Ostia.

"He's quite right," the Abbot nodded. And Ugolino looked at the Bishop with new respect. "He is a simple fellow," he thought, "but if ever I could get him to understand what some of those tangles of mine are about, I would get a clearer answer from him than I do from Rome or Paris." Aloud, he said only, "Perhaps we think too much about the big church and not enough about the little churches."

"I have thought of that, too," said the Abbot. "Without the big church, it falls apart into the confusion of the heretics; but without the little churches, what are we going to do with all of them down there?" He went to the window. The moon had come out, and the light lay white on the tile roofs of Assisi, rising like steps below them.

"It is under those roofs that you would like to do something, isn't it, my lord?" said the Cardinal gently.

"Yes, and I doubt if Saint Benedict himself would know how to do it."

"But if not he," asked the Cardinal, "who then?"

"I have wondered sometimes if Francis might not be able to do something about it."

The lower jaw of the Bishop of Assisi's generous mouth dropped, but the Abbot was the busy host now. "Let me take you to your lodging, my lord," he said, "and you, my lord, too," to the Bishop of Assisi.

But the Bishop of Assisi shook his head. "I like to go through the streets when they are quiet. I suppose it is the way a mother feels when she looks upon her children all quiet and asleep after the day's brawling."

As the Bishop of Assisi made his way down the moon-whitened paths, Francis crept into the little hut of the priest of San Damiano.

"What are you going to do now?" he asked when he discovered his guest in the morning.

"I'm going to rebuild San Damiano." Francis had eaten some of his mother's good bread and he had drunk a little of the wine, standing in the doorway and sniffing the hemlock-sweet air. He felt his strength returning to him.

"With what?" asked the old priest in alarm.

"With the stones which the passers-by will give me."

"But so few pass by here."

"Never mind," said Francis cheerfully. "God will send them."

And God did. Some of them were townspeople out on their errands into the plain. Francis held out his hands to them, "Give me a stone for San Damiano," he begged. Some of them, laughingly, went and picked up stones by the road and, dusting them off, with mock solemnity handed them to Francis, who bowed solemnly and said, "In the name of God and San Damiano and Our Lady, I accept it." It was curious to see how, at that blessing, the jest lost its flavor, and more than one fumbled in his purse and put a coin on the stone. Presently some of Francis' old friends came riding along and asked cheerfully how the madman of San Damiano was doing and would the crucifix talk for them if they made a large enough gift. And Francis, smiling, promised them that if they made a really large enough gift the crucifix would speak in them. Some of them laughed at this; some looked uncomfortable. One or two muttered, "It sounds like the Patarins to me." But most of them sheepishly gave Francis a coin or two and rode off a little damply back to town.

And so it went until one day a group of ladies came riding down the hill with a squire or two in attendance. They were dressed in all their spring finery as if riding to some wedding, and their laughter was like music above the old stones. They looked curiously at Francis, standing with outstretched hand and crying, "My ladies, a stone for San Damiano and Christ and His Blessed Mother!"

"It is a big prayer for a little church," said the eldest of the ladies, who rode at the head of the little troop. For a moment Francis' eye rested with delight on the fresh colors of their long gowns—peach, soft green, and that bright yellow of the jonquils. So Flora and her nymphs must have looked when the ancient mythologists saw them.

"But not too great a prayer for a great lady," said Francis bowing. The lady laughed and took from her woman's silken purse a silver coin and held it out to him, and all the ladies followed. Then they rode on, laughing together, their laughter sweet as the sound of the bells on their palfreys. Only the last of the ladies paused. It seemed to him that in that moment's graciousness she was the fairest of all—slim and pale in her green gown with a white veil over her golden hair. Then as she leaned toward him, he saw with astonishment that it was the Lady Clare, the unknown bride of that night so long ago at the house of the Offreducci. He stood still as before a dream that had come into the daylight. She looked at him, and he thought she was about to speak, but at that moment one of her companions called gaily to her, "Come, Clare. This is one beggar who does not need you." And Francis heard the snort of the curled and silk-bedecked youth who had ridden up to her side, "Beggar!" He saw the flush, like the flush on the throat of an amaryllis lily, on the slim neck of the Lady Clare as she bent over and put her coin in his hand. Then she turned and rode away, and her escort spat one word at Francis, "Hypocrite," and rode off, leaving him staring at the dust.

The old priest Nicholas roused him. "If you want your stones now, you certainly have silver enough to buy them."

As from a long distance Francis turned and looked at him. "Yes," he said, "I will go up to the stonemason's."

"No," said the old priest with a surprising access of energy. "Your father will hear of it; but if I go, he can hardly complain."

But the old priest was quite wrong, for the next night the stonemason at supper told his wife of the sudden wealth at San Damiano and of the cartload of fresh golden stone which he had promised for the morrow. And the next morning before his wife could visit any of her neighbors, the stonemason and his men loaded the cart and sent it down the road to San Damiano. By high noon the gossip had reached the shop of Peter Bernardone—"A whole cartload of stone for San Damiano! The old priest paid for it in silver."

"Whose silver?" roared Peter Bernardone.

"He has been begging by the wayside," said the Lady Pica.

"Hypocrite!" Peter Bernardone cursed his son. "Who would give a madman in the gutter silver coins like that?"

And the cloth merchant sent his servants around to some of his oldest friends, bidding them bring staves and their stoutest servants to take a madman. Some answered the summons because they wanted to see the excitement; others because they were standing by a sorely tried fellow merchant; and some because they thought that the world was coming to a pretty pass when young men defied their fathers like this. Only before they started, the Lady Pica faced her husband with all his comrades.

"Peter Bernardone," she said, "if you lay a hand upon my son, I will ask every drop of blood from you!"

There was a time when Peter Bernardone would have been very proud to see her stand there so much a lady and yet so resolute before all this company. But now he only wondered if she knew that he had already been to the Palace of the Commune and appealed to the Consuls. Francis had refused their summons on the ground that since now he belonged entirely to the Church, only the Bishop could judge him, and the Consuls had not dared to risk the possibility that the Bishop would support him. Now Peter was sure she must have heard this when she suggested that he appeal to the Bishop.

"Is it not in his court that one argues all the family troubles that cannot be kept within the four walls of the house?" she asked coldly.

Bernardone scratched his head, and all around him the voices of his friends rose: "That is an idea. She has a head on her, that woman. Peter Bernardone, it is the Bishop who will do you justice."

A small boy outran the crowd going down to San Damiano, and meeting a servant of Leo, bade him tell his master. One of the lepers heard the noise of the tumult coming and ran to San Damiano. So the priest heard while the mob was still an echo on the hillside.

"Go into the little room behind the sanctuary and pull the chest against the door. It is cedar; it will hold."

"No," said Francis. "So long as I hide from my father, I am his prisoner. I will go out and meet them."

The first of the crowd, with Peter Bernardone striding angrily ahead, came into view as Francis left the church. He saw those in the front ranks clutch their staves at sight of him, and then as he came steadily on, they paused. But his father never slackened his pace. Francis went up to him and knelt down. "My father," he said.

But Peter, putting his hand on his forehead, thrust him away. "You are no son of mine!" And again the word "Hypocrite" fell on his head like a blow. Then Peter turned to his neighbors and cried, "Take him!"

Then someone in the crowd shouted, "Remember the Lady Pica!" And although they laid rough hands on Francis, they pulled him out of the reach of his father's blows.

As they began to drag him along, Francis protested, "I will come with you gladly. You don't need to pull me." So they let go of him, but they kept their staves ready in their hands. Although they had been noisy enough before, they were all quiet now, watching Peter and his son curiously. But Francis, as he strode along, kept his eyes on the dust, for a great emptiness filled all his being. He looked ahead. The road to Assisi stretched up the hillside, and it seemed endless. He tried to pray, but no word stirred the heavy silence within. "The road to Calvary was a long road," he thought, and then he fixed his mind on putting one foot ahead of the other. By no stretch of imagination could he ever reach the top of this road, for his breath tightened in his chest, and his whole body burned with exhaustion. But he could take one step more if he put all his thought on that alone.

Only when they reached the courtyard of the Bishop's palace and Francis sank down on one of the stones by the door for a moment while the crowd pressed into the vestibule of the Bishop was he able to catch his breath. He could hear the crowd roaring within, and then the sounds died away, and one of the Bishop's servants came to him and courteously bade him come in. At sight of him, the crowd drew back so that there was a clear lane to the low dais on which the Bishop sat. Peter Bernardone was standing before the Bishop, gesticulating, and Guido was listening to him with a puzzled look on his face. The puzzled look deepened when Francis knelt down before him.

"Francis, what is this story that your father tells of you?"

Francis looked up at the Bishop, and then he looked at the face of the man standing there before him, that dark contorted countenance, and as the fire played through all his being, he sprang to his feet. "My lord," he cried, "I have no father." And then as he heard the hiss of breath all over the room, and his father started toward him as if he would throttle him, Francis stretched out his hands to the Bishop. "I have no father. I renounce all part in Peter Bernardone's wealth, and in any inheritance I might have looked to have from him. And all I have of him I return to him," and as he spoke, he tore off the tunic of rough wool in which he stood and the shirt beneath, and the sandals on his feet, and he stood naked in his drawers. Then he flung his clothes upon his father, and after them the leathern girdle and purse. After a moment's hesitation, Peter Bernardone stooped down and gathered up the clothes and shook them defiantly before the Bishop; and then, choking with anger, he strode out of the palace. Astonished, the Bishop gazed after him, took the cloak from his own shoulders, and wrapped it about the naked young man. As he did so, Francis said, "I have no father but Our Father Who art in Heaven," and he began to repeat the words of the Lord's Prayer, and over all the room those words echoed and re-echoed. Now a loud sound of sobbing burst out, and the Bishop came down from his chair and took Francis to his bosom, and holding him in his arms, led him into his own chamber.

"Do not be afraid, Francis," said the Bishop. "Even though you have renounced your inheritance, the brethren up at San Benedetto will take care of you."

But Francis slipped from the Bishop's grasp, and he knelt down at his feet. "My lord," he said, "I have only one Father, and he will provide for me as he provides for the birds of the air and the grasses of the field." And he took off the Bishop's cloak and handed it back to him.

For a long minute the Bishop stood and looked at him. Then he bade one of his servants go and bring him a pilgrim's tunic and cloak. They were old and worn and stained.

"These, at least, you will not refuse as my gift," said the Bishop.

"I take them from your hands as from the hands of God," said Francis, kissing the Bishop's hand. Then he put on the tunic, but the cloak he held from him and looked around until he saw a piece of chalk on a chest by the wall. Then he spread the cloak out on the floor and drew a great white cross on it. "You have given me my livery, my lord," he said.

Again it seemed to him that the Bishop wanted to say something but could not find the words. Only as Francis knelt down again before him, he raised his hands, and he ended the words of blessing with, "Go in God's keeping."

"Amen, my lord," said Francis, and he ran out of the Bishop's palace into the courtyard, where the crowd was still waiting. Some of them knelt down and said, "Pray for us, Francis, on your pilgrimage." Now it was as if a great wind had blown through him and were carrying him along, and they all fell back and made way for him as if they had felt that invisible pressure. And so he came out the gates of the Bishop's palace and down the winding road to the gate to the hills. Here he found Leo waiting, holding the arm of the Lady Pica, who put out her hands to Francis. But he slipped from her grasp and knelt down at her feet. "Give me your blessing, my mother, and pray to Our Lady for me on the way I must go."

Her voice fogged with tears, the Lady Pica obeyed, but before she could touch him, Francis rose and was on his way.

"Where are you going?" shouted Leo.

"God only knows," Francis shouted back as he strode off. It seemed to him there was nothing in the whole world but this great wind bearing him along under the shining sky of God's presence, and his heart sang within him, "Free! Free at last!"

5

It was only after hours of walking as on air that Francis tired at last and took refuge in a haystack. Here, snug for the night and looking out at the stars, incredibly large and bright, he laughed, "Not even the Pope himself has so fine a canopy nor so sweet a bed." Once he half awoke as the straw tickled him, but sheer exhaustion brought sleep again. Presently, something else stirred him, and he woke to find a couple of field mice chasing each other over his face. And then it seemed to him the whole stack had come alive. "Clearly the inn was full before you came," he said, as he stretched out in the open meadow, wrapping the Bishop's cloak about him.

He awoke to find the sun on his face and to hear voices over his head. Some haymakers had come into the field and found him. Francis greeted the little company of peasants in their short gray tunics so cheerfully and called down the blessing of Christ and Our Lady upon the day so reverently that they were reassured. And when he asked them if he might join in their labor for no wage beyond a share in the noon dinner, they made him one of them. He not only sang a French song of the sweetness of the fields and the beauty of the spring flowers, which he had learned from his mother, but taught them the tune so that as he sang the words, they could hum with him. And as they ate their dinner of black country bread and goat's cheese, Francis spoke so winningly of My Lady Poverty, whom he had taken for his bride, that a great contentment settled down on the little company, and presently some of them began to nod.

"I am a proper enough preacher," laughed Francis, "for I have put you to sleep."

When they started for the fields again, the peasants were disappointed to find that Francis was taking his leave. "Stay with us and you shall sup with us and bed with us, too," they pleaded. "There is a hut up there in the village for the unmarried men."

But Francis shook his head.

"Where are you going?" asked the peasants.

"God only knows. I shall keep moving until He speaks." And then as an uncomfortable look came over the faces of the men before him, Francis pointed in the direction of Gubbio.

"You'd better know where you are going there," said the oldest of the peasants, "for there are brigands up there in the rocks."

"Brigands?"

"Have you not heard?" asked one of the women. "Up there beyond the old church of Caprignone. You know, where the Black Madonna is."

As Francis stared, another woman hastened to explain, "Yes. The Madonna of the Devils. Who else would give Our Lady a black face but those who could think of no color but their own?"

"Oh," laughed Francis. "Have you never noticed in the pictures of the Three Kings how some of the painters have given one of them a black face for the men whose faces are black? Did you not know that God has made men of other colors, and one of them was among the first to bring gifts to Our Lord's manger?"

"You have told us many strange things," said the leader thoughtfully, "but if you will not stay with us, at least be careful."

"Is there no lord in the castle there?" asked Francis.

There was an uneasy laugh. "At the Castle of Biscina. He is of the same kind. Men say"—and here the voices fell cautiously—"that he shares the spoil."

"I will go and look at your Madonna," said Francis. "And having nothing about me for the brigands to steal, I do not think I need fear them."

But the peasants shook their heads. "A bird with no feathers to pick they will dash against the rocks."

"Not unless God permits it." So Francis left them standing in the field, and he went on gaily, with the wind sweeping a silken path before his feet through the ripe grass.

As he had guessed, the Black Madonna of Caprignone was an old painting, seemingly more ancient even than the crucifix at San Damiano, and whether it was age on the rude pigments or the smoke of the votive candles that had burned for centuries before it, there was no question that the face of the Madonna was black as Gaspar's own. Yet in the poise of the head and in the cradling of the child, there was something of the tenderness of all Madonnas. It was a bare little church, hewn out of the mountain side, with its only light the sunlight from the little window above the Madonna's altar. Yet the woman cradling her child in her arms made a softening in the harsh darkness.

"It must have been a great fear that built that," said Francis to himself as he came out again into the sunlight. Thinking of the chapel, he must have lost the path, for presently he found himself in a little glen. There was something fascinating in the cool green light that seemed to be reflected from the earth rather than from the sky. "It is such a place as the bird took the knight to in my old romances," Francis thought with amusement. As he stepped down into the glen, he saw that the walls where they showed between the trunks of sycamore and ilex seemed to be washed with ferns, and below, the floor of the glen was alive with water pattling softly over rounded stones. "It must be a very ancient place," he thought.

He was astonished at how cold it was, and looking around, he saw that in a little pocket of the rocks the winter's snow still lingered on. Within a stone's throw violets and pink orchids were growing, and Francis wondered how the spring flowers would look in the snowbank. But before he could move, the quiet of the glen was shattered. It seemed as if a horde of wild beasts were breaking in down the narrow path by which Francis had come. Then he heard the ominous jangle of steel on stone, and he thought of the peasant women's devils and the farmers' bandits, and he braced himself to face a scowling fellow with hands on hips, stumbling down the rocks.

"You vagabond!" shouted the man. "What are you doing here on my lord's territory?"

Francis drew himself up and flung the Bishop's cloak about him so that the chalk cross hung as straight as possible. "I am a herald of the Great King," he said, turning so that all might see.

There was a moment's silence of astonishment, and then the leader laughed, throwing back his head so that the muscles of his throat bulged angrily. "That is a new one," he said, "and yet"—his eyes narrowed—"your voice is a gentleman's. Let us see your credentials."

"Neither scrip nor purse have I," said Francis, flinging the cloak back and holding out his hands so that one could see the tunic falling straight against his body.

"Ha, a heretic!"

"No! A poor penitent!"

"Let us see," and the men seized Francis and shook him until the leader with an oath exclaimed, "Not a pin on him. He is mad." Then they took his cloak and dumped him into the snow, shouting, "Go back and tell your king that this is the way we treat mad fools. Tell him to send us somebody better gilded next time." And they went off laughing and cursing.

Francis lay in the snow, finding the coolness soothing to his bruises and praising the providence of God that had preserved the snow for comfort in his need. Then he stood up and tried to straighten out his poor tunic, but it hung in tatters about him. At first he was too sore and too confused to think where he was going, and then he began to be afraid, for the next brigands would have no cloak to steal, and there might not be any snow to soften the rocks. He had come out of the glen now onto a desolate piece of roadway. It was ancient country with an old gravestone here, and there the base of a column set up as a barrier to mark the road. "Civilized men must have lived here once," Francis thought ruefully, "long before ever the faith was preached." And then he heard a bell, swinging slowly through the woods, from a little height above.

Slightly higher up on the hillside stood an old church and a convent beside it. Rather a large convent it seemed to Francis as he walked slowly around it looking for the gate.

He saw the porter's eyes narrow as he measured the apparition at his door. Francis, remembering the kind of neighbors among whom he lived, sympathized with the man.

"Who are you?"

"A seeker of God's will."

The porter scowled. "There is no shelter here for heretics."

"Thieves took away the cloak the Bishop of Assisi gave me. And this tunic he gave me."

The porter laughed. "That looks more like the thieves' than the Bishop's. But you seem well enough spoken. What is a man like you doing with the riffraff of the roads?"

"I ask only the chance to work that I may cover myself decently with one of your servant's castoff tunics."

The porter smiled. "If it's work you want, get 'round to the kitchen. The cooks will give you your belly-full of their sluttishness."

The porter was quite right. The walls of the old stone-vaulted kitchen were black with soot and the tiles at his feet shining with grease. A fat old monk gave Francis a broom, and as Francis set himself to sweeping out the cavelike room, moving stiffly with his sores, the old glutton took pity on him. "Go, skim off some of the fat from the top of the stew and put it on that crust over there." And when the night came, he pointed out a corner in the fireplace where the new kitchen boy might sleep. It was warmer than the open fields, but there were no stars overhead. And those were not field mice that Francis heard rustling in the wooden hutches at the opposite end of the kitchen.

By the end of the week the cook, like so many lazy men a connoisseur when it came to other men's industry, declared that his new aid might be mad but he was certainly no idler. When Francis asked him if he would not give him the castoff tunic that had now become the object of his dreams, the cook shook his head. "I will ask Brother Prior to give you a lay brother's tunic, and I will keep you here in the kitchen with me." And when Francis protested that he had never thought of anything so exalted as a Benedictine lay brother's status, the cook's easy-going complacency changed. "A habit you may have, but not a rag to go out and join the rest of these heretical vagabonds of yours."

So Francis went back to the road. "If the saints will not aid me, perhaps the sinners will," he said to himself. So when he came to the outskirts of Gubbio, he asked the way to the tower of the Spadalunga family. The man whom he stopped, a small knowing-looking craftsman with a hammer in the pocket of his leather apron, laughed at him.

"If you were a wandering minstrel, beggar, you might get a welcome there. He keeps a cheerful enough household, the Lord Frederigo, but I never heard that he was given to deeds of mercy."

The Lord Frederigo's porter thrust Francis away from the gate summarily enough, but Francis raised his voice in a little French hunting song, and at the sound the master of the house put his head out of an upper window and asked what in God's name went on here. When Francis stood out so that he might see him, the young lord laughed, "Why, here you are! They told me in Assisi that you had gone mad and your father had chained you in the straw!" Then he looked at him more closely. "I must say you do look mad." But as Francis went on singing, the face above sobered, "But madman or not, your voice is as sweet as ever." And Frederigo began to curse the porter for not knowing the difference between a vagabond and a mad gentleman.

Frederigo made Francis sit with him at table and asked him was it really less trouble to be mad than to keep pretending one was sane? Then as Francis quietly told him of his adventures, he asked him if the prank was worth all the beatings. "You're a little fellow, after all,

Francis," he pleaded, "and a temptation to any bully you come across. You are lucky it was only a snowbank. It might well have been a heap of rocks, and then you would be rotting there now."

Francis insisted that it was no madness, but Frederigo only shrugged his shoulders. "They say that is the final proof." He was all for calling his friends to a feast the next day that they might enjoy the madman, but Francis begged him for a cast-off tunic of one of his servants, and Frederigo, who was not an unobliging fellow when it did not interfere with his own pleasures, swore that he would do better. Indeed, when he thought about it, it seemed to him an amusing thing to send his servants out to buy the traditional gray tunic and leather belt and boots and wallet and staff of the pilgrim. There would be much gossip, Frederigo reflected with pleasure, as to who in his household was going on a pilgrimage, and doubtless it would come to the ears of his aunt in the Benedictine convent on the outskirts of the city, and the old lady would flutter to know whether her graceless nephew was at last in the way of conversion. Indeed, when the pilgrim gear arrived, Frederigo insisted on trying it on in front of a mirror and swore that he would order another outfit for Francis and come with him. But when Francis soberly reminded him that there would be no turning back, Frederigo sighed and began to tease his friend, "It is only an excuse for a holiday, this wandering around the country of yours, Francis." And Francis had to admit, somewhat shamefacedly, that never had he enjoyed any holiday as much as this freedom of the road. "But do not forget the brigands."

The warning was quite unnecessary. Francis chose another road back to Assisi, and in the pleasant company of field workers who gladly gave a cup of water or a heel of bread for a song, he forgot the world's violence, forgot it until he came into his own city. There it was a little group of boys teasing a dog by tying an old pewter pot to its tail that first reminded him. Without thinking, he asked them how they would like a pewter pot tied to their ankles. Then as he calmed the nearly frantic beast, one of the boys recognized him. Now it was with great relief that the young ruffian shouted, "See! It is only Old Bernardone's mad son!" and the boys began to shout and jeer, and as always happens in the back alleys of a city, some apprentices and other idle fellows took up the cry. It was with a mob at his heels, therefore, that Francis came into the city square. Above him, he could hear the shutters opening, and on the balconies the voices of women, but this time it was not of

Bernardone's mad son that they spoke but "that proud Pica's son!" Some of the young ruffians in the crowd began to shout, "Where, my Lord Francis, is that bride of yours?"

Francis thought he had known almost everyone in Assisi, but some of the faces and voices were quite strange. As he tried to take shelter in the doorway of the new cathedral, the mob surrounded him, and someone let a stone fly. Then someone else began to tug at his tunic, and with sudden despair, Francis saw himself again the ragged beggar who had taken refuge in Gubbio. Incongruously he thought, "What would Frederigo think of this adventure now?" Then he stretched out his hands and he cried out, "God give you peace, my brethren!"

They began to laugh. "Peace! It will take more than that to drive away your devils."

"For the love of God, my brothers," he began again.

"Peace," said a sharp voice. "And now the love of God . . . So go all the Patarins."

Then a girl's voice screamed out, "Look! He's going to take refuge in the church!"

"Where else," asked Francis, "shall a penitent sinner take refuge but in the church?"

"That does not sound like a heretic," said a cooler voice, and the crowd began to fall back as an imposing figure strode forward. Francis turned. It was one of the richest men in the city, Bernard of Quintavalle. Doubtless that quiet, dark-colored gown of good Flemish wool which he was wearing now had come from Peter Bernardone's shop. It was not so many years ago, either, that Francis had thought it a good jest to sing a merry song under Bernard of Quintavalle's windows in the middle of a spring night. Now he turned with relief at the grave pace of the former magistrate. Some of the rabble had already begun to draw back. "Francis," Bernard asked, "will you not come and have supper with me?" The invitation was given with such respect that Francis could not refuse. There was muttering, even giggles of muffled laughter as he followed the merchant through the crowd, but no one dared to stop Bernard of Quintavalle's guest.

"He who sups with the devil," cried a raucous voice from the edge of the crowd, but Bernard paid no attention, and there were indignant cries of "Hush!" and "For shame!" as the mob began to drift off.

Bernard said nothing to Francis until they reached his door. Then he stood aside courteously and bade him enter. Once within, he commanded his servants to bring water that Francis might wash after the road, and then he invited him to his table. Like the robe which the rich man wore, it was a sober and solid meal, but to the vagabond with the chill of fear only now subsiding in his empty stomach, it was a veritable feast. Only when he had refused any more food and had drunk a little of Bernard's good red wine did his host begin to question him.

"You heard what they said, Francis," he began, "the word they called you."

"Do you think," said Francis, putting his elbows on the board, "that it is mad to believe what Our Lord said, that even as God provides for the birds of the air and the flowers of the field, so will He provide for us if only we have faith enough?"

"Faith enough," repeated the magistrate thoughtfully, "that is a large order. One must not ask of men more than men can do," he said, sipping his wine soberly.

"But did not Our Lord's disciples do just that?"

"Do not forget that they had Our Lord with them."

"But even after Our Lord left them, did they not follow the evangelical counsels?"

"It was a long time ago when the world was younger."

"But each generation of men is new, and the world is new for them, and does not Holy Church teach us that Christ is with us even to the end?"

"There are many things, Francis," said Bernard, "that the preachers say in the cathedral on Sunday that no man takes literally, and I do not think that even the preachers think he should."

"But suppose they did?" asked Francis eagerly. For now it seemed to him that Bernard was looking at a possibility which he had never considered before. It was a long thin face that Francis looked at in the candlelight, with a look of habitual caution in the downcast eyes and of steady control in the small mouth. And yet behind those firmly molded lines of cheek and jaw there was a sense of strength leashed and, as Francis had learned that evening, courage enough. Bernard of Quintavalle would not stand idly by when wrong was done, but would he step beyond the ordered lines of his own clear and tested routine?

"Suppose," said Francis, "that Christ should come again in Umbria."

Bernard raised his eyes to Francis', and Francis caught a flicker of light in their gray depths. "How many would know Him, I wonder," the rich man mused, his hand, with the old seal ring, relaxed around the glass. Perhaps after his day's business he was only playing with ideas, all the unceasing vigilance of the man of affairs for a moment relaxed.

"Not know Him?" said Francis with the fire leaping again in his heart. "That were indeed to be old, to be dead."

"I wonder," mused his host, and then he roused himself. "We have both of us had long days. Do you stay with me tonight."

"Nicholas, the priest at San Damiano, will give me shelter."

Bernard shook his head. "It is a long way for a man who has dodged a mob."

"They did not know."

"They never do," said the magistrate wearily. "That tale I know all too well. You can go to San Damiano in the morning, but I will give you a pallet in my chamber tonight."

Francis was surprised. He had always thought of the rich man as rather aloof and self-contained. That was why it had seemed such sport to tease him in those days now so unbelievably remote—so much remoter, Francis saw suddenly, than the days of the Apostles of which they had been talking.

"We shall have no difficulty sleeping, either of us," said Bernard when they both had commended themselves to Christ and Our Lady, and Bernard of Quintavalle had carefully set the night light on a chest where it would not shine into the face of his guest sleeping on the pallet. In his great bed Bernard composed himself and began to snore lightly. "He is no fool," he said to himself, as he took pains to keep his breathing low and even. He must have fallen asleep, because when he opened his eyes again there was a shadow between him and the light. "He has come to look at me and see if I am really asleep," he thought, as he closed his eyes again. Then he heard a rustle, it seemed to him away from his bed, and he opened his eyes again. Now he could see the night light and a darker shadow in the shadows where he had put his guest to sleep. "He is kneeling by his bed," he thought, and he took care to deepen his snoring a little so that his guest's suspicions should not be aroused. Then he heard a whisper, and as he listened, he noted that it was repeated over and over again, steadily and rhythmically. "He is praying," he said to himself, and moving very slowly so as not to disturb his guest, he rose on one elbow so that he could look through the bed curtains. Now he could see the face of Francis. Though the soft light of the night lamp fell on it, it seemed to him that its radiance came from within, and now the whisper had risen to the volume of a low cry. Presently he could make out the words, "My Lord and my God."

He could see the little man now quite clearly in the light by his pallet in the corner. He had raised his hands, and he was completely absorbed in his prayer, saying over and over again only, "My Lord and my God!" He was weeping now, Bernard noted, and experimentally he shifted on his pillows, making a little noise that could not have failed to catch his guest's attention. But Francis seemed completely unaware; so Bernard sat up in bed and moved over to the edge. In doing this he made quite a bit of noise, but Francis never broke the rhythm of that prayer, "My Lord and my God!" Only now he was sobbing, and the familiar petition became a prayer for mercy. Presently, Bernard pushed the curtains quite aside and sat on the edge of the bed, but Francis was still completely unaware of him. Now he had ceased to weep, and he was repeating the phrase, "My Lord and my God," with accents of wonder and surprise, as if he had suddenly become aware of the goodness and bounty of God and did not know how to give thanks for the divine forgiveness. A little prickle of excitement ran down Bernard's spine, and he took the coverlet from his bed and wrapped it about himself, but still the little man went on praying. Now it seemed to him that he was giving thanks to God, but always it was the same single phrase, "My Lord and my God."

Bernard had known Francis in the old days, had known him as a great many older citizens of Assisi had known Peter Bernardone's surprising son, a fine businessman, everybody agreed—Bernard himself had bought the stuff of a couple of gowns from him. But all the wit and the gaiety and the song of which men spoke so often in Assisi seemed to be wasted in revelry. All right for a young man for a spring or two, but not year after year. And now this most astonishing thing of all—religion; not as a good Christian takes it, soberly as the framework of one's life, but extravagantly as he had done everything else. Bernard knew that piety is sometimes the last posture of the self-dramatizer, when all other poses have failed. So Bernard had taken his chance to test Francis, and now as he watched him, all doubt went out of his mind. Presently Bernard found that he was weeping with Francis and that that chant, "My Lord and my God," was rising to his own lips. He was an austere man, not given normally to many words, and least of all to any words of feeling. He could not have said the words aloud even if he would, but he found himself saying the words with Francis within his own spirit. So he slipped quietly from his bed, and kneeling down, he bowed his head; and presently he was asleep from sheer exhaustion.

When he woke next, it was dawn, and his guest was lying on his pallet asleep with a smile on his lips. Bernard was cold and stiff, or he would have thought it all a dream. Only there was a lightness in his heart so that it seemed as if time itself had rolled away, and he was a boy again. He was a boy, awake before the dawn because his father had promised him that that day he would take him to the law courts, that he might see what the mysterious adult world was like in which his father spent his days when he was not at home. So now he dressed, and when he had finished his preparations for the day, he turned and saw that his guest was standing by his pallet, waiting for him. Then Bernard of Quintavalle went and knelt down in front of Francis, and now for the first time he repeated aloud the words of the night's prayer, "My Lord and my God."

Francis started, and for a moment he looked puzzled, and then he flung his arms about Bernard and kissed him.

"Take me with you," said Bernard. "Wherever you go, I will go, and whatever you bid me do, that I will do." And his eyes fell before the blinding radiance on Francis' face.

As he waited for his answer, the little man shook his head. "That we shall ask of God for both of us," and he bade Bernard come alone the next morning to the parish church of San Nicolo for Mass.

But when the time came, Bernard was not alone. With him was a man of his own years, at sight of whom Francis drew back, for he was the Bishop's own canonist, Peter Catanii. As Francis stood there peering at Peter in the uncertain light of dawn as if he could not believe his eyes, Bernard took Peter's hand and they both fell to their knees before Francis. "I was but waiting for Bernard's word," Peter said stiffly, as if now he were embarrassed. But Bernard was astonished to see how readily the little man's arms stretched around both of them.

"And now," said Francis, "we three will go to the church of San Nicolo and we will ask the priest there to say Mass for us, and when he has said Mass we will ask God what we should do."

The priest of San Nicolo was not up yet. At first he was a little cross. "Can you not wait until it is dawn?"

"We are in a great hurry," said Francis. And then the priest saw Peter and Bernard, and at sight of Peter Catanii he arose and said, "I will be there as soon as I can make ready."

When the priest had finished saying Mass, he paused at the door of the sacristy and he said to Peter, "Is there anything else I can do for you, Master Peter?" But Peter looked to Francis.

He said, "You have done us the greatest service and that which only you, a priest, can do. The rest is God's." Then when the door of the sacristy had closed upon the puzzled priest, Francis went up to the altar and opened the book of the Gospels that lay upon it. He turned to his companions and said, "Let us pray that God will make His will clear to us, and that the text which I shall read will be the word which He has given us." And so he opened the book and, looking down at the illuminated page, began to read aloud the first words on which his eyes fell, "If thou wilt be perfect, go sell what thou hast, and give it to the poor." In his joy his feet danced as he kissed the book of the Gospels and put it back on the altar. Then he bade Bernard open it and read.

And Bernard read, "Take nothing for your journey; neither staff, nor scrip, nor bread, nor money." Again Francis cried out with delight. And they closed the book, and then Francis turned to Peter—"Now do you open it."

Though his voice shook a little, Peter read in clear tones the first verse he came to, "If any man will come after me, let him deny himself, and take up his cross, and come follow me." Bernard kissed the page and burst into tears.

Francis flung his arms about his companions, crying, "God has spoken. This is what we have to do, all of us."

When they had dried their tears of joy, Peter turned to Francis and he asked, "All of us? Are there others?"

"Yes," said Francis. "There are hundreds, and thousands of us, stretching out to the end of time; and so will we all do until God rolls up the heavens and flings them away like an outworn garment."

6

Outside the church Francis turned cheerfully to his companions, and embracing them again, bade them Godspeed. But Peter for the first time put out a hand and held him. "What do we do now?" he asked.

And Bernard, seizing him by the arm, too, said firmly, "You are our leader, the master we have chosen."

"No," said Francis, and his voice sharpened so that both men drew back. "There is no master here but our Master Christ."

"But," protested Bernard, "we are your disciples."

"There are no disciples except His. We are three companions," he said, taking the hands of his friends and swinging them wide.

"But what do we do now?" asked Bernard.

"You have had the day's marching orders," said Francis gaily. "Beyond that God will tell us."

"Will you come and help me?" asked Bernard.

"No, this you can do better without me."

"Where are you going?" asked Peter.

"I'm going back to Saint Benedict's church of the Little Portion. It is the right size for my strength. You, my brethren, will build a greater." And with a light wave of the hand, he went down the street, leaving Peter and Bernard looking at each other.

While Peter, somewhat fearfully, went off to see the Bishop and Bernard to see his steward, knowing that it would take all his years of experience in putting complex matters simply to make clear to him what he wanted done, Francis went down the road from Assisi into the plain, singing gaily. This time he did not take the road to San Damiano, for that road had become crowded of late with all the people who had gone down to see the restored chapel and the crucifix that had spoken. The new stones in the front and side walls stood out rawly in the spring sunshine, and there were not wanting those who pointed out that the madman might be a saint but he was only an indifferent mason. There were not wanting, either, a stonemason or two who stopped to smooth a rough place in a wall. The old priest did not sleep in the sun so much these days, and there was a pleasant chink of silver in the alms box as he took visitors through the little church. He was, as Francis had told the Patarin, a simple, guileless man. Now he made no effort to repair the little shack by the church wall, but he kept the oil lamp burning before the altar, and when the Lady Clare came by one day with one of the women of her household and left him some fine linen for the altar, he not only washed the old marble but went up into the city and got a couple of new brass candlesticks to grace the linen. And he bought a new and larger pot that he might have a little porridge for the beggars who now came to ask for food. Only he always insisted that the last portion must remain in the pot lest Francis should come in later that night and need it. When he heard of this, Francis rebuked the old priest, "Do you not know that it is only the empty pot which God can fill?" And he laughingly accused Nicholas of tethering him with a rope of charity as menacing as ever was his father's iron chain.

So Francis came no more to San Damiano. But farther down into the plain by a different road farther to the west, little more than a path through the fields, he found another decaying church. This was even tinier than San Damiano, and if anything, more ruinous. Wandering in the plain perhaps a year before, Francis had come upon the church of the Portiuncula. Actually it was nothing more than a little stone hut, crumbling into the rich earth, but Francis had recognized it as the church to which his mother had brought him when he was a child one summer day. She had sat down on one of the fallen stones, and with him setting in the grass at her feet and resting his head on her knee, she had told him one could never judge things by their outward look, for this little church was a grander thing, if one knew it, than even the great new Cathedral of Assisi's patron, San Rufino. Somehow that had caught the child's attention, hovering on the edge of sleep, and he had asked his mother how a little hut not much bigger than a pigpen and falling apart at that—how that could be a greater church than the wonderful new Cathedral on the Piazza. Then his mother had explained that this little church had been here when there had been no church in the town above, nothing but the heathen temple.

"Then St. Benedict came here," said Francis, for even as a child he had loved to climb up the hill to the Benedictine abbey with its great view of the country, and almost the first thing that he remembered of those early visits was that St. Benedict himself, who stood so tall and majestic above the high altar in the abbey church, had been the first one who had brought the Order into this land.

"No, it was here long before St. Benedict," she said. "It was here even before Our Lord came on earth."

"But this couldn't have been a temple," the child had protested. "There are no pillars in front of it."

But Pica insisted that some men said it had been a temple, though there were, also, those who said it had been a tomb. Not that it mattered much, for all that had been redeemed. Three pilgrims coming back from the Holy Land in the early centuries had come upon the little building, and they had cleaned it out. There was still a Roman sarcophagus over there in the bushes, which the peasants had filled with water for their cattle, and anywhere around here one might come upon a fragment of an ancient idol, the once white marble now green from the rains. Francis was falling asleep again when his mother told him that they had called it St. Mary of Jehosephat, and with delight he had made her repeat the strange name. Then they, too, had gone away, and men had forgotten again as they do, and then Saint Benedict had come into the land, and he, too, had cleaned it out again and doubtless repaired it. It seemed to the Lady Pica that that was what men were always doing—someone building something and then going away and forgetting it, and then someone else coming along and throwing out whatever his predecessors had left behind, and cleaning up, and then after a little while going away and forgetting again. Only Our Lady, like a careful mother, would remember even when her children had grown up and gone away and forgotten her.

Remembering all this now in the bright summer morning, Francis knelt down against the stone where perhaps his mother had sat when she told him these things, and put his head upon his hands and wept. For he had heard up in the city that the wife of Peter Bernardone was ill with that light cough that she had had before, and Francis had tried not to think of it, for his father had sworn that he would kill him if he crossed his doorstep; and that would bring no comfort to the Lady Pica, caught again between her husband and her son. So now Francis knelt down and asked Our Lady, torn as she must have been so often between the justice and the mercy of God, to remember that day and to let Pica know that though her son had gone away, he had not forgotten. And then as he looked into the dark little building, he thought to himself, "This is the right size for you, little man, Francis," and he set about cleaning it again.

Afterwards, he looked around the little clearing in which the church stood. All sorts of wild things had closed in about it—briars and weeds and stunted saplings of ilex and sycamore, and vines throwing their nets over all the underbrush. But here and there as he pushed aside the tangle, he could see single stones and presently heaps of stones, half buried in the silt of past winters. Then he remembered something else which he had heard as a boy, whether from his mother or from the monks up in the abbey on Monte Subasio he could not remember, that it was here that Benedict had built the first abbey with little sheds as modest as that old chapel, to shelter their prayer and labor. "There are stones enough," he said to himself, "and I shall not have to trespass on any man's possessions for that at least." So he set himself cheerfully to dig out some of the old stones and to carry them to the church.

Of course, some of the peasants soon found him—a child running after a curious dog, a shepherd looking for a straying ewe, a farmer's wife who had come for water to a little spring beyond a clump of ruins. All of these had stared at Francis with curiosity and had replied, civilly enough, to his greeting, "May God give you peace!"

Another day Francis was discovered by a group of young men from the town out fowling. He had stood up to look at them, his face streaked with sweat, and to his delight he had found his brother, Angelo, among them. But Angelo only laughed when he saw him, and turned away to his companions, and said, "Go and ask my mad brother to give you a drop of that mason's sweat."

"It is not for sale," said Francis quietly. "It has been bought by a richer merchant than you."

They all laughed, but it was an uncomfortable laughter, and they soon rode on.

Here, too, Francis was found another day, prying with a broken piece of sapling at a clump of stones lying imbedded in the earth. "You're hardly the right build for that, friend," cried a cheerful voice, and Francis looked up to see a strapping peasant youth, who might easily have posed for some ancient Apollo but for his leathern skin and a certain look of cheerful tolerance of the world's folly on his handsome features. He took the sapling from Francis' hands and poked at the stones with it until it broke in his strong grasp. Laughing at the surprise on Francis' face, he tossed it into the bushes and without difficulty lifted first one and then another of the stones, and one by one he set them easily on the wall which Francis was rebuilding.

"You really are not very good at this, you know," said the young peasant as they worked.

"I know," said Francis humbly. "If my Master had had a better workman, he would not have sent me."

"Your master? Up there?" The young peasant pointed to the city. But Francis pointed to the clear sky above.

The peasant laughed. "You're an odd fellow." Then his eyes narrowed, "Are you that madman that they're all talking about?"

But to that Francis made no answer. When they had made that little portion of the wall straight, the youth looked at him and said, "Whatever you are, you must be hungry. Come with me."

It was a little group of peasants eating their dinner in the field where they were working. The young man, whom they had greeted as Giles, smiled at Francis, "If you will take all that about the sparrows and the lilies seriously, then the least we can do is to see that you are not disappointed."

"That is no way to talk, Giles," said one of the older women, but the rest of the company laughed gaily and slapped Giles on the back and said he was always one for having his joke. When they had finished their dinner and lay around on the crushed grass, Francis began to sing to them in their own Umbrian tongue. It was a complaint of an old man about his son's folly, and though the older women looked dubious, the father laughed and all the young men, and presently they began to sing with Francis. And then Francis led them on to a little hymn to Our Lady, and this time the older women sang with shining eyes, and all the girls on the outskirts of the little company. When it was time to go back to their work, the old farmer came up to Francis and said, "Madman or not, any time you want, there is a bowl of food for you if you will come and sing with us."

Francis thanked him and called down the blessing of Heaven on such friendly hospitality. But as he went back to Benedict's St. Mary of the Little Portion he thought, "Food for a song is a fair enough exchange at a lord's house but not in the fields of these hard-working farmers." And so the next day he slipped back to Assisi as soon as ever the sun stood high overhead, before the farmers could call him to their dinner. "I seem always to be running away from food," he thought to himself, "an odd plight for a beggar." So he went up to the new cathedral in the heart of the city and, finding a quiet corner, he knelt down to pray.

Now for the first time it came to him that he was not alone, that he had two companions, and doubtless more would be added. He was under no temptation to play the master, but what answer should he give them when they asked him to tell them something of the way along which he had been before them? It was almost three years now, he thought. That was all the time that Our Lord had needed to teach the world His lesson, that lesson which after all the centuries men still had not come to the end of learning. And then he thought of that old question, "Suppose Christ came again in Umbria?" The fresh coolness of the new cathedral fell like balm upon his weary spirit, and putting his head down on the marble railing around an unfinished side altar, Francis fell asleep.

It was evening when he came out of the church and hid in the shadow of the doorway to watch the throng in the square. They were the same men doubtless who had thrown the stones, but now they seemed completely unaware of him. It would be tempting providence to try again, but he had not eaten all day. He thought of the kitchen at Bernard of Quintavalle's house. Francis knew how long it took to make a bargain over a bale of cloth, but he had no idea how long it would take to sell a house. Nor had God given him companions for this. As he waited indecisively, he felt somebody come near him, and he, who even as a child had run out to greet every stranger, shrank back with the memory of the mob in his mind.

But it was the voice of Leo that spoke to him, "I have been looking for you all day."

Francis found the darkest corner of the base of the Cathedral and pulled his friend down beside him.

"I have seen my uncle," Leo began.

"What does he say?"

Leo shrugged his shoulders. "What would you expect? He is a doctor and a canon of the Cathedral."

"I suppose he said it was madness."

"Well," said Leo more cheerfully, "he said anything was better than the mooning 'round I'd been doing, waiting for something that would never happen."

"Then he will give you your share of your inheritance?"

"He will release me from my inheritance, rather." There was a wry note in Leo's voice.

"Of course, what he does with the money does not matter so long as you no longer feel tied to it."

Francis felt the young man beside him relax. "Of course, he said if it was religion I wanted, why not do it properly? My inheritance would buy me a proper benefice, or if I was too lazy for that, then the Benedictines on Monte Subasio would be very glad indeed to add my land to theirs."

"But what did he say when you said you wanted to give it to the poor?"

Leo hesitated. "I am afraid I didn't do it very well, Francis," he said at last. "I told him it was like the early Disciples and the saints in the Golden Legend—I thought he would explode then." Leo, folding his arms around his knees, rocked a little on his seat by the Cathedral door. " 'The Golden Legend! The Golden Madness! That is the trouble with all you young men. Your heads are buzzing like a beehive with scraps of phrases from poets' romances. This is Assisi, you fool, in the year 1209, and the poor are a mob of dirty, feckless, thieving rascals who will listen to no counsel but what the Patarins give them.' "

"What did he propose then?" asked Francis quietly.

"What you would expect," said Leo with contempt. "A chantry in the new Cathedral to pray for my ancestors' souls that some, at least, of the inheritance they had built up might redound to their good, and some burses at Bologna that better men might do the studying I refused to do."

"But doesn't he see?" said Francis, forgetting the nephew in his indignation at the uncle. "We have the chantries in the cathedrals, and we have the burses at Bologna, and the churches in the fields are falling into decay, and in the dark streets of the towns men are stifling for want of the sweet air of the Lord's Gospel."

"I tried to tell him that," said Leo helplessly, "but he only laughed and told me that it was as he had thought, I had been listening to the heretics."

"No," said Francis quickly, "we have never said that he should not stay there in his library with all its leather-bound books, writing out all those fine-spun theories of his in his neat hand. All we have said is that that is not enough."

"Oh, I said all that, though of course not as well as you would."

"And in the end?" said Francis.

"Oh, in the end—you know, Francis, he's not really a bad fellow for all his crustiness. In the end he suggested what he thought a reasonable compromise. Half of it to San Lazzaro. It was a sink, he said, in which to throw good money; but still, God knows, some beginning should be made."

"But that," said Francis, "is a fine idea. Why not all of it?"

"The rest, he said, to buy from the Benedictines the little patch of waste where he has heard you've been poking around. I should take orders and be the chaplain there, and you—"

"No," said Francis and then as he felt his friend shiver a little, he suddenly remembered. "Have you eaten today, Leo?"

"No," said Leo, "I had forgotten. Shall we come back to my house?"

"No, we shall eat at the table of the Lord." Francis felt Leo looking down on him and he seized his arm. "They are at their supper now. You take that street, and I will take this, and we will come back here to the Cathedral doorway. There is enough light from that lantern there for us to eat by, even before the moon rises."

"Beg?" said Leo incredulously.

"It is the calling which God has given us."

So the two friends parted. Francis knew his face was dirty enough and his dress torn and stained enough so even his family would have failed to recognize him. But still out of some remnant of delicacy or of cowardice, he told himself, he had chosen a street where he was not likely to be known. So he went confidently down the dark alleys to the kitchen doors. At his first knock the door was opened a little, and then, when he began, "For the love of God—" it was banged in his face with a rattle of the bolt. He had a little better luck with the next. It was an old woman who put her head cautiously out the door, and when she saw that it was a little man who stood there, she bade him wait, and then she thrust a hard lump of bread into his hands and bade him in God's name be gone.

"This is hardly enough for two," thought Francis, and he went on down the street. "A little hard cheese, a bit of salt meat, some cold beans in a leaf—it is little enough for two hungry men," thought Francis, but it was all the street yielded. So giving thanks to God and Our Lady, he went back to the Cathedral, and dusting the stone of the step under the lantern with his tunic, he spread out the thin parings of his quest.

"Now let us see what you have, Leo," he called cheerfully, as his friend came up.

But Leo hesitated. "Come now, don't be embarrassed," said Francis. "Whatever God has given to us, it is a feast." Then he saw with astonishment why Leo had been hanging back. For Leo had a whole half loaf of fresh bread, and a big hunk of soft cheese, and even a piece of fresh meat.

Francis laughed joyously. "Even here, Brother Leo, the world goes by the looks of things. The housewives took pity that so fine-looking a young man should be begging his bread." And Leo hung his head in shame. Francis said grace and began to eat joyously. He swore that the hard lump of bread was the sweetest he had ever tasted, and he made Leo taste it, too, and they both laughed when Leo hesitated to join his companion in its praise.

At the laughter two men came across the square with a torch and looked at them. "It is the madman," said one. "Francis, I've been looking all over today for you—over at San Damiano, and down at the old place in the fields."

"Why have you been looking for me?" And then he recognized the speaker as one of the Bishop's servants. "The Bishop wishes to see me?"

"At once."

Leo looked at him in the light of the torch. "Are you sure you ought not to wash up a little?"

"Oh, the Bishop will understand," said Francis confidently. But he was not so sure when they came into the Bishop's presence and Guido frowned as he looked at the two friends.

"Sit down," said the Bishop, pointing to two stools. "What is this I hear of your taking to yourself disciples?"

"Not disciples, my lord," said Francis, "only companions."

"Companions?" repeated the Bishop. "That is all right for him," the Bishop pointed his cross at Leo, "although God knows his uncle is angry enough. He has told his secretary that he can read no more, that all the lines blur together."

"But surely," began Francis and then he decided to hold his tongue, for though he suspected that the Bishop had too much good sense to spend any time on all that hair-splitting of the Biblical commentators, still he could hardly expect him to listen to any disparagement of the most distinguished scholar in his diocese.

"It is bad enough when you take off a young man like Leo, who if his uncle is to be believed, has not been up to much good anyway, but a man like Bernard of Quintavalle is another matter altogether."

"My Lord, the Grace of God moves . . ."

"The Grace of God! Half the madmen in history have thrown the blame for their folly on heaven."

"But no one can call Bernard mad."

"That is it, precisely," said the Bishop, rising and beginning to pace back and forth across the tiles of his study floor. "When madness seizes fools, that is bad enough, but when it seizes wise men, men of mature years and settled place—" the Bishop's voice was rising. "Do you know what has happened today?" he said, suddenly stopping and thrusting out one long, bony finger at Francis.

"I have heard, my lord, that Bernard has gone into the country to free himself of some farms—"

"Look here," said the Bishop, "I have been willing to believe that there was no real harm in you for all your fantasy and folly, but you talk like a heretic now."

"But the Gospels say—"

"The Gospels! First, it was this crucifix, and now it is the Gospels. Do you know what happened today? Peter Catanii, my own canonist, came to me and told me that he had resolved to join—" the Bishop hesitated, and then with indescribable contempt, he finished his sentence, "the Poor Penitents of Assisi!"

Francis rose and stretched out his hands to the Bishop. But Guido bade him sit down as if he were an unruly schoolboy.

"The finest legal mind in the land," the Bishop went on, "and you put him to carrying stones and plastering mud on worthless church walls. Presently, no doubt, he will be begging with a mob throwing stones at him!"

"My lord—" Francis began again.

"Be still," said Guido, and he turned to Leo. "Your uncle tells me that you will become a priest, and that you propose to put half your inheritance into the lepers' hospital. God knows they can use it, and perhaps I have thought too little of them, though a man can do only so much." And now that his anger was ebbing, the Bishop sat down, a tired old man. "And the rest you want to put into that briar-patch around the old church. The Benedictines will be glad enough to exchange it for some of that land by their walls."

"No!" said Francis.

"I was not talking to you," said the Bishop, and he turned back to Leo.

But Leo shook his head. "I have chosen Francis for my master, and what he says I will do."

"Not what I say," said Francis hotly, "but what God says. 'Neither staff, nor scrip, nor bread, nor money.' My lord, if we take even that briar-patch down there, we shall be tethered to it. We shall build a wall around it like the Benedictines around their abbey, and presently men will look over the wall and covet what is within it, and then we will put men with staves at the wall, and they will get other men to come with staves against it, and there only will be fighting, my lord, where there was peace."

The Bishop rubbed his hands over his face wearily. "God knows," he said, "there is something to what you say. Mad as it is, there always is. There is fighting enough, even among men of religion who have sworn to keep the peace. But then, if you are worried about walls, let Bernard keep this house of his within the city walls, and companions or penitents or whatever you call yourselves, let the four of you live there like decent men."

"No, my lord," said Francis leaping to his feet. "Within the walls or outside, it does not matter. A house will hold us prisoner, and we shall think of that house when we should be thinking of the whole roofless world, and we will huddle there when we should go out looking for the stray children of Israel."

The Bishop stared at the little man. "What then, in God's name, do you think you are doing?"

"My lord," said Francis, "we are simply trying to live the Gospel, to behave as we would behave if Christ, Our Lord, were to come again here in Umbria."

"Christ in Umbria," said the Bishop and he flung his hands over his head. Then Francis and Leo slipped to their knees and waited at his feet. Presently the Bishop turned to them. "I do not know. I do not know," he said, and now he was no longer looking at them but at the crucifix on the wall opposite his chair.

"That is all we ask, my lord," said Francis, "your blessing that we may find out."

And fumbling the words, the old man repeated the blessing, and as the hand with the violet-stoned ring completed the last cross, he pushed them away.

III: To the Four Quarters of the Earth

1

It was like Bernard of Quintavalle that he made no effort to burden his new companions with all the business of converting his scattered properties into silver. Only when at the end of some weeks he had passed the last bill of sale, did he go down to the Portiuncula and ask Francis to come up early the next morning and help him give his fortune away. That night as Francis scraped the bottom of the wayfarer's pot at San Damiano, he told the old priest Nicholas how in the morning Assisi would become like Jerusalem when the new converts brought their wealth to the feet of the Apostles. Nicholas, who had by now acquired an extensive experience of converts, old and new, and some not yet converted at all, looked sober at the prospect Francis so gaily sketched, but he did not have the heart to cast any shadow on the bright picture of the young man's imagination.

The dawn was breaking when Francis reached Bernard's door and already dark shadows were coming down the alleys. "I hope they don't rush us," said Bernard nervously, as he handed Francis and Peter heavy leather bags. Then as the three friends took up their places at the door, there came a wild cry of delight, and it seemed as if all Assisi were rushing upon them.

"May God give you peace, my brothers," Francis pleaded without any effect. But just as the first sturdy figure had fallen upon him, came the harsh clapping of wood and a raucous voice shouted, "Unclean! Unclean!" From the crowd came a cry of astonishment, which soon turned to anger, and then terror.

"The lepers! The madman has turned loose the lepers on us!" the mob screamed as it fell back.

"No, my brothers," shouted Francis, standing on the stone by the door. "They will but take their share. There is plenty for all." So as the sun rose and the light came down between the houses, the rest waited muttering, while the two lepers came up. Francis threw his arms about them, while a shudder ran through the bystanders, and then Bernard put a handful of silver in the worn purse which the lepers carried. But even when they had gone, the rest hung back as if there were danger in the lips that had kissed that horrible decay.

Then a reckless voice cried out, "There is no stain on the silver, at any rate," and again came the rush.

"There is enough for all, my brothers," cried Francis. "Let the cripples through first, and the old." But they seemed not to hear him.

A couple of stout fellows thrust through the crowd and laid hold upon Bernard's tunic and reached out their hands as if they would snatch the bag from him. But there was a cry now from the rest, and Bernard shook them off. Then he gave each of them a couple of coins and bade them let the next have their turn. Bernard was a man who was accustomed to having his low voice obeyed, and even in this mob were men who had often enough bowed to him; so they pulled the stout ruffians back, and slowly the crowd began to line up for their money. To Francis it all seemed disappointingly slow and dull. So he took a handful of silver out of his bag and flung it on the pavement, but the resulting scramble was so violent with people in the back knocking sticks out of the hands of cripples and striking down an old woman and a child, that Francis had sadly to admit that Bernard's way was the better.

Indeed, Francis to his astonishment was forced to admit that the sturdy beggars of whom he had heard so many complaints in his father's house were more than a fiction. These fellows were dirty and ragged enough, and yet he had to admit that they were, also, menacing and even violent. Presently, as the sturdy ones retired to the end of the street, slimmer figures, but more supple and agile, began to elbow their way through the throng. This time there were women as well as men, and even a few boys.

Now cries of indignation arose all over, "Thieves!" and "Whores!" The objects of this vituperation moved so fast that they seemed to pluck the coins out of the givers' hands before ever they had left the bags, and they slipped away before the wrath of their neighbors could strike. It seemed to Francis that some of these sinewy shadows must have come out of the very paving stones at their feet. One, indeed, was so bold as to thrust his hand into the pouch which Peter held and flourish the handful of coins in his face before Peter knew what he was doing. There was a roar of anger all over the street and cries of "Throttle him!" But the thief was gone, back into a dark alley before anybody could move. After that, even Francis held his leathern pouch more cautiously.

Now came some of the halt and the lame, and Francis' spirits rose again. But there was a sudden jeering, "Look! He has trussed his leg up, the old scoundrel!"

Another cried, "Take that arm out of your blanket!" and the whine of the professional beggar rose over the taunts, and the clenched fist came out.

Francis said to himself, "Who of us shall say who is worthy and who is unworthy?" and he began to sing a hymn pleading for divine forgiveness, but not in French this time. Then the crowd fell back as a tall, somber figure strode forward, and an angry voice cried out, "Hypocrite!" It was Sylvester, the priest, who had sold Francis some of the stones for San Damiano. "Hypocrite!" he cried again, and here and there a voice took up the cry. "You robbed me of those stones which I gave you cheaply as to a beggar, and here you are throwing a fortune away on all the riffraff of the town." The three companions looked so astonished that jeers of laughter broke out all around them.

Then Francis said icily, "Greed in a priest is so fearsome a thing, we must exorcise it if we can." And he took a handful of silver from the pouch and flung it into Sylvester's outstretched hands. Some of the coins clattered to the pavement, and again there was a wild scramble as men and women tore at each other to pick them up.

Francis cried out in pain, "Brothers! My brothers!" Then he looked at Sylvester, who stood clutching the coins. "Father, forgive me," he said, "because I, who am not worthy, spoke harshly."

For a moment Sylvester stood there, and then he opened his hands slowly and the coins dripped like water from them. As he turned away, no one moved; all stood there gazing at the coins. Then a couple of boys darted forward and began to pick them up and to pass them around to those who had not yet shared in the giving.

On the edge of the crowd, Francis heard two men arguing. "He called him a greedy priest," said one.

"He is no heretic," said the other. "He asked his pardon."

The silver was all gone before noon, but all afternoon the beggars continued to pour into Assisi, and worried shopkeepers put up their shutters, and sober citizens asked each other what the world was coming to.

Even the Bishop, who had gone up to sup with the Abbot Simon and to ask his advice, grumbled over the Abbot's good wine. "Of course, like any Christian, I am all for leaving the world, but why they cannot do it in an orderly fashion and come up here to join you!"

"I think," said the Abbot with a smile, "it is precisely the orderly fashion that they do not want."

"That is it. That is what bothers me," said the Bishop. "Wherever he goes, there is all this upset."

"There is the other side, too," said the Abbot thoughtfully. "There are those churches restored; the lepers are certainly not starving. One of our men was down with some of the farmers today, and he said they were singing hymns in the fields there after their dinner. Anyway," he reassured his guest, "there's no danger that many of your rich men will give their holdings away to beggars and go off with the madman."

But the Bishop shrugged his shoulders. "After Peter Catanii, I do not know."

As it turned out, the Bishop was quite right. Even as they were talking, Francis was out begging his supper, and this time in a quarter of the city where his friends lived. For a little while he had stood shamefacedly at the edge of the Piazza San Rufino, where the house of the Offreducci rose. As the sound of singing came out cheerfully to him, he thought, "Here where I have been lord of the feast!" And then he said to himself, "It is pride which makes you hang back." And so he went into the courtyard, bright in the long twilight of summer. In the old Roman sarcophagus he could see some red flowers, geraniums perhaps, where the lilies had been. He looked up to the gallery above, but it was quite empty.

As he strode into the banqueting hall, one of the servants tried to stop him, but Francis raised his voice firmly, "For the love of God, and Christ, and Our Lady, my brethren," and Martin heard him and turned toward him with astonishment. Then as the whole room followed his look, he waited, and Francis came in, holding out his hand.

But Martin shook his head. "Did I not see you giving silver away in the street today?" he asked.

There was a roar of laughter over the hall. "No man eats silver," said Francis, and the laughter died away.

"Even madmen get hungry," said a mocking voice.

"Here!" said the young master of the house, and he took a broken piece of bread from his place and threw it onto the floor. But Francis went over and picked up the bread, and calling down the blessing of heaven on its giver, he said grace over it and began to eat. It was as if a ghost had come into the garlanded banqueting hall, and all the bright figures sat there as if frozen in their places. Then when he had eaten, Francis gave thanks again, and bowing to the company, he went out.

As he came out of the hall, he saw the Lady Clare standing over beyond the sarcophagus as if she were waiting to speak to him, but at that moment a young man whom Francis recognized as a cousin of the Offreducci of Coccorano, the young Faverone, came running up to him with a plate of meat and fresh bread, and he held it out to Francis— "For a hungry man, a little bread is nothing."

"For a hungry man," said Francis, looking at him, "a little bread is everything. But I have brethren; so I shall take your gift to them."

"That is not enough for more than one," said the young man. "Wait."

Francis stood for a moment by the sarcophagus holding the plate. He turned around, and it seemed to him that the Lady Clare was trying to speak but did not know how to begin. Then before he could find any way to help her, the young Faverone was back with a loaf and the remains of a joint on a platter. "I will help you carry these," he said.

Francis turned back to look for the Lady Clare, but she was gone. "Perhaps she wanted to give me an alms, too," he thought. Then he had to give the young man all his attention, for he wanted to know where his companions were lodging that night.

"I have not thought that far," said Francis, laughing at the young man's astonishment. "Supper was far enough for the present. As for lodging, we shall think of that later."

"And yet you gave a fortune away today."

"No, it was Brother Bernard who broke the last of his chains."

At the side of Bernard's house was a little arch into a courtyard, where in old days men had unloaded supplies from the country. There Francis found Bernard and Peter and an old servant of Bernard's, who was pleading with him, "You at least will sleep in your old chamber this night, my lord!"

"No, it belongs to another man."

"But at least," persisted the old servant, "let me bring you out one of your own beds."

"I have no bed. I have told you, fool," said Bernard gently. "I have nothing but this robe in which I stand."

Here Francis interposed, "I have brought you your supper, at least," and he looked back at the young man waiting behind him. "I think, too, that I have brought you another brother."

And the young man fell down at his feet and said, "Let me be one of your followers."

"No," said Francis. "We are all of us brethren here, and only in love shall any of us strive to be first."

Now the word flew all over the town and the surrounding countryside: one of the young Offreducci had walked out of the banqueting hall of his family. That madman had walked in, and he had looked at him, and he had followed him out into the night, and he had not come back. Some of his kinsmen had gone looking for him down in the underbrush around the Portiuncula, and they had found him there, carrying stones like any peasant, and he had laughed in their faces and said that this was where he was at home. Some of his old friends laughed now, but more grew silent as they heard the story. It was now more than three years since Francis had ceased to come and sing to them, and that loss they had all but forgotten, but now he had come back, and he had plucked one of them out as if with a magician's spell; so the story grew as it went from high tower to high tower.

"Thank God, at least," said the Podestà, "there will be no distribution of wealth at the Offreducci palace. Those robbers will know how to keep their own."

And the Bishop took his comfort, too. "It will do no harm if a few of those rioting sprigs of nobility sober up and take to honest labor." But the Bishop was much less cheerful when a week later he learned that Sylvester, the priest, after having thought over Francis' rebuke, had gone down to the Portiuncula and joined the Poor Penitents. "Peter Catanii was bad enough," said the Bishop, "but a priest and a parish priest at that!"

"He should have asked his Bishop's permission, certainly," said the Abbot Simon gravely.

"Thank God he didn't," said Guido.

"One of our men reported," said the Abbot Simon thoughtfully, "that there are several others down there, a handsome young peasant, a fellow that looks half-simple, or half-mad—he was not sure which—and probably some others by now. You might send someone down to look around."

"No," said the Bishop. "I'm going myself." But before he could tear himself away from his thronged antechamber, word came that the company down at the Portiuncula had broken up, and that they had gone off in pairs for some sort of mission or other, and the Bishop heaved a sigh of relief at the thought that for the present, at least, his troubles were over.

But he found out soon enough that he was quite mistaken, for reports began to come in from neighboring bishops. True, they were harmless enough for the most part. Two fellows calling themselves Penitents from Assisi had come into one town and had begun to preach along sound enough lines: penance, going to church, frequenting the sacraments. But when they began to beg, one or two solid citizens had protested that they had beggars enough of their own without any more coming in. Then some of the more lawless elements had begun to throw stones at them, and they had been glad enough to slip out under cover of darkness.

Another report told of an heir who had been bewitched and gone off with these vagabonds, and there were stories, too, of honest farmers' sons who had taken to roaming with them. But in general the reports agreed that the Penitents from Assisi had worked for their bread when they had a chance, and that what they preached could hardly be called heretical unless taking the letter of the Gospels literally was to be so termed.

The Bishop was ready to admit that it might have been worse, when reports began to come in of some sturdy rascals who had got lodging for the night on the ground that they were Poor Penitents from Assisi and had robbed their host. The priest Sylvester bothered the Bishop, too, wandering about without leave of his bishop and worrying proper home-staying parish priests as to whether they should allow him to use their altar for Mass. There was at least one story, too, of a young man who could not get on with the wife whom his father had given him and who had run away from home to join the Penitents. To do them justice, the latter had sent him home soon enough, and yet there was the threat of scandal. And now stories were beginning to drift back of crowds of listeners who had wept at the preaching of the madman from Assisi, and of thieves and bandits who had been converted, and even of a pair of neighboring lords who had made peace with each other. The Bishop noted that people were no longer laughing, and presently they had begun to talk as if this were some sort of "movement."

So as soon as the Bishop heard that the Penitents had come back to the Portiuncula, he went down with one servant to see them. He found them busily at work cleaning out the little church and carrying fresh stones for patching a piece of wall that had given way in the winter rains. It was as cheerful a company as the Bishop had seen in the spring fields, and he sat there watching them from his mule for several minutes before anybody noticed him. Then they all came flocking around him, kneeling down for his blessing with a simplicity that made it quite impossible for the Bishop to invoke episcopal authority even against the runaway priest, Sylvester.

"How many are you now?" he asked as they crowded around to help him down from his mule.

"We are Our Lord's own twelve," said Francis proudly.

"But," said the young peasant with the odd face that bothered the Bishop, "there are plenty that are looking at us, and we shall have more before the summer ends."

"What will you do with them?"

"Oh, we will put them to work. Surely, there is work enough, my lord."

"Twelve is enough for a convent," said the Bishop quietly. "Many a convent has started with fewer."

"My lord," pleaded Francis earnestly, "no convents!"

"The weather is fine now, but what will you do when the winter comes?"

"Oh," said Francis easily, "we will send them out again, two by two. My lord, let the brethren tell you their stories!"

But Guido shook his head. "Another time. There are other stories which I have heard, too."

"You know, my lord," said Francis gravely, "how it is. There were two rascals who said they were Penitents from Assisi; and now men talk as if there were a dozen."

"It is precisely because men talk," said the Bishop firmly, "that wise men take precautions."

"Do not coop us up," pleaded the odd-faced brother.

"Be still, Brother Juniper," said Francis. "My lord, you know that we shall obey you in all things that we can without disobeying Him who is the Master of both of us."

"Am I, who will have to answer for the souls of all of you at the Judgment Day, likely to ask you to do anything against His commands?"

"But, my lord, we have sworn on the Gospels that we would take poverty for our lot: 'Neither staff, nor scrip . . .'"

"Then the more important it is that you have some rule to guide you."

"But we have the Gospels, my lord."

"The Gospels! Men have had the Gospels for more than a thousand years, and do you think the Gospels have kept them from the sin and the folly that disgrace human history?"

"That," said Francis, "is because men have forgotten the Gospels. All we are trying to do is to remind them. We are taking the Book out into the fields and to the alleys and the byways, and we are making men look at the pages they have forgotten."

"It is not easy," said the Bishop, "to keep the pages clean in the fields and the alleys and the byways. Only the heretics claim they can do that."

But Francis flung himself at the Bishop's feet. "You know, my lord, that we have never claimed any perfection in us but only in Him who sent us."

The Bishop raised him gently and then he put the hand with the great ring on his. "This is not Palestine of the first century, my son. This is Umbria of the thirteenth, God forgive us all."

"Then what do you wish us to do, my lord?"

"If you will not settle properly in one place, then do you at least make yourself a rule of life so that men will know what they undertake when they join you, and so that the rest of the world will know who belongs to you, and who steals your name. And then take this rule to

Rome and get it approved as men desirous of perfection have always done."

"To Rome!" said Francis, with shining eyes.

The Bishop shook his head. "Be sure you have that rule."

2

When Bishop Guido returned to Assisi, he sent word to the Abbot Simon at the Benedictine abbey and asked him if he would come to his palace that day to see if he could help the Penitents. Francis would not wait for him, however, but dictated to Brother Leo, whom he had taken for his secretary, the three texts which they had read in the church of San Nicolo.

"It is not enough," said Peter of Catanii.

"Then add to it the rest of what Luke says."

"Even so, this is merely a series of Scripture texts. It is no proper rule."

"It is our charter. You have said so yourself, Brother Peter," said Francis.

When the Abbot Simon came that night, Francis had a rule ready for him and the Bishop.

"But this is all negative," said the Benedictine when he had finished reading the very brief document. "It says that you shall not have any houses or possessions. What are the positive things that you are doing and will do? And there is no mention here of the good works that men say that you do, and I think you will not deny—taking care of lepers, preaching the Gospel to the poor . . ." The Benedictine went on quietly, putting the case for these unconventional religious brethren as generously as he could. Even Francis was astonished that the low, reasonable voice of the Abbot could make it all sound so normal, even so well-established.

"Well," he said at last, "simply write that we will do whatever good works God gives us to do."

"Are you sure of that?" said the Abbot. "Will you open a school?"

"Oh, no!" Francis drew back hastily.

"There is no reason why you should," said the Abbot quietly. "But there are limits on what you undertake to do, and I think you should face them."

"Then," said Francis, "I will let Peter and Bernard tell Leo what to write."

"Francis," said the Abbot gravely, "you are the head to whom they look."

"No, Our Lord Christ is the head to whom we all look."

"Even among the twelve," said the Abbot Simon quietly, "Our Lord chose one. He was not the one whom He loved most, nor was he the best educated, nor perhaps even morally the best. But Our Lord chose Peter, and the others—John and Luke and all the rest—took him for their head."

But Francis protested, "You know, my lord, better than any of these that I am not made to be a ruler."

"I think Peter must have thought that in the beginning," said the Abbot.

And then the peasant, Giles, who had come in without anyone noticing him in order that he might bring word to the others back at the Portiuncula as to how their companions were faring with the ecclesiastical dignitaries, said, "When I left home, I took you for my father. Shall we not say, then, that Francis is the father of us all?"

"No," said Francis. "Our Father in heaven is the father of us all. I am only your little brother."

"It does not matter what you call it," said the Abbot Simon; and then he turned to Leo, "Why don't you write it, and then when you have written, let him read."

It took several days more of work before they finally got something which Francis would admit came near his intention, and then he said it sounded too much like the lawyers. So, taking the points which they had made, he dictated them afresh to Leo.

That evening when Francis had read the latest revision, underscoring two points again and again—that devotion to poverty was the mainspring of their enterprise and that always the brethren should count themselves among the least of men—the Bishop looked at the Abbot. "How do you think that will sound to the Cardinal of Ostia?"

"Like nothing he has ever heard before," said the Abbot cheerfully. And then as the brethren waited, "But I suspect that with all the things he reads and hears, he will say that he could well do with something new. Take it with you."

The Bishop gazed with astonishment at his friend, and then he wrote out his own letter to the Cardinal, telling him that these men,

however odd, were still faithful children of the Church. Then he
wrote a letter for the Cardinal to give to the Pope, if ever it should
come that far, saying that the Poor Penitents had their bishop's blessing, and he would do his best to see that no ill to the Church came of it.
"God knows that is a lot to undertake," said Guido, shaking his head
at the little man standing before him. But Francis swore that they
would do nothing of which the Bishop would ever be ashamed to hear.
So it was arranged that Francis, Leo, Bernard, Peter, Sylvester, and
Giles should go to Rome. All the brethren would have liked to go, and
Francis would have liked to take them all, but the Bishop had pointed
out that six men were enough to inflict on the hospitable. Although
he was burning to go, Giles offered to stay. But Francis would hear
nothing of it. It would give the Pope a very wrong impression of them
if they left Giles at home, for they were really simple men like Brother
Giles rather than learned like Brother Sylvester and Brother Peter.

The Bishop offered fresh tunics for the journey that they might
come to Rome looking like pilgrims and not beggars, but that suggestion Francis rejected out of hand. If they did see the Pope, the Pope
must see them as they were. And so with the Abbot's offer of bread for
the journey. For this, as for everything, they must trust to the goodness
of God. Clearly both ecclesiastics regarded this as a discouraging beginning of the mission to Rome, and Bernard and Peter looked grave.
But Francis was firm. There was no point in getting the Pope's approval
for something they had no intention of doing.

But just before they reached the Flaminian Way, Francis to the
astonishment of Bernard and Peter called the little company to a halt
and said to them, "My brethren, this is a great mission on which we
are going, and it is only right that we should put the direction of it in
the hands of one of us who shall be the leader, and his voice shall be
the voice of God to us."

Perhaps Bernard was tired of the long arguments over the rule, for
he looked quizzically at Francis and said simply, "We will do what you
wish as we always do."

"No," said Francis, "you know I have no talent for business, but you
have had much experience in telling a man to come and he cometh—
and the rest of it."

"He is right, Bernard," said Peter gravely. And seeing that Francis
was in earnest, the rest of the company agreed.

"I will then," said Bernard, "if you will tell me what to do."

But Francis had already begun to sing a marching song of the pilgrims coming from France to the holy city. So it was Bernard who decided when they would offer their services in the fields they passed through, and when it was foolish to linger to work and they might accept charity. Always Francis was the first to agree to whatever Bernard suggested; so they came with only reasonable delays and in good order to Rome. Only then did Bernard notice the quickening of Francis' breath and the excitement that warmed his song. He was not surprised, therefore, when Francis gaily brushed aside his suggestion that they stop first at one of the pilgrim hostels, and wash their faces, and dust their clothes before presenting themselves at the Cardinal of Ostia's door.

"Oh, no, Brother Bernard," he said. "It is still early in the afternoon. Let us go on to the tomb of Peter."

Remembering the story of Francis' first visit to Rome, Bernard watched him closely as he knelt down at the tomb of the first Pope. But this time Francis seemed completely unaware of anyone around him, and after only the briefest of prayers he arose and took Bernard's hand.

"Now let us go," he said. And as they hurried along out of St. Peter's, he told Bernard that since it was still early in the afternoon he was sure the Pope would not have left his audience chamber.

"But shouldn't we see the Cardinal of Ostia first?" asked Bernard.

"Oh, no. If the Pope will see us, why waste time?"

Bernard started to marshall his arguments, but Francis was already dancing ahead on light feet. It took all Bernard's breath to keep up with him, and Peter and the rest straggled behind. Only when they reached the door of the Lateran Palace did Bernard invoke his forgotten authority. "We cannot go into the Pope's presence looking like this."

"How else should we look?" asked Francis in astonishment. "We are pilgrims come to Rome, and the moment we get here, we throw ourselves at his feet as good sons should."

"The porter will throw us out as vagabonds," said Peter.

"Then I shall cry for the master of the house," responded Francis with perfect seriousness. "Do you think a little dust will blind the Pope's keen eyes? God has brought us safely here. Why should we waste the time He has given us?" And Francis would hardly stand still until Bernard could show the letter from the Bishop of Assisi to one of the Pope's chamberlains. As Bernard talked, Francis hung back a little, and the chamberlain looked from Bernard to Peter, and he saw that in spite of their rough dress these were men of substance; so he passed them on to another ecclesiastic.

"The public audience for today is ending," said the latter. "Come this way." And he took them down a little hall to the Pope's audience chamber and bade them go up and kneel down at the foot of the Pope's throne.

As they came into the room, Bernard saw with relief that the Cardinal of Ostia was standing with several other high-ranking ecclesiastics to one side of the throne, and he wondered if it would be better perhaps to try to get his attention first. But while he wondered, Francis darted forward and flung himself on the ground and kissed the Pope's feet. Perhaps the Pope was weary from the day's throng of pilgrims, for as Francis rose to his feet and flung his arms wide before him, Innocent asked, "Who let this swineherd in?" And then fixing an eye on the little man that had made many a more important man quail, he spoke sharply, "Little swineherd, go back to your pigs in their sty." And he shook his robes as he stood up from his throne.

Bernard and the rest had fallen on their knees as Francis went forward, and now they arose uncertainly, and Bernard looked for the Cardinal of Ostia and tried to catch his eye. But the Cardinal was looking as if fascinated at the little figure of Francis darting out of the audience chamber.

"That has ended our hopes," said Bernard, and he seized Peter Catanii's arm, and they strode out of the antechamber as fast as they could. They had almost reached the door when one of the Pope's servants caught Peter's arm.

"My Lord of Ostia would speak with you."

The Pope was standing by his throne talking with some of the cardinals, and as Peter came up, he heard his voice clear and ringing. "I'm not sure but if we had a little more regard for decency we should have to worry less about heresy."

As Peter knelt down, the Cardinal looked at him. "You were an intelligent enough man when I saw you in the Bishop's place," he said severely. "What are you doing here in this madman's company?" But before Peter could answer, there came a shout at the door and then a tumult, and as the Pope stopped and looked angrily around, a little figure shot through and fell at his feet. And at the stench, the cardinals drew back and the Pope looked down.

"Get away from me, madman!" he called sharply.

As Francis rose to his feet, he looked up into the angry face of Innocent. "I have done what you told me to do, my lord. You told me to go to the pigs and I have," and he flung his reeking arms wide.

For a moment, the angry Pope stood speechless, looking from the man before him to his companions, standing frozen with horror behind him, and then to the cardinals at his side.

"What you told me to do, my lord, I did as I always will!"

Innocent thought that the lips of the Cardinal of Ostia were trembling, and he spoke to him sharply. "My Lord of Ostia?"

But the Cardinal said only, "Obedience is hardly the mark of a heretic, Your Holiness."

Innocent looked down at the grotesque figure before him, with the slime of the pigpen dripping on the marble floor. "Get out of here," he said. And then as the little man still stood, and his companions wavered, Innocent's face softened. "Go out and clean yourself up and come back here tomorrow, and I will listen to you." As Francis knelt down to grasp his feet again, the Pope pulled his robes away from him. There was a little titter now in the room, and the Pope swept the company with a dark eye that had suddenly grown cold. Then as the little man rose to his feet, he turned to him again. "Wait a moment! Where did you find that pigpen to roll in?"

"Over there, back of the stables beyond Your Holiness' palace."

"But how did you know where to look for it?"

"Oh," said Francis, "as we came in through the city and they said, 'There are the Pope's stables,' I smelt the pigpen, and I thought the Pope's pigs smell no better than any peasant's pigs." Now there was a roar of laughter all over the room.

"Get you gone!" said Innocent. Then he turned back at the door and looked at the Cardinal of Ostia. "Come tomorrow morning, and tell me what you can of these madmen from Assisi."

It was with some uncertainty that Ugolino went into the Pope's presence the next morning. There had been, he knew, a letter from Germany that must have made yesterday's episode seem a grotesque trifle. But as he dropped to his knees, the Pope pushed the parchment away. "What is this madman of yours up to now?" he began abruptly.

"He was at my door at dawn, Your Holiness, with his rule."

"Never mind the rule," said the Pope. "Ugolino, do you ever dream nights?"

"Dream?" said the Cardinal. He had often told his friends that serving Pope Innocent might or might not be the world's most important job, as his flatterers said, but it was certainly the most interesting, for one never knew quite where the mind of His Holiness might be. You would think you had followed his thought, and then suddenly he would be challenging you from the opposite direction. Now Ugolino remembered one other thing about the Pope. He might not believe what one told him, but it was very difficult to surprise him. So now the Cardinal of Ostia smiled. "As a matter of fact, I did have a dream last night."

"What was it?"

"Oh," said Ugolino, "I would not take it too seriously."

"Who said anything about taking it seriously? What did you dream?"

Again the Cardinal spread his hands, palms up. "I was a long time falling asleep. It was the first time I had seen that little madman, though I had heard about him often enough."

"But what did you dream?" persisted the Pope.

"I was out on a lake," said the Cardinal, "on Trasimene, which I crossed once when I was up in that Umbrian country. There was a sudden storm in my dream and a high wind, and the boat was overloaded. Indeed, for a moment I thought it was sinking. And then—" the Cardinal paused and smiled.

"And then—"

"I don't know how to put it."

The Pope studied the face in front of him. "Christ walking on the waters?" he asked, his eyes narrowing.

A look of sadness came into the Cardinal's face. "Oh, no, my lord, not even in my dreams am I worthy to see Him. But there was a light, only I could not see what was beyond the light, and there was a voice spoke though I could not hear what the voice was saying."

"A very good figure for all of us," said the Pope thoughtfully. "And was that all?"

"Not quite all," said the Cardinal, frowning a little. "Of course," he said, "this is what caused it all. You see, the little madman was in the boat with me, and when the voice spoke, he scrambled out of the boat.

Naturally, I tried to stop him, but he was too quick, and he began to walk on the water."

"And he began to walk on the water?" said the Pope.

"Yes, absurd, isn't it?"

But the Pope did not smile. "There is something infectious about his madness. I had a dream, too. I dreamed that I was lying there in my great bed, and I could not sleep. Through the curtains of my bed I could see the Lateran Church. It was very close, and yet it was small enough so that I could see it all. It seemed as if I could put out a hand and touch it, and as I looked, the church began to tilt, as if it were going to fall over my bed. When I tried to cry out, the voice was strangled in my throat so that I could not make the servants either by the bed or at the door hear. And then," said the great Pope, "just as I thought it would fall over the bed, a little man appeared and he shored up the wall on his shoulder, and it was steady. When the wall was quite straight again, the little man turned toward me and it was—"

"The little madman from Assisi," said Ugolino.

Innocent nodded.

"Bernard and Peter never struck me as fools," said Ugolino, watching the Pope. "There is something catching about it," and he smiled as he had so often, to break with a jest a deadlock in men's minds.

"I'm not sure," said the Pope thoughtfully, "that I should mind if this madness spread a little further. Have you read the rule?"

"If you can call it that," said the Cardinal cautiously.

"Does it make sense to you?"

"Yes," said the Cardinal, "if you take those Gospel sayings of theirs literally."

"You're quite sure? You remember that's what the heretics are always doing."

"Oh, this is totally different from the heretics," said the Cardinal. "There's no talk here of other people's sins or of the corruption of the Church, but only of making all things new again. They say the little fellow has been cleaning up and rebuilding some little churches around Assisi, at that."

"I suspect that that's the way he sees it. Did you ask him what he meant by it all anyway?"

"Oh, yes," said the Cardinal. "I told him that all I could see wrong in the rule—and mind you, I'm quite sure that although Peter and Bernard have put the points in some sort of order, the curious stuff of the thing is his—I told him I could see no harm in it, but it seemed to me that it was more than men could do. Then he asked me what I thought Our Lord meant when He said those various hard sayings of His. And when I began to tell him what some of the commentators had said, he reminded me that he was a simple man, and though he honored Jerome and Augustine as holy men and great fathers of the Church, yet he did not want anything of them. All he wanted to do, he said, was to behave as if Christ were there in Umbria, and they were His twelve disciples. Simple enough, isn't it?" said the Cardinal wryly.

But the Pope paused as if he had caught the sound of some distant voice, and then he said thoughtfully, "Christ in Umbria! Brother Ugolino, no one puts us, however much they may despise us, among the world's fools; and we work long days and we wake longer nights, and God only knows what shall come of our best counsels. Christ in Umbria? Let the little man try it."

So the Pope summoned Francis, and he told him that he might go on with the way of life indicated in the rule, and he gave him the responsibility for the guidance of the fraternity. Then in the Pope's presence, the brethren promised obedience to Francis, and Francis promised obedience to the Pope. Innocent would have ordained Francis priest on the spot, but he declared himself quite unworthy. All he would agree to was the diaconate for himself, and the small tonsure for the brethren not yet in orders. As for parchment or written license, they were quite unnecessary once the Pope had spoken.

When the Pope had given his blessing, Francis, followed by his brethren, went out of the audience chamber as if literally he were walking on the bodiless air. The great Pope looked after him, and for the first time in all his years he wished he were the young Lothario Conti again, and the world young to be saved by his faith and good will. Then he turned in a business-like way to the Cardinal of Ostia and said, "Watch this venture. Curb the wind if you can, my lord."

3

But since they stopped frequently on the way back to preach, or to work in the fields for their bread, or to visit lepers, or even to clean up a neglected church, the autumn was well advanced when Francis and his companions returned to Assisi. Francis would have gone straight to the brethren at the Portiuncula, but Brother Bernard pointed out that in view of the Bishop's friendly letter to the Pope it was hardly courteous not to tell him of their success. So it was agreed that they should go to the Bishop's palace before they took the road to the plain. Francis was disappointed, therefore, when they reached the Bishop's palace to find that the Bishop had already had a messenger from the Cardinal of Ostia, and that the Cardinal was disposed to take a real interest in the future of the new brotherhood.

"The Cardinal has written to the Abbot Simon," said Guido, "and the Benedictines have given me the deed to the Portiuncula and to the land around it."

But Francis would still have none of it. "My lord," he said, "we have espoused My Lady Poverty and we cannot accept any deeds to property. We have the Pope's approval for this, too," said Francis.

"But do you not see," said the Bishop, when Francis had told his wonderful story all over again, "this doesn't mean that he has approved any rule for you? It means simply that he has given permission for you to try to see what you can do. And you may be sure that any approval of a rule will depend," said the Bishop severely, "on the use you make of this opportunity. What do you think the Cardinal of Ostia will report to the Pope if you fling this generous gift of the Benedictines back in his face?"

Francis was adamant. They had the Pope's permission. Nobody could gainsay that. In vain the Bishop appealed to Bernard. "Are you not the leader of this undertaking? I'm sure it was because he saw the mission in the hands of so experienced a man as yourself that the Cardinal of Ostia recommended you to His Holiness."

But Bernard was emphatic. Francis was the leader, and if he said they could not accept the Benedictines' deed, then that was the end of the matter.

Appealed to again, Francis took refuge in whimsy. "What do you think we should do with the Abbot's parchment down at the Portiuncula? Thrust it up under the eaves where the winter rains will drip on it through the thatch and spoil the fine writing?" he asked.

"You don't need to take it down there," said the Bishop in exasperation. "You can leave it here with me."

"That is true," said Peter, who had been watching the altercation. "You need never touch the deed. It can remain in the Bishop's hands."

Francis would still have none of it. "I should be then the hypocrite that my father called me," he said, and his face darkened, and Peter knelt down and asked for his forgiveness. "It is hard for a lawyer to forget his craft," said Francis. And then at the pain on Peter's face, he, too, knelt down and asked forgiveness in turn.

So the Bishop was forced to report to his friend the Abbot that their kindly arrangement had come to nothing. "Never mind," said Simon. "With the deed or without, we will not disturb them, and they will be sure at least of a roof for the winter."

But he had reckoned without Francis. As soon as the brethren at the Portiuncula had welcomed them with delight, and the priest Sylvester had led them in singing a Te Deum in the little church, Francis told his companions that they must give up the Portiuncula. It was a blow, for all through the summer the brethren who had been left at home had worked hard at clearing away some of the land around the little church and making a garden. They had even raised some walls at the side of the church, which would take only thatching to give them shelter in the winter. But Francis shuddered when they showed him their handiwork so proudly, and he told them that this was only the beginning of temptation. If they went on with the little shelter by the church, they would be presently taking the Benedictines' deed, and then they would be holing themselves up in a fortress here when without the fields were white with the harvest to be reaped. In vain, the brethren who had remained reminded Francis that they had preached and worked in the fields and tended the lepers, and their work at the Portiuncula had in no way interfered with their living the kind of life he had taught them.

But Francis was obdurate. For him, a shadow had come over their loved refuge. "Men have heard the angels singing here," he said, "but I tell you the devils are closing in." So he left the Portiuncula, and while the brethren went out to help the farmers with the harvest and so win bread for the lepers, and for themselves, and for the poor who had taken to coming to the little church, Francis took Brother Giles with him and went to look for a new spot where they might settle—in a desolate region in the plain below San Damiano. It was in a loop of the little river, the Rivo Torto, that Francis found what he was looking for, a deserted barn or shack of weatherbeaten timber with the freshening autumn wind blowing through the broken slats of the wall, and the torn thatch swinging crazily in the sunlight.

"No one has been here for years," said Giles.

"That is why I asked you to come with me. Have you ever heard of any man owning this wilderness?"

And Giles who had lived in this region all his life could not remember. As a boy he had followed a stray calf to the loop of the river and been frightened by his playmates with tales of ghosts who had been heard in the ruined shed. The roof was fairly intact then, but there were bats under the eaves, and the boys had frightened each other out of the place soon enough. Even the tales of the haunted ruin had been forgotten in the intervening years, and Giles was quite sure that they would not be troubled by any claims of ownership. So in the next weeks when there was a little time in the early morning before they went to the Portiuncula for Mass, or in the evening when they had returned from the harvest or from preaching in the neighboring villages, Francis led his companions in patching the rain-gutted walls and replacing the decaying thatch. And as they stuffed the spaces between the planks of the walls with mud, Francis happily bade Leo write down that henceforth all the shelters of the Companions should be of wood and mud and thatch. "Stone is a temptation," he said. "A man with a stone house is tied to the earth."

"But at least we can use the little church," said Sylvester wistfully.

"Only," said Francis, "until we can have a wooden church. For churches, also, should be made poor and simple so that men will not be tempted to adorn the stone and the mortar but will think only of the miracle of the presence of God that is forever renewed within their walls." But it was too late now to think of building a chapel of wood and mud; so Sylvester continued to go to the Portiuncula to say Mass on its ancient stone altar, and the peasants continued to come in now and then to receive the sacraments, or to bring a child for baptism, or to ask Sylvester to come and visit the sick and dying. When they came back from the market and tried to make little offerings to Sylvester of the coins they had brought with them, Francis bade Sylvester refuse them. "For presently you will have a treasury for the church, and then the robbers will be tempted to break in. But let them give us food, which will sustain all the brethren; and whatever is left over, we can give to the lepers and the poor." He was quite inflexible on this point. When the son of one prosperous farmer sent a handsome copper pitcher full of wine to Sylvester for a gift for his services to his father on his deathbed, Francis bade Sylvester return the copper pitcher when they had drunk the wine. However, the farmer insisted on replacing the copper pitcher with two clay pitchers full of country wine, and these Francis allowed Sylvester to keep, for in the rough red country earthenware there could be no temptation.

When the winter rains came, and it was no longer possible to work in the fields, and even the road to the leper hospital was deep in mud, then Francis proudly gathered up all his brethren into the little hut at Rivo Torto. Their dozen now had grown to a score, and Bernard, who could never quite give over his habit of careful planning, asked Francis how the little hut could hold so many.

"It will be like a choir," said Francis gaily, "and each man will have his little stall against the wall, and there will be a space down the middle where we can pass." So Francis bade the brethren lie down, each with his head to the wall and his feet to the center of the hut, and as he said, there was just room for each of the twenty to stretch out on his straw and to turn without jabbing his neighbor's ribs. Likewise, between their bare feet their was an aisle down which one might just pass. "Is it not like a church choir, Brother Sylvester?" asked Francis, surveying the recumbent brethren with pride.

"Yes," said the priest, "if every man keep his place and sing in tune."

So Francis bade Sylvester lead them in a simple little office, with one side answering the other in a rude chant. Sylvester offered to teach the whole company some of the Psalms of the Hours that they might praise God in proper fashion. But Francis, who had seen the anxiety on the faces of Giles and Juniper, bade him remember that not all the brethren knew Latin. So for the canonical hours Sylvester had to be content with a very simple chanting of the Paternoster, with a rhapsodic paraphrase which Francis added to each petition, and a few antiphonal verses of praise for a close. And when the singers for cold and weariness flagged, Francis would take a couple of sticks and, mimicking a violplayer, would sing until presently the whole laughing company was singing with him. "There is not a fairer choir in Christendom," said Francis with delight as the rain beat on the thatch above their heads, and the voices rose, rough and warm. Outside some shepherds, bringing in the last strays of their flocks, heard the singing; and two of the lepers, bogged in the mud on their way back to the hospital, heard it, too. And so the legend was started that the angels were singing not only as of old about Saint Mary of the Angels, as the peasants of the region were accustomed to call the Portiuncula, but also about the thatched eaves of the little shed in the bend of the Rivo Torto.

But it was not all singing that winter in the hut, for though the brethren huddled together for warmth, the north wind found its finger's breadth under the eaves, and the rain washed away the mud. There was hunger, too. There was little work on the land, and too many beggars were knocking at the doors of the villages and the farms and even the houses of Assisi. The beggars must be taken care of first, too. Many a night Francis led the grace over a pot of porridge that had been liberally watered that there might be enough thin gruel for twenty men.

One night one of the younger brethren, the son of a prosperous farmer, awoke screaming with fright and brought half the brethren tumbling to his side. "I am dying with hunger!" he cried, and when a wood faggot had been lighted, and all the startled sleepers looked upon the frightened youth clutching his thin belly, Brother Juniper laughed and bade him tie the cord lower.

"A little pinching outside and you will not feel the pinching inside," said Juniper. "You farmers don't know how more experienced men of the world handle these things."

And the young man, embraced by the flickering light of the faggot and the anxious hovering of his brethren, was ashamed and hid his face in his arms and began to weep. But Francis went to the shelf near the door, which Brother Giles had built so that any food left over for a chance beggar might be safe from the rats that scampered through the open door, and took a few crusts of bread and offered them to the young brother. But when he refused to eat the crusts which he eyed ravenously, Francis sat down at his side and began to gnaw companionably at a crust, assuring him that hunger was nothing to be ashamed of. And he apologized to all his brethren that he had not thought enough of the patient beasts that carried their valiant spirits, and the next day he sent Giles and Leo up into Assisi to beg for bread. "They like their beggars handsome, these finicky townsmen of ours," he laughed. "The country folk in the plain here are less fussy."

"Then," said Brother Juniper, "let us you and I, Brother Francis, go together into the fields. Nobody is meaner-looking than we."

That night there was enough for all to eat, but Leo and Giles reported that more than one door had been shut in their faces. Apparently their refusal of the Benedictines' gift was known in the town, for there were several who taunted them and said, "Go up to the Benedictines and let them take care of their own."

And among the farmers there were one or two, also, who asked, "Are you mad? When you might be living at the Portiuncula, piling yourselves up in a sty that is worse even than the lepers have?"

"But the Portiuncula belongs to God," said Francis.

"Then let God take care of his own," retorted the farmer. And the word which Francis had not heard for a long time was spat at him again, "Madman!"

It was perhaps that revived charge of madness that before the winter was quite over emboldened one of the peasants to thrust open the door of the little shed at Rivo Torto before the brethren had arisen one morning, and while the astonished men blinked in the gray winter dawn, the churl shouted, "Come in here, ass, and join your brethren." Before any of them could move, he drove the animal into the aisle between their feet and bade the creature make himself at home. The peasant was nearly routed by the laughter of the brethren, but the ass stubbornly refused to leave the dried hay which he had begun to eat. And when Francis began to remonstrate with the peasant, the sullen fellow insisted that he had bought the land on which the shack stood the harvest before, and it was time that he drove the squatters out.

There was nothing for it but to return to the chapel of the Portiuncula. But though pilgrims had lain on its stone floor for centuries, twenty were too many for continuous occupation. So Francis went up with Peter Catanii to see the Abbot Simon on Monte Subasio. The porter at the gate did not recognize them, and he scolded them, "It has been nothing but beggars all winter," he said, "and the cooks are weary even of baking their bread."

But when the Abbot saw Peter and Francis, he exclaimed in horror, "It is a poor return to our friendliness that you starve down there without letting us know."

"We have survived the winter," said Francis stoutly, "but we have been driven from our nest and called squatters."

"You know—" said the Abbot and then he broke off. "Let me at least feed you before we talk. No man's reason was ever sharpened by hunger." And when he saw that Francis and Peter ate but a little of the good loaf of bread and thrust the rest into their sleeves, the Abbot sent his servant away for more loaves. "Look," said he, "if you will not take a gift, let us rent it to you."

"But wherewithal should we pay rent?" asked Francis.

"Pay us in kind with what you have there."

"I do not know what you would find," said Francis. "Even if we cleared the ground, it would be a long time to a crop. But wait a minute—" he said. "I noticed that the loaches were running in the stream as we came away."

"Lent is coming," said the Abbot. "A basket of loaches! That shall be your rent."

"But we shall lodge there, my lord, only so long as we pay our rent."

"Yes, a basket full of loaches every Lent."

"It is but for now," said Francis with surprising caution.

"As long as you like," said the Abbot.

So they went back to the Portiuncula, and as soon as the warm spring sun had dried out some of the bushes and a patch of earth, Francis and his companions built a shed like the one at Rivo Torto, of wattle and mud. They laid saplings across for a roof, and with mud and dried leaves from the floor of the wood near-by they made themselves a dormitory to which they might come back from the day's labors, for now that the fields were drying, the farmers were cleaning out their barns and beginning to plow, and there was work for a man to do. So there was food, and when Mass was said in the morning and the brethren started out for the day's labor, it was possible to leave one of them behind to prepare the meal for the evening. It was a happy homecoming when the brethren who had been nursing the lepers, and the brethren who had been begging in the town and preaching, and the brethren who had been working in the fields heard the Angelus and turned their faces home, for now there was a steaming pot to crouch around in their hut as they told of the day's adventures.

But even this pleasant arrangement had its problems. One day Francis came home to find the young brother who had been left in charge of the preparation of the supper standing in front of the little hut looking down the road.

"What are you waiting for, Brother Angelo?" asked Francis.

"Thank God somebody has come!" replied the young brother.

"What do you mean?" And then Francis noticed how excited the youth was. Usually Angelo Tarlati was a rather composed youth, as was to be expected of a young man who had already made his mark as a knight. But now his eyes were shining, and Francis' heart went out to him.

"What happened?" said Francis. Now a couple of the other brethren had come back from San Lazzaro, and Francis saw the glint in the youth's eyes as they waited in expectancy.

"Some robbers came!" he said. "Three of them," and his voice rang out with excitement.

"But what is there to steal here?" asked Francis.

"They tried to steal our supper! The supper of the brethren!"

"Perhaps they were hungry," said Francis. The youth's face fell, and then a look of indignation replaced the excitement. Francis had worried about him when he first came, for he had looked like someone who might be swept away by an enthusiasm, and Francis was not sure how long he would stay.

"They tried to seize the food," said Angelo, "and I told them the food was being prepared for honest men who were laboring for their supper and not for thieves and wastrels like them!"

But now it was Francis' eye that flashed. "What a rude way to talk to people!" And then as the boy's indignation collapsed like a pricked bladder, Francis moved in on him inexorably, "How do you think men will ever be won to love God and repent of their sins if you treat them so rudely when they come to you?"

"But," said the young brother, growing a little angry now in his disappointment, "it was my charge to protect the food of the brethren."

"It is your charge," said Francis as the brethren gathered around, "to feed the hungry. Which way did they go, these 'robbers' of yours?"

"They went over to the wood toward San Damiano."

"Then go, and when you have found them, kneel down and apologize to them for the way you have talked, and bid them come back and sup with us." Then as he saw the youth look at the wood and at the sky where the sun was already beginning to dip toward sunset, Francis took compassion on him, and he asked Brother Giles to go with him. Then as he saw Giles look hungrily in the direction of the steaming pot, Francis promised, "We will wait for you."

It was dark before Angelo and Giles brought the three robbers back. The latter had lain down to sleep in the wood, a little ashamed that they had let one man rout them, but there had been stories of angels and of devils about the strange company in the clearing around the Portiuncula. Then, too, the young brother had been so indignant that they had not been sure that he did not have reinforcements within hearing. So they had wasted the afternoon, and now, when the young brother flung himself at their feet and Giles stood by watching, one of the robbers remembered that they had heard that these men were mad, too; and another decided that if there were more reserves like Giles in the company, perhaps they had better accept a fair invitation to supper. So the robbers came back, and when they reached the house by the Portiuncula and found all the brethren still waiting with watering mouths around the steaming pot, they looked at each other in astonishment. When Francis in the name of all the brethren invited them to sit down and take their portion first, one of them looked at the others and said, "Indeed, they are mad!"

But one of the robbers, who was not much older than Brother Angelo himself, said, "It is a miracle!" and he began to eat hungrily. Only when they had all eaten and had said grace did Francis ask them why they lived by robbery when they might live like honest men.

One of the robbers rose abruptly then and thanked Francis for his food but asked if he might be excused the sermon. There was a little cry of anger among the brethren at the insult, but Francis bade them be still. What they had given, they had given freely for the love of God, and no man could be compelled to take what God himself had left man free to accept or reject. So Francis bade his companions let the man go; and as he watched him go, Francis began to weep. Brother Angelo wept, too, and then one of the robbers—the young one—began to weep, and he threw himself at Francis' feet and begged him to let him stay with them.

But Peter Catanii looked grave; so when Francis, drying his tears, had embraced the young robber, he asked Peter why he did not rejoice, too.

"What credit do you think it will do us with the Bishop or the Cardinal when it gets around that we are a refuge for thieves?" asked the canon lawyer.

"It was a thief who went first with Christ to Paradise," said Francis. And then he turned to the other robber.

But he said only, "Give me time to think." In the morning he was gone; but the young robber arose with the brethren and when he had listened to Mass, he sought out Brother Leo and asked him to hear his confession that he might again be a member of the Church and begin to work his way to some deserving of the new fellowship that had embraced him. And Francis laughed gaily and called him Brother Angelo's convert and bade him follow Brother Angelo, whose turn it was now to go into the fields and look for work.

By now Francis was used to the resentment of the families from whom he snatched his converts. In vain he assured them that the eldest son who left his father's fields, or the young lord who rode down the drawbridge of his ancestral castle, or the young merchant who tore himself away from his father's shop or left the caravan to find its way home without him, or even the young student who gave up his studies at the university, or the priest who left his chaplaincy in the house of a noble lord, would in the brotherhood of the Poor Penitents return riches beyond any hope he had taken from those who relied on him. Francis knew that it was not only the secular powers of this world who blamed him, but the great doctors at the university who saw their brightest hope put on beggar's dress and take to wandering through the fields, and the bishop who had at last seen a worthy shepherd installed in an unruly parish—these, too, were disturbed. "What would happen to the world," said one indignant bishop who met Francis on the road, "if all of us left our places and turned vagabonds?"

It seemed as if the return to the Portiuncula were a signal for recruits to flood in, for Francis was kept so busy receiving new brethren and coming to know what manner of men they were, and deciding what work they could best do, that he quite forgot about the world outside. It seemed to him sometimes that he was like the mother of a busy household, with no time to think of anything beyond the immediate personal needs of her children. He was shocked when this absorption of his was brought home to him by the news toward the end of the next autumn that the Lady Pica had died. Some of the beggars had brought it, passing on, as was their wont, scraps out of their budget of gossip. Sylvester the priest said the Vespers for the Dead for her in the little chapel of the Portiuncula, and Francis and all the brethren who were at home knelt and made the responses as best they could. And then Francis and Leo went up to their old parish church of San Nicolo, where she lay in front of the altar with tapers burning at her head and feet.

Francis took one look at the still face, looking so clear and haughty and aloof against the white linen folds, and he began to shake with sobs. His brother Angelo, who had been watching the bier, turned at the sound and started up with an angry hiss, "Murderer!" And then a couple of the servants laid hold upon him, and Leo took Francis' arm and pulled him away.

There were a good many people in the church of Francis' childhood. Francis saw them only as dim shapes as he made his way to the door, and the stranger that his mother's face had become to him seemed to Francis a symbol of all that old life in Assisi. But the next morning when the priest Sylvester had said the Mass for the Dead at the Portiuncula, Francis came out of the little church to find a horseman waiting for him. He was a handsome young fellow in a bright cloak, and with his recent return to Assisi still in his mind and the shade of that old life around him, Francis noted that it was good solid stuff such as might have come from the shop of Bernardone. And with an effort Francis, peering into the face of the young man, recognized another young cousin of the Offreducci.

"Paul, I think you are," he said.

The young man's face lighted and then sobered. "I bring you a message from the Lady Clare," he said.

"Come," said Francis, leading him aside where they could sit on a broken tombstone.

"She heard," the young man began awkwardly, and then he plunged, "she thought you ought to know that the women who watched with your mother told everybody she died content. She spoke of the prophecy of the beggar at the door that great things would come of that child, and she said she was sure that great things would come." He turned aside as Francis put his head in his hands, but he was still there when Francis looked up.

"I put her in Our Lady's keeping long ago," he said gently. "I knew she would not fail." Then he saw that the young man still lingered. "He must be curious," he thought, and aloud he said, "Would you like to come in and see our church?" Then he took the young man over to look at the dormitory and at the new workshop for the making of wooden bowls and wooden spoons where some of the older brethren, who were not used to working in the fields, and the sick, might yet earn their bread. He picked up a rough fiddle which lay on the bench and he struck the strings, and he began to sing a little French hunting song which he used to sing with the young heir of the Offreducci and his other friends. At that the grave young man smiled. Then they went out again, but the young man still lingered.

"I wonder," thought Francis. And then as they stood in front of the church, the young man seemed to gather up his courage. "That was not all the Lady Clare bade me say to you. The family has told her that she has dallied long enough, and like a good Christian woman she must marry."

Francis looked at the young man. He looked a good deal older than his years now, and as Francis thought of the young girl, drawing her veil across her face on the gallery so long ago, the sweetness of the lilies in the sarcophagus came back to him.

"She has sent me to ask if she may join your company."

"But you have seen that there is no place for a woman here."

"She will go wherever you tell her," said the young man. "But she wants you to receive her vows."

"But a single woman—" said Francis. "Even if it were a company of angels—"

But the young man smiled. "You do not know my cousin. She is quite sure there are others who will join her."

"But our way of life—" and Francis spread his hands as if to embrace all the clearing.

The young man laughed. "She told me you would say that, and she bade me ask you who it was who followed Christ to the Cross, and who was up first on Easter morning."

And as Francis' eye sparkled, the young man knew that the Lady Clare had won her point. "Tell her," said Francis simply, "to let me know when she is coming." But the young man went off with shining eyes, for a moment reminding Francis of his own days of impossible dreams, and he thought to himself, "He will come, too."

That night when Francis told Bernard and Peter of Lady Clare, they looked at him as if he had at last taken leave of his senses. "The Lady Clare!" said Bernard, as if by repetition of the name he might reduce the problem to manageable size. "She is one of the richest heiresses in Assisi. Did you ever know the Offreducci to let anything slip out of their grasp?"

But Peter looked thoughtful. "Even when I was in the Bishop's house, they said the Lady Clare was talking of becoming a nun. And I remember the Abbot said once that her fortune would put that convent on Monte Subasio on its feet. But the Bishop asked the Abbot Simon did he really think that the Offreducci would let the Lady Clare's fortune get into the Benedictines' or anybody else's hands but their own."

"Brother Peter," said Francis with relief, "that is an idea. The Prioress at San Paolo, thank God, is a much simpler woman than her brother on the hill. She gives her good bread with only a prayer and a blessing, and she never preaches any sermons about order, or taking thought for the morrow."

"Happily for us," said Bernard dryly.

"Thank you, Brother Peter," said Francis. "That is the answer. We will receive our Lady Clare here, and then we will take her to the Prioress."

"But if you think," said Peter, "that the Benedictines will let her out of their hands while she is there—"

"She will come with empty hands," said Francis gaily. "Tomorrow we must clean out the church that it may be fine for the Lady Clare."

"You don't think she's coming tomorrow night, do you?" asked Bernard, relieved to find that the scandal was not likely to be unmanageable.

"No one knows," said Francis, "when the bride cometh." And they all laughed.

But Bernard was surprised the next day when Francis before dawn aroused Leo and Giles and told them to go up to the old Cathedral of Santa Maria Maggiore and take the blessed palms from the Bishop's hands and bring them back here to their altar. And not for the first time Peter marvelled that Francis who thought so seldom of the world's opinion yet so often remembered to remind the Bishop that though they might live like outlaws down in the thicket here, they did not forget that they were members of his flock.

Leo and Giles brought back more than the blessed palms from the Solemn Mass in the Cathedral at Assisi that Palm Sunday of 1212. They had thought it proper to hang back until the last among the halt and the ragged with whom was their proper place. And so they had seen the Lady Clare kneeling there in her place by the wall near one of the Offreducci tombs. She had looked like a vision from paradise, dressed in her richest gown, gleaming with jewels. Her mother and her sisters and their cousins, who had been among the first to go up to the altar and take their palms from the Bishop, were standing around her, but with her bowed head she seemed frozen in her place. Then the Bishop saw her, and he came down from the sanctuary and handed a palm to her, blessing her as he gave it to her, and her face, that had been so pale, flushed, and as the Bishop handed the palm to her, he smiled so that it looked like a painting on a church wall, where the Blessed Lord gives the palm of martyrdom to a saint.

"There is much talk of it in Assisi," said Brother Leo. He had heard two women talking about it as they came out. One said to the other, "He knows that she wants to be a nun, and he is sorry for her now that they have made her promise to marry."

A couple of young men came up just then and heard the woman's remark. One of them laughed, "Imagine burying all that beauty in a convent! Who is the luckiest man in Assisi?" But Leo and Giles thought they had listened to enough gossip, so they hurried home.

That evening an old man who looked vaguely familiar to Francis brought a message. "It will be tonight," he said, "after the moon has risen." Then Francis recognized Gualo, an old servant he had often seen in the house of the Offreducci.

"But will they not stop her?" asked Bernard, as Francis took the old man into their little shed of a refectory and set bread before him.

"They have not blocked up the door of the dead since her father's funeral," said the old man.

"The chapel is ready," said Francis gaily when the old man had gone; "how about the choir?" But Francis had hardly finished telling the astonished brethren that the Lady Clare was coming that night before there was a rush to the river.

Brother Juniper laughed with delight, "If one sister can wash the faces of the company, then—" and he shrugged his shoulders. But Francis looked thoughtful.

"Have you said anything to the Benedictines?" asked Peter.

"No, the birds fly too swiftly across Monte Subasio."

It was Brother Giles who found some wild anemones against a half-buried column in the woods. He put them with some vine leaves on the altar where they shone brightly in the light of the tapers.

When the moon had risen, they all went through the woods toward the road from San Damiano, and on the edge of the woods they waited with their lighted torches; and as they waited, they sang a little hymn which Francis had taught them. It was an old French hymn in which the angels welcome the spirit of the newly dead to the joys of paradise. Only one or two of them knew the words, but they hummed as Francis and Leo and Peter sang. Presently they heard footsteps on the road above, and then they came out of the wood, lifting their torches high so that the road was lighted as if for a ball. And a slim shrouded figure slipped out of the darkness into the torchlight, and then behind, another slim figure. Now the veiled figure flung aside its cloak, and the Lady Clare stood there, shining like one of the blessed in the dress which she had worn in the Cathedral that morning. While the brethren stood dazzled at her jewels sparkling in the warm torchlight, she came and flung herself at Francis' feet. And as Francis looked down into the face now turned to his, so frankly as if this young woman were offering all of herself in her clear gray eyes, Francis raised her and lightly embraced her, scarcely touching the soft shoulders under the rich gown. Then the Lady Clare presented her companion to him, her cousin, Pacifica di Guelfuccio.

Francis took Clare by the hand. Now the singing of the brethren rose to a triumphal paean, and so they came through the woods. When they reached the little church, all the brethren stood around in an arc about the low entrance, and then as many as could get into the little church went in to help Brother Sylvester sing the Te Deum. Some shepherds, upon whom the night had fallen in their quest for some strayed sheep, heard the singing in a wood nearby. One of them was terrified and said, "It is magic," but the other said, "It is only the angels that have come back again to St. Mary's."

When the service was over, Clare knelt down on the steps of the altar, and she put her hands between Francis', and she swore the three vows of chastity, and obedience, and poverty. Francis cut off her shining tresses and held them up so that they gleamed like gold in the torchlight; then he laid them with the bright flowers on the altar. And Clare went out of the church with bowed head with her cousin following behind. When she came around the corner of the church in a few minutes, all her fine robes had gone, and she stood in front of the altar in a plain gray dress such as the peasant women wore, and Francis tied the rope girdle about her slim waist, and over her shorn head he laid a length of black linen. Taking her hand, he turned her to face the brethren, and as their eyes shone in the torchlight, Clare's clear eyes fell, and the blood glowed in her pale cheeks. Then, still singing, with Francis leading Clare by the hand, they went with flaring torches through the woods to the little Benedictine Convent of San Paolo in the marsh beyond.

They had a hard time waking the portress, and she shrieked at the sight of all the torches, but Francis stepped forward, and he called out, "Mother, it is I, Francis." Presently the Prioress herself spoke sharply from the window above, "What are you doing here at this hour, Francis Bernardone?"

But Francis answered gaily, "Mother Prioress, I have brought you the bride."

She closed the shutter with a snap, and in a moment she was standing in the doorway with a little huddle of nuns at her back.

"What folly is this of yours, Francis?" she said still more sharply. Then as Francis bade the brethren go back to the Portiuncula, she opened the door wider and she saw Clare standing by Francis.

"A beggar?" And then as Clare knelt down in front of her, the old woman looked at her keenly. "A rope and a veil," she said. "What trollop is this, Francis?"

"Look," said Francis, "surely, you have seen the Lady Clare."

The candle in the Prioress' hand nearly fell to the ground. "Do you know what you are doing, either of you?"

"Perfectly, mother," said Clare, speaking in a low voice that yet thrilled through the stillness of the night. "I have taken my vows in the Portiuncula between the hands of Francis here."

"So we have asked your shelter, mother," said Francis.

"None too soon," said the old woman, and she pulled Clare and her cousin in through the door and shut it. In a moment she looked out the window again, "This is mischief enough for one night, Francis."

But Francis laughed, "God will reward you, mother," he called gaily. Singing, he started back with Brother Leo to the Portiuncula. "And who shall say, Brother Leo," he said as they stumbled over an old root, "that dreams never have their perfect fulfillment even in this world."

The next day Francis had a difficult time getting the brethren out to their day's tasks. It seemed that everybody had some excuse for remaining home. "They want to see the fun," said Juniper, and Francis was angry, and then ashamed when Bernard reminded him that the Lady Clare's brother, Martin, would doubtless come with a large company, and he would hardly hesitate to beat up whoever stood in his way. So Francis was forced to agree that Giles with Leo and Bernard and Peter and a couple of stalwart young peasant fellows should stay. It was afternoon, however, before Martin came roaring down with a noisy company of relatives and servants of the Offreducci into the little clearing.

When Francis barred his way in front of the church, the irate young man threw himself upon Francis, snatching the front of his tunic and shaking him. There was a rush from the waiting brethren, but Francis bade them stand back. Then with surprising strength, he thrust down the hand of the irate young man. "Are you a Christian?" he asked.

"A Christian! You incontinent rascal!" thundered the angry young man. "Where have you hidden my sister?"

"You can look," said Francis, opening his hands. "But remember this is the house of God, and these poor shacks are under the protection of the Bishop and our lord, the Pope."

"More of your romantic nonsense," sneered Francis' erstwhile friend. "If you think you can bully me with any notion that the Pope has any time to think of such trash as this!" The young Martin tore through the church. He bellowed when he saw the golden locks still lying on the altar, but when he thrust his hand toward them, Francis again barred his way.

"Mass has been said at this altar," he said, "and it will be sacrilege if you touch anything on it."

There was an uncomfortable muttering among his fellows, and the young man drew back, shaking his fist in Francis' face. Then he tore through the shacks, jabbing the straw savagely with his sword and dashing the wooden bowls and spoons to the earth. But there was obviously no place for anyone or anything to hide. In the little shed leaning against the church, he found Clare's rich dress, and he flung it with anger in the dust and trampled on it. It was at that moment that one of his men came up and whispered to him.

"So you took her to the Benedictines!" he roared.

"She is in God's keeping," said Francis stoutly.

Having made a wreck of the Portiuncula, the angry young man and his followers rode off toward the Benedictine Convent. But as Francis had said, the birds flew swiftly between the convent and the abbey, for when the Assisians reached the priory, they found that not only were several Benedictine servants waiting but a couple of stalwart servants of the Bishop, too. And the Prioress not only told Martin what she thought of his manners in a fashion that made all his companions fall back as the sight of the guardsmen had not, but she produced the Lady Clare, who stood there calm and unflinching before her brother and told him plainly that she had come of her own free will and had made her vows in proper form, and he knew where he must go if those vows were to be broken. To the astonishment of Francis, the Lady Clare was the calmest of all those involved in the day's transactions, and her brother was forced to go back.

The next day the Bishop sent for Francis, and with Bernard and Peter, Francis went up to face him. The Bishop was still smarting from what seemed to him a trick, for his servants had reported to him that the nuns in the convent went in fear of their lives from Clare's family. On the other hand, when the Bishop had sent for the head of the family, Clare's uncle Monaldo, and had asked him why he had not controlled his nephew better, Monaldo declared that his men had told him that Clare had flourished the palm which the Bishop had given her in their faces as evidence of his approval. The Bishop therefore had decided that Clare had better be sent to the convent of Sant' Angelo on Monte Subasio, where the brethren from San Benedetto could come to the nuns' rescue. And he added a little tartly that if Francis had thought of embarking on a career of stealing ladies from their homes, he had better reconsider it fast.

But a little more than a week later, Agnes, the younger sister of Clare, stole out of the family stronghold and took her way with an old servant up Monte Subasio to the convent and announced that she had come to join her sister. Clare at once sent word to Francis at the Portiuncula, and the anxious Benedictine sisters appealed to the Bishop. But before either could move, Monaldo, the uncle of the girls, had appeared at the Benedictine convent with a dozen armed knights. And though Agnes clung to the very altar, they penetrated the enclosure and dragged her to the door. The frightened girl cried to her sister to save her, and Clare ran to take her place at the altar. The nuns cried out stoutly at the sacrilege, and as Monaldo dragged his niece down the rough mountain side with the thorns and the brambles catching at her hair and tearing her dress, the frightened girl clutched at the very earth and screamed to her sister for help.

Suddenly the knight who had been helping Monaldo drag his niece found that she had become like lead, rooted to the ground, and he was unable to move her further. Astonished, he went to join his companions now making haste to put a distance between themselves and the threats of the nuns, which already had begun in their abashed ears to assume the proportion of curses. Finding herself for a moment alone, the girl Agnes scrambled to her feet and ran back to the convent just in time to find a couple of the convent's servants, whom the Prioress had at last galvanized into action, ready to help her. News of

Agnes' deliverance reached Francis almost as soon as the news of the assault on the convent, and by the time Francis reached the convent, the nuns were already giving thanks for a miracle.

Francis lost no time in cutting off the hair of the frightened Agnes, and as soon as she had ceased her weeping, he received her vows as he had received her sister's and clothed her in a tunic he had borrowed from a younger brother and girt her with the cord of the Order. Then he set out for the Portiuncula to bring the glorious news of this third sister who had joined them. But before he could reach the Portiuncula, the Bishop's servants overtook him and bade him attend in the Bishop's palace the next day.

With his customary directness, Francis declared himself ready to wait upon his lordship at once; but this the Bishop had obviously foreseen, for he had given instructions that he would not see Francis until he had had a chance to make inquiries of the other people involved. But the Bishop soon found that he had overestimated the difficulty of collecting information. Monaldo was in the vestibule of the palace the next morning to complain of the kidnapping of his nieces, and the Abbot Simon was hard on his heels to protest the sacrilege of Monaldo's breaking into the convent. The Bishop allowed Monaldo and his nephew Martin to listen to the Abbot Simon's quiet but precise account of what had happened, and he assured Monaldo that excommunication of him and his entire family would hardly do justice to the enormity of his crime. As for his claim to a return of his nieces, they had made their vows in due and proper form. There was nothing he could do about that unless he could prove force.

But Monaldo, a giant of a man, was not so easily routed. "There is more than one kind of force, my lord," he said.

"What do you mean?"

"There is witchcraft!"

But that was an unhappy inspiration, for although the Bishop had never claimed to be a very profound theologian, he was quite competent enough to assure Monaldo that the penalty for faith in witchcraft might be even graver. Monaldo was now beside himself with rage, but he had quite enough experience to know when he was completely defeated. So, glowering, he withdrew, leaving Abbot Simon to thank the Bishop for his intervention and then to inform him that the Benedictines could hardly be expected to deal with the predicaments into which Francis' recruiting methods would be sure to land them.

There was nothing for the Bishop to do, therefore, but to go up to the convent to see Clare and Agnes and Pacifica. Clare, speaking for all three, made it clear that while she was grateful to the Benedictines for their hospitality, it was the company of Francis that she had joined. When the Bishop reminded her that no order, or lack of order, on earth was any excuse for women gallivanting around the countryside, Clare reminded him that she had given her vows of obedience to Francis, and she would abide by his instructions.

Sitting there in the convent guest room beside the astonishingly cool young woman in her plain dress and her simple black veil, and looking from her to the worried Prioress and the Abbess, the Bishop reflected that they might have done much worse than Clare for the first recruit of the new women's company.

So he went home and sent for Francis. "If only you would give me some warning of these inspirations of yours," he said wearily.

"But it was no inspiration of mine," said Francis. "It was the Holy Spirit that moved the Lady Clare."

"I think the Lady Clare is no fool," said the Bishop, fixing his gaze severely on Francis. "Whatever this nonsense of yours about a fixed dwelling, surely you realize that women must have a fixed abode—an enclosure from which intruders can be kept out."

To his great relief, Francis agreed, but he insisted that there must be no ownership, no rent or income. The brethren would beg for the sisters' bread as well as their own. But in the end, Francis had to agree that the sisters could accept from the Bishop's hand the loan of San Damiano and the little priest's house attached to it, and whatever additional buildings the Bishop should think necessary for their protection. There were several clerks at the Portiuncula, and it was agreed that the service of the church and the little convent should be in their hands. For the old priest Nicholas was sleeping now in a grave on the other side of the church, and the Bishop would be glad to have San Damiano taken care of. So Francis agreed, and in a few weeks when the Bishop's steward had reported that a proper wall had been built around the old hut, with a proper convent door in the wall where those who craved the sisters' services could knock, Francis and a dozen of the brethren went up to the convent and brought their three sisters down in triumph to San Damiano. As they stood before the old crucifix at the end of the little service of dedication, Clare knelt down at Francis' feet and asked for his directions. But Francis took her by the hands and raised her, and said simply, "Do you pray for us." That night at supper at the Portiuncula, Francis told his brethren that nothing should be too hard for them now that they had Sister Clare and her companions to pray for them at San Damiano.

5

When Francis received Clare into the Order, nothing was farther from his thoughts than what her coming might mean either to the Order or to himself. It was the perfection of the symbolism that had entranced him; that the bride who had drawn her veil across her face now so many years ago had come and put her hands between his and sworn her vows seemed to him the final manifestation of a dream come true. When Bernard and Peter had tried to point out the difficulties of admitting women into the Order, Francis had cut them short by reminding them of Our Lord's example, and by asking them if it was charity to deny to those whose weakness needed the best chance of perfection that help.

He had not even thought, as he once would have, of the possibility of fresh recruits, for the Portiuncula was overrun with new brethren now, and Francis often begrudged the time and thought that must go into the building of fresh dormitories and the initiation of new and untried novices.

Every time he sent a couple of brethren out for a preaching mission into the country or the towns about, there were fresh problems. There were the recruits of all kinds and degrees of promise. There were problems of inheritance. There were offers of houses. It seemed to Francis now that he spent more and more of his days talking over these matters with Bernard and Peter, and though it was he who usually cut the knot and came up with the solution, he begrudged the time it took to dispose of all the difficulties which Bernard and Peter were always conjuring up. Yet he had learned that in the end it saved time to listen to Bernard, and anything that Peter thought of would occur to the Cardinal of Ostia, also. But still it seemed a poor way to spend one's days.

Yet as he knelt with Clare before the crucifix at San Damiano, he had a sense that he was returning to his beginnings. And when he stood with her and her two companions in the little hut that was to be their dormitory and their refectory and their workroom and made a suggestion or two out of the Rivo Torto experience—like having each sister have her fixed place—the quiet gray eyes of Sister Clare understood so readily his meaning, and her sweet voice promised obedience so quickly that Francis' heart was warmed. But he reminded himself that she was very young and quite inexperienced, this young woman who gazed at him so gravely. "She will ask too much of herself," he thought as he walked back through the woods to the Portiuncula.

Francis felt that his fears were confirmed when the first report came that Clare was sending over to the lepers a large share of the food which the brethren carried up to her each day. But Brother Juniper laughed at Francis' fears. Had he not noticed, he said, that every man who could went up the road to see the Lady Clare. Francis looked so startled at the idea that Brother Juniper laughed and hastened to explain, "Can you blame any man for preferring his blessing in music rather than in the cackling of some of these old crones?"

In spite of himself, Francis laughed. "You need not worry," said Juniper, "Sister Clare is a better almoner than you or I." And Francis had to admit on his next visit that Juniper was right. For those who came to San Damiano said grace over their food and ate it in a decent fashion, sitting on the ground in front of her door, while Sister Clare talked to them or read to them from the Gospels in a voice that was pure music. Afterward she looked at their sores and bathed them, and wrapped them in clean linen, and sent body and soul away refreshed.

"It is a hard life for a woman," said Bernard of Quintavalle, when Francis told him.

But hard life or not, Francis soon found that it had its magnetism. First it was a couple of girls from one of the leading families of Assisi, and then there were three who came at once, and presently the Lady Clare sent word that they must really extend their dormitory. The additional strain on their providing drew no complaint from the brethren, for the ladies never ceased to express their gratitude and their wonder at the generosity of their benefactors. But Francis wondered if all of these girls who were coming in understood what they were undertaking.

He need not have worried. Clare apparently talked very carefully with each girl who came to seek admission, and she did not hesitate to send back two girls from the most distinguished families. Francis had wondered how she could be sure so soon. He had agonized himself over doubtful candidates, and usually it had been only after weeks of vain endeavor to make the young cuckoo at home in the nest that he had owned himself beaten, or the unsuitable candidate had given up and crept away in the night. But Clare had seemed so sure.

"That girl has never been able to stick to anything," she said of one. "She has always been a silly thing, given to romantic posturing," she said of another.

Francis was frightened that this might be feminine prejudice, the fruit of the gossip of which she must have heard so much. So he asked Leo and Sylvester the next time they went to Assisi to keep their ears open for anything they might hear of the unsuccessful candidates. Leo went to see one of the dowagers of his own family, the Lady Monica, whom Leo had long ago discovered to be a shrewd judge of character, masculine or feminine, and she assured him that Clare was quite right. When Sylvester asked the family chaplain in the other household his opinion, though the chaplain spoke with becoming reserve, he made it clear that he did not think that the young lady of the house belonged down at San Damiano. Indeed, she had already forgotten about it all a month later and was making preparations for her marriage to the young man whom her father had picked for her. Francis thought ruefully that he wished it were quite as simple as this to make sure of the judgment of all the superiors whom he had watched setting up housekeeping in shed and cave and taking in their first companions over the countryside.

And he noticed something else as he went up to San Damiano. Overcrowding was likely to be a noisy and mussy affair, as he knew all too well, but even when more than a dozen young nuns had crowded into what were now the two little sheds against the old church, all was clean and swept, and there was a cheerful quiet that fell like balm on Francis' weary spirit. Clare never seemed hurried, and she never raised her low voice, and yet even while she was talking to him, she missed nothing of what was going on. The quiet answer she gave to each inquiry was obviously final. Francis never ceased to be astonished how when he came to her with some fresh suggestion, she seemed to be all ready and waiting for him. So quick was she in her understanding that once or twice as he went back home to the Portiuncula, he wondered if she had not been ahead of him, and he mused afresh how little Our Lord had said in the Gospels of the weakness of women, and how much he had taken them for granted, and how well they had repaid his confidence.

Indeed, there were some problems that Clare seemed to have found the solution to that still baffled him. One was the problem of books. Even words themselves had always seemed to Francis a very poor instrument of communication unless, of course, they were sung. How much more direct were look and gesture, he had often thought. And all the fuss men made of learning, as if the wisest of men were anything but a child at the feet of divine wisdom! He had always been grateful when some generous ecclesiastic gave a Missal or a Book of the Gospels to be chained to the altar of a newly restored church for the brethren to use. And he had taken it for granted that Brother Sylvester should now and then linger in the chapel with the old breviary he had brought with him. But when one of the younger brethren who was also a priest had come and asked Francis for a breviary that he might say his office, as was fitting, Francis was alarmed and shook his head.

"No," he said to the astonished young fellow. "For if you have a breviary, you will sit in your chair like a bishop and you will say to Brother Giles here, who cannot read, or to Brother Juniper, 'Brother, go and fetch me my breviary that I may read it.' "

"That nonsense, at least, Sister Clare will not have to worry about," Francis thought as he went up to San Damiano as he so often did now when he was disturbed. "If I did not stop it," he thought, "we should presently be like the Benedictines, with lay brothers working in the fields, and the clerks kneeling in the church." But when he got up to San Damiano, he found that Sister Clare had assembled her sisters in the refectory, and they were all sitting with heaps of coarse gray wool before them, sewing, while Clare in her sweet voice was reading the office of the day.

"You must be expecting a lot of recruits," said Francis, pointing to the heaps of cloth.

Clare looked startled, and then she smiled. "You have all been so good to us that I dare not let us spill out of that new dormitory just yet. The dresses are for some of the beggar women who come to us. If they look decent," she added, "it will be a little easier for them to keep their self-respect." Not for the first time Francis looked at her and wondered how a girl in a noble household could have learned some of the things she knew.

"Do you never wish, Sister Clare," he asked teasingly, "that you could go out the door and down into the fields?"

"Often."

"What would you do if you could?"

"I should gather the women together," she said, "teach them the prayers, and explain the creed to them."

"But why the women?" he asked.

"Because it is the women who have the children first." She looked at him in surprise. "And in the winter these children who have no school to go to must spend much time with their mothers."

But he shook his head. "You have enough to do up here."

"Yes," said Clare with her warm smile. "You must never think that I am not content with what God has given me to do."

That night Francis told Brother Peter and Brother Sylvester of what Clare would do if she were free to go into the fields.

Sylvester smiled. "She's already finding ways, as it is, to get the women to come up to her door. They bring up a sick child, and when she has looked at the child and given it medicine or bandaged it, she will get the mother to pray with her. The Lady Clare's prayers are going over the countryside, they say."

"Maybe the Benedictines are right after all," said Francis with a sigh. For earlier that day he had learned that two young brethren sent out from a cave outside of Spello to preach in the hill country had been set upon in the marketplace of a village and tossed in a ditch. They were not badly hurt, but it had been all that the elder brethren could do to keep them from rushing out again upon martyrdom.

"Do you never feel oppressed by the responsibility?" asked Brother Francis of the Lady Clare another day. She had just told him of a foolish novice who had excited the whole dormitory by crying out in the night to them of a dream she had had that Our Lady had come into the chapel of San Damiano and crowned Sister Clare with roses. Sister Clare had blushed as she told of the folly.

"But what did you do with the girl?"

"Oh, I set her to scrubbing out the dormitory. She will be so tired she will sleep tonight without dreaming."

"But how do you know what to do? Don't you worry?"

Clare looked at him with her clear eyes. "If it were just me, of course I should worry," she said, "but I pray Christ and Our Lady to help me, and then I ask, 'What would you have me do?'"

"It is because she is shut up there within that limited area that she is so sure," he said to himself that night as he lay awake in the dormitory listening to the heavy breathing of some of the brethren and to the snoring and the thrashing of others, and wondering if perhaps he had not made the wrong choice after all. For he had been in the church of San Giorgio outside the eastern gate of the city that day. It had been the anniversary of the day when he and Bernard and Peter had opened the Gospels, and when the Mass was over, the priest had asked him if he did not want to preach. Francis had simply stood on the steps of the altar, on the lowest step as befitted a man who was only a deacon, and he had told the people of the three openings of the Gospel, and of the great freedom and the joy that had come to the three companions who had gone out to follow them, and of the sweetness of my Lady Poverty, whom they had taken for their bride. And as he spoke, he had been so moved that he had wept, and all over the church men and women had wept with him. And when he had finished his sermon, they had crowded around him and asked for his blessing, and some of them had said that if they were not married people with families, they would follow him and his Lady Poverty.

Then Francis had been abashed, for he had not meant that they should think of following him. So he arose now, moving cautiously so as not to disturb the sleepers on either side of him. He groped his way into the chapel. It was very still here with the only light that of the lamp burning on the altar, and he knelt down and he buried his face in his hands. "If they had paid no attention to my preaching, I should have had nothing to worry about," he thought. "It was because I spoke of myself and of what had happened to me," he thought again. And then he remembered Sister Clare, and he prayed that he might ask only what Christ would have him do, and then he went back to his place in the dormitory, and he fell asleep.

But when a couple of days later he went over to San Damiano again, he told Sister Clare of the people in San Giorgio who would like to embrace the life of Penitence but must think of their families. "They are not the only ones, you remember," said Clare. "There is your friend, Luchesio, and his wife up at Poggibonsi. You said yourself that they have made their love for each other and for God in each other a hearth to warm all who come near."

"That is true," said Francis, "though I don't remember that I used that figure." He looked keenly at Clare, and he thought she blushed. "But it is a good one," he added.

"You found a place for us in your bounty," said Clare. "There is no reason why you should not start a Third Order for those who are married and in the world."

The confidence of the Lady Clare restored, as it so often did, Francis' humor with himself, and he smiled as he said, "Would that not be even more difficult than the Order of the Poor Ladies?"

But Clare did not smile. "The mother of one of my young sisters here came to see her daughter yesterday, and she reports that her brother, who is with the Benedictines up at the abbey, says they are getting ready for the visit of the Cardinal of Ostia. Why don't you ask my lord Ugolino what he thinks of it?"

Francis said nothing, but he was amused as he started for home to think that Sister Clare in her enclosure so often knew of things which for all his brethren wandering over the countryside he had not yet heard.

Though he must have known that every monastery or bishop's palace at which he and his retinue had stayed in their progress from Rome to Assisi had sent on word that the next house might be ready, and the great abbey on Monte Subasio would have been prepared almost to the hour for his arrival, the Cardinal, with one of his secretaries, turned aside from the road just before he reached Assisi, and sending the rest of his retinue on, he went down into the plain to the Portiuncula. He had taken the precaution of dressing himself as a simple priest; so there was no excitement when he came into the little clearing and went straight to the chapel. There he found the familiar little figure kneeling in a corner. He waited until Francis rose from his knees and turned and saw him. Then as Francis knelt down and asked for his blessing, the Cardinal smiled. "This is the proper place to find the head of the Order, even if it is a bright sunny day."

But Francis looked pained. "My Lord, you know there is no head of this brotherhood but Christ."

"How many brethren have you now?" asked the Cardinal, sitting down on the steps of the altar and motioning to Francis to do likewise.

"I have no idea."

"What sort of shepherd is this, who knows not the number of his sheep?"

"That I leave to God," said Francis simply.

"That is all right for God, perhaps," said the Cardinal, "but when the bishops tell me that your beggars are overrunning the land like locusts, what shall I tell them?"

"It can't be more than a few thousand," said Francis.

"Nearer ten thousand would be my guess," said the Cardinal, "and I am not in the habit of exaggerating my figures, I assure you."

Francis looked thoughtfully into the Cardinal's face. At first glance it looked like the face of any high-ranking ecclesiastic—placid, a little fleshy perhaps, with a look of high expectation in the glance. But there was something speculative in the eyes of the Cardinal of Ostia, a little ironic twist to the corner of his mouth that suggested that unlike so many of them, here was a man who would not easily be put off the inconvenient truth, who would not let sleeping dogs lie.

"Is it not marvellous, my lord?" said Francis, standing up and looking into the Cardinal's face.

The Cardinal did not smile, but a shadow flicked in his level gaze. "You have an affinity for marvels, little Brother Francis," he said. "I have no objection to one now and then, but the average bishop, I assure you, has no taste for marvels until they are safely wrapped up in a tomb."

Francis sat down, and then he turned to Ugolino, and he held out his hands to him. "Tell me, my lord Cardinal: is it better that I stay here?" and he stretched out his hands as if to embrace the whole little settlement, "or go up to one of those caves in the mountains and—" he hesitated.

"What would you do in your cave?" asked the Cardinal. That at least was one of the things that you could count on with Ugolino—he would look at an idea even if presently he would reject it as foolish.

"I should pray."

"You are praying here."

"Yes, but there is so little time to pray here."

"The Benedictines do a good deal of praying up on the mountain."

"I didn't mean the Benedictines," said Francis hastily.

"That I quite understood"—the Cardinal's voice was a little dry now—"What do you think would become of all this around here"—and the Cardinal swept his sapphire-ringed hand in a majestic circle—"and up in the town, and in the other towns, and all the places where your locusts have run? What would happen to them if you went up into your cave and stayed there? To say nothing of those women whom you've taken under your protection."

"Sister Clare would take very good care of them."

"I have no doubt," said the Cardinal with a smile. "But don't you notice that it is of Sister Clare that you speak first with assurance? As for the others, they are not shut up in an enclosure with the Bishop's eye upon them. What do you think would happen to them if you hid yourself away in a cave?"

"Some—" Francis began and paused.

"Precisely," said the Cardinal. "What any head of any order in Christendom would say if he were speaking candidly. No, Francis, you have started something, and you must see it through."

But Francis shook his head. "Sometimes," he said thoughtfully, "I am not sure where we are going."

"Who is in this world?" asked the Cardinal. "But until there is someone else who can do the work you are doing, I think your course is clear." And the Cardinal strode out the door, leaving Francis standing in the middle of the church looking after him.

When that night at supper the Abbot Simon said teasingly to his old friend, "I hear you discharged your responsibility down in that briar-patch today. What did you think of it?"

"It is like nothing else in Christendom," said the Cardinal. "That is why I shall report to the Pope that it must be protected against all the bishops' complaints."

"And the little man?"

"He is beginning to suspect that he is in over his depth."

"Then?" The Abbot Simon raised his brows.

"That also," said the Cardinal, "is not so common that I should like to waste it either."

6

There was rejoicing when the papal messengers arrived with their great pouches at the Portiuncula that late winter day of 1215 and handed one of their parchments with its dangling seal to Bernard and Peter. The latter had heard of their arrival in the neighborhood while he was waiting the day before in the antechamber of the Bishop. For although Peter always protested that he could no longer be counted on to look at things as a canon lawyer should, from time to time the Bishop insisted on asking his advice. Peter knew, too, that when the messengers left the Bishop, they went up to the abbey on Monte Subasio to deliver to the Abbot the Pope's summons to a great council to be held in the Lateran Church in the spring. Peter had wondered if the messengers had a scroll for the Portiuncula, too, and then had hastened to add that, of course, they could not think of anything so magnificent as that. But the Bishop rebuked him. The Cardinal of Ostia, he was sure, would not let the Pope forget the head of what was, after all, an approved order with an approved rule. Bernard and Leo refused to entertain any doubt whatever as to the correctness of the Bishop's judgment, but Francis, when Peter reported this conversation that evening at the Portiuncula, declared that the Pope was much too busy with the great of the world to look so low as the Friars Minor at the Portiuncula; so he would keep the promise he had made to go up to see Sister Clare, whom he had neglected of late. It was with great pride, therefore, that as soon as he returned to the clearing, one of the young brethren ran out to take him to the church and to point to the great seal hanging from the altar.

"It is not an invitation," said Peter when he had read the summons to Francis. "It is a command."

But Francis shook his head. "It is addressed to the cardinals and the bishops and the mitred abbots and the other great lords of the earth. It is not for such as the Friars Minor." But only a couple of days later a messenger came from Ugolino with an invitation to Francis and any companions he might choose to stay with him in the Cardinal of Ostia's palace near the Lateran.

"See," explained Peter, "he does not urge you to come; he takes it for granted that you will."

"It is only fitting," said Leo gently. "We are a great company now, and you are our father—"

"So far as this earth only is concerned," Francis interrupted sharply.

But Peter seemed not to have heard him. "The Pope will preach the Crusade. It is the duty of all Christians, whether or not they can go on the Crusade themselves, to labor for its success."

They had come out now into the open space before the little church, and as they stood around Francis, they all fell silent, waiting for him to speak. It was so quiet that Francis heard a bird singing in a tree overhead and suddenly he laughed, "A bird sang in a wood."

Leo smiled, but the younger men looked puzzled.

Francis hastened to explain, "My brethren, this is not the first time I have been asked to go on a crusade. In the days of my vanity I went forth, and Christ himself turned me back."

"It is Christ who calls you now, through His vicar," said Peter.

So Francis agreed to go. He was not sure that he would even understand what they were talking about, for already the report had come to
the Portiuncula that the Pope had sent to the schools of Bologna for
a half dozen of their leading doctors to come and give their counsel on
his proposals for the reform of Christendom. It was a long time since
Francis had heard any news of his father, but now Leo learned from
some of his relatives in the city that the old Bombarone had been
boasting that his son, Elias, had been invited to the council in Rome
like the Bishop and the Abbot on Monte Subasio, and Peter Bernardone had laughed and said that for the matter of that, his son had been
invited, too. He might be a beggar in a sack of canvas which neither
Peter nor any self-respecting cloth merchant would have in his shop,
but no man could deny that when he preached, he drew greater crowds
than all the doctors in Bologna. And mad or not, everyone knew that
some of the greatest in the Church had gone down the path to the
thicket. And here Francis' brother Angelo was heard to observe bitterly
that in this at least men still followed Scripture, and the good and
faithful son received little credit beside the prodigal.

Francis winced at that, but he said only, "These things are all in
the past." And he began to consider whom he should take with him.
Leo, of course, for he was the firstborn of the Brotherhood—but Leo
protested that he might be good to take notes but if counsel should be
asked, what could he offer? So it was agreed that Peter should go, too,
and Giles, for men must not think even for a moment that their company was made up only of the learned and well-born. Then Francis
reminded Bernard that he had led them when they went to Rome not
knowing what welcome they should find, and now that they were going
as invited guests, it was only right that he should lead again.

Bernard smiled at the proposal. "Not lead, Brother Francis. I shall
only hover between you and the Cardinal and try to make some truce
between heaven and earth."

But nobody could have been kinder than Ugolino. He gave the
Friars Minor a bare room in his great palace with pallets on the
marble floor, and when Francis insisted that they must sit in the lower
places at his long table, he smilingly bade his steward remember that it
was a host's duty to satisfy his guests. However, when the day came for
the formal procession into the Lateran Church, the Cardinal insisted
that Francis and his brethren should appear in his entourage. They
could walk with his secretaries if they liked, but they should come in

his company that everybody might see that they were the sort of men for whom he would publicly answer.

Happily, however, the Cardinal was to enter at the end of the great procession, just before the Pope himself. Francis and his brethren had no vestments or robes to worry about; so they could stand in front of the crowd that filled the square before the church until their time came to fall into the Cardinal's train. In that throng, jostling each other against the walls of the basilica, Francis knew that there must be men who had listened to the heretics' preaching and whose gorges would rise at the very thought of the splendor which now unfurled before them, but their mutterings would be lost in the rising crescendo of acclaim as one magnificent figure after another, followed by its glittering train, swept across the cleared space in the piazza. For here was all the pride and the glory of the visible Church on earth. No vision of romance which any of the loved singers of Francis' boyhood had conjured up could compare with this magnificent procession. The richest of damasks and brocades and velvets and linens from the looms of Constantinople and Flanders and France and Spain had been embroidered by the hands of thousands of nuns and great ladies all over Christendom. Now they flowed along in a shimmering flood of colors and patterns that seemed to distill the splendor of all the world's flowers, while on ring and pectoral cross jewels blazed in the sunlight until the eyes of the beholders were dazzled.

They were handsome men for the most part, the men who carried this splendor—tall and well-fashioned, with a look of command about them. "Power chooses its own," thought Francis, and then he noticed how often they were getting old now, these men under the mitres, and presently came one who seemed bowed by the very weight of his robes, and with pity Francis saw that the old man was little more than a skeleton. "It is death that is worming its way beneath those brocades—" and he wondered if death should win and the old man crumple within, would the robes still be carried on by the splendid procession? And then he thought, "Look at that youngster, pressing with hot breath behind him, or that crafty-eyed little man who is watching the youngster—he has no chance to slip into the robes, but he knows the strings that will make the puppet dance." A great cheer broke into Francis' thoughts, and he saw that the Cardinal of Ostia had arrived with his splendid suite. It was characteristic of Ugolino that he should have included even the humblest of the clerks who worked in his household.

Among them Francis and his companions need not feel that they had spoiled the splendor of the procession.

It was a long one, and Francis and his brethren had already found their places on the scaffolding near the altar so that they could watch the Cardinal himself come down the main aisle of the Lateran Church. He was quite as splendidly dressed as any of his colleagues, but though he was already an old man, one could not imagine that his robes would march on without him if anything should happen to the man within. His keen eye swept the sanctuary before him as if he were checking to make sure that his directions had been carried out. For him this magnificent procession was one more task that he had been given, and he seemed completely unaware of the applause as he scrutinized the now nearly filled benches. Then as the Cardinal took up his stand with the other cardinals at the entrance to the sanctuary in a glittering scarlet bank, as the archangels might have girded themselves on the battlements of heaven, there was a deafening roar, and the splendid figure of Innocent appeared, high above the heads of the crowd, swaying a little as with measured steps his bearers carried his litter down the aisle. At first Francis could make out little but the glitter of white and gold and the gloved hand lifted in blessing. Again, he had the feeling that the cheers of that vast throng might have borne that litter over their heads without need of human hand. Then he could see the Pope's face, and he was shocked to see how cavernous and weary it looked.

"He has been dreaming again," thought Francis with compassion, "and this time the morning has brought no reassurance." So though there was nothing in the gaze which the great Pope turned on the crowded pavement before him to invoke pity, Francis began to pray for him. Now Innocent was scrutinizing the benches as the Cardinal of Ostia had, but where there had been a suggestion of complacency in Ugolino's eyes when he saw that his plans had been effective, there was no complacency in the eyes of Innocent, and Francis wondered how long it was since he had seen anything on which his eyes could rest with unalloyed pleasure.

When the Solemn Mass was over, and the Pope rose from his throne to speak, Francis saw how impatiently he waited for the cheers to cease, and how the ruby in his ring quivered in the light of the tapers on the altar. When the Pope's voice rose, it was clear and ringing, and yet as he went on speaking, Francis noted that it was a little slower than he remembered, and the speaker seemed to be breathing heavily as if he wished to make haste and could not. And then Francis, like every-body else in the vast basilica, was lifted up by Innocent's eloquence, so that he forgot everything but what the Pope was saying, for the Pope was speaking of the Crusade—not of this campaign or that, but of the great Crusade, the effort to recover the holy places from the hands of the heathen, which had as yet not even begun to be accomplished. For the holy places were still in the hands of those who had no idea of what had happened there, and who daily blasphemed in a thousand ways out of pure ignorance.

"But the great blasphemy," thundered the Pope, "is not the ignorant blasphemy of those who know not what they do. The great blasphemy is the blasphemy of those who know what the holy places mean, of those who owe to what happened in those places everything of good they have in their present lives and every hope of salvation for the future, and yet who make no real effort to recover them!" True, Inno-cent went on to admit, individual men and even hosts of men had gone to recover the holy places, and many of them had died; and here, as in everything else, the martyrs were the saving remnant. But here, as in everything else, the princes of this world had their hearts set on other things. Those to whom most had been given were precisely those who had least thought of paying their debt.

Francis had heard his father's friends in Assisi complain of the waste and folly of the Crusade, and he had heard the Patarins mock at the feeble and corrupted leadership of the great churchmen. But here spoke the voice of him who of all men on earth had the most right to speak, and yet it seemed to Francis that what he said was sharper than anything he had ever heard from grumbling merchant or mob-raising Patarin. But in the blaze of the great preacher's indignation there was an undertone of sorrow and even, it seemed to Francis, of despair. Something of this presently began to permeate that great audience, sitting there triumphant in its splendor, and where everybody had at first been looking complacently around the brilliant throng, more and more, Francis noticed, the eyes fell and the faces grew still. He had heard men say as they waited for the procession to get under way that if sacred oratory were the highest of the rhetorical arts, then they were about to hear one of this world's greatest delights, for no orator was finer than Innocent at his best. But it was not pleasure in listening to a supreme example of an art which most of the audience practiced from time to time themselves that made these faces grow cold and

rigid. As the great Pope surged on in his wrath and in his despair, something weary came into the faces about him, and ringed hands began to
tighten over brocaded knees.

"Sometimes I have wondered," thundered the Pope, "if Our Lord
has not preferred to suffer the desecration of the ignorant rather than
the blasphemies of those believers, every act of whose days is a betrayal
of His passion!" The Pope did not linger long on the violence and
cruelty and injustice of the great lords, or even of the kings who tore at
each other's throats like jackals and stained with blood the fair sunshine of God's earth. "We can meet our enemies," said he. "The
Church was cradled in persecution, and it was weaned on barbarism."
But how could it hope to survive the treachery of those who betrayed
it in high places from within? Then it seemed as if Innocent realized
that he had gone to the utmost bound where his audience could be
expected to follow him.

Now his voice sank. He should have despaired, he said, as all thoughtful men would have despaired, if it had not been for Christ's promise
that He would never forsake His Church; so now even in this latter
day of Christendom's corruption there was hope. There was the hope
of the saving remnant of those who in all the mockery of God's world
still heard His call, of those who bore in their souls the ineffable mark
of their redemption. "And what is that mark?" he asked. "And how
will God know them?"

There was a mystical symbol, he went on to explain, the Greek letter
Tau, the letter that was the shape of the headless cross on which many
Biblical authorities believed that Our Lord had suffered. Wherever
men remembered Christ's passion, wherever forsaking the world and
the flesh and the devil as they had sworn to do in their baptism, they
strove with themselves in mortification, asking only that the will of
God might be fulfilled in them, then here were the men who were so
marked. There were not many such men, the Pope went on to say.
Probably there never had been many, but they were still there even in
the Christendom of this year of 1215. Many of them were humble men,
living and working in obscurity, but they need never fear. God would
know his own, and if ever the Crusade to which he now called Christendom were to succeed, it would be because of these men. So the first
preparation that they who took up the challenge of the Crusade should
make was this preparation in their own spirit. Not every man could
give silver or gold for the Crusade, though many could give who had

not yet thought of it. Not everybody could take his sword and his horse and go, though there were many who could take the sword and the horse and the men-at-arms with whom they had been laying waste their neighbors' land. But every man from the humblest to the greatest could prepare for the Crusade in the reform of his life. And every man who held any office, secular or religious, from the smallest to the greatest, could make the first exercise of his office the teaching and the encouragement of the reform; and above all, he could remember that the most effective sermon was still the preacher's example.

"The Pope could hardly have given you greater support if he had called you by name," said the Cardinal Ugolino that afternoon.

Francis said only, "My lord, there is so much to do and I have done so little. I beg you to let me go straight back to Assisi."

But the Cardinal said no, he must listen to some of the discussions now that he had come. "And besides, there are some men whom I would have you meet."

Francis protested that of all that brilliant company there could be none interested in meeting one so humble as himself.

The Cardinal laughed, "I shouldn't say that humility was the principle of selection for this or any other council, but there's many a man here who knows that he could do with a little, and there is one man in particular whom I want you to meet. He is the Spaniard, Dominic Guzman."

Francis drew back. "Everybody knows that he is the most brilliant of preachers!"

"And the least effective, if one can judge from the results," said a peculiarly vibrant voice. Francis turned to face a gaunt, dark face with fine eyes and full lips, very firmly held. Francis stood abashed in the presence of the great preacher, but he remembered one thing that he had heard of Dominic, and that was that when the papal delegates had gone to Toulouse with a great and splendid retinue that filled all the countryside with fresh murmuring, Dominic had waited until they had left the region, and then he had gone in with his men, dressed like poor pilgrims. The remembrance of this gave him courage to look up into the face a head above him. Dominic smiled, and Francis flung his arms wide and embraced him.

Then Dominic began to talk, not of his debates with the heretics nor of the house of studies that he had founded at Paris, nor of any of the things that Francis knew were beyond his understanding; but he talked of the two orders which they were founding and of the way of life which they were asking the Pope to approve. When Francis heard Dominic say that the Pope had told him that the Council would presently rule that all new orders must take the rule of some order already in existence and recognized, he looked so appalled that Ugolino hastened to reassure him, "You remember, you have had your rule approved; so you will not need to worry."

"Then," said Dominic, "let me join my order to yours, and we can take your rule."

But Ugolino shook his head and smilingly warned Francis, "He has a genius for order and for organization, this Dominic. As the Portiuncula looks beside the abbey on Monte Subasio, so the abbey on Monte Subasio will look beside any order which Dominic organizes."

Dominic countered with the suggestion that he would gladly choose Francis for his superior, but Francis protested that he had had trouble enough with clerks from Bologna. Whatever should he do with clerks from Paris, to say nothing of Dominic? But Dominic begged Francis to give him the cord from his gown as a pledge of brotherhood between their two orders, and though he said that he had decided that he would take the rule of Augustine for his men, if he must choose, still he assured Francis that he would include his own prescription of poverty. When a little later the Pope sent for both Dominic and Francis and, explaining that he knew he would never get anywhere with any sort of reform unless he could get a new model of bishop, suggested that they should nominate their best men for bishoprics, Dominic joined Francis in declining the proffered honor.

"How then," said the Pope, "am I to reform when the reformers will not help me?" But Dominic agreed with Francis that that was not the calling for which they had enlisted their men. A little exasperated, the Pope bade them both come and listen to some of the debates of the sessions. "It is all very well," said he, "for you to dodge the problem of rule. If you will not face it, men less good will."

"He is right," said Ugolino, when somewhat shamefacedly they came back to him. But with a sigh, "I do not see how you will ever come to understand it until you have been in our shoes."

So neither Dominic nor Francis dared refuse when Ugolino asked for their company the next day at the sessions of the great council. These were mostly questions of organization, details of rule and practice, which the doctors in their furred robes were debating. Dominic settled back to follow the debate with the enjoyment of an expert who is quite aware of the basic issues that lurk behind the wrangles over form, but Francis soon wearied. One of the doctors from Bologna, however, caught his eye. At first sight he did not look at all like a doctor with his bulging eyes and his great jaw. Rather he looked like a man who had worked in the fields in his time, and yet the attention with which he was following the debate was so intense that it seemed to Francis almost an extension of the man's vital force.

Dominic, in a lull in the debate, noticed Francis' fascination. "You know him, of course. He is a countryman of yours, Elias Bombarone."

"No," said Francis, and then he remembered that old Bombarone had said that his son Elias had been invited to the council. So this was Elias Bombarone, of whose brilliance and of whose steady application to scholarship Francis had heard ever since he was a day-dreaming schoolboy. It was astonishing now to find him so alive-looking.

"I'll see that you meet him after this session. And yet," Dominic added with a candor that surprised Francis, "I'm not sure that I ought to let him meet you. We are all praying that he will come and join us."

"But he belongs with you," said Francis.

For a full moment Dominic gazed at Francis without speaking. "Of course, I think so, but do men always know where they belong?"

"He should go with you," Francis repeated humbly, and then as the debate resumed, he forgot about Elias Bombarone. They were debating the terms of monastic holding of property with not a word of the Tau, and now Francis knew that he was wasting time. So he slipped out of the basilica and went back to Ugolino's palace to find his comrades. On the lonely stretches of the Campagna he could forget about all this irrelevant prattle of property and could think about the Pope's Tau.

But he found only Giles at Ugolino's palace; so leaving word for the others to follow, he started back with him. They were halfway across the Campagna before Francis remembered that he should have asked Bernard's permission to return, and then he remembered that he had taken no leave of the Pope; but it was too late to turn back. When Bernard overtook them, Francis knelt down and confessed the disobedience and was gravely forgiven, but it festered in his memory during the next weeks that he had been discourteous to the Pope. So when some weeks later he came back from a mission in the country and heard that the Pope had come to spend the summer heat in Perugia, he started out at once for the papal court. Since all of the elder brethren were out preaching the Pope's crusade and the younger brethren were helping the farmers in the fields, Francis went alone.

As he crossed the old bridge across the Tiber, he thought of the night when he had been dragged into captivity. There was a great coming and going over the bridge now, for the papal court was large, and all the merchants of the countryside were hastening to make their profit of its residents. But Francis lagged a little crossing the bridge, wondering how many of the swords and the shields of the long-ago battle were still rusting under the water below. Then he thought, "What a fine thing it must be to be Pope, that one's very presence can make a peace!"

But when he reached the Bishop's palace where the Pope was staying, he found the gates barred, and no one would tell him why. He walked around the corner of the building to a little postern gate which he remembered having noticed when he was released from prison. Now he was astonished to find that first one and then another horseman was riding out. "I will ask one of these messengers," he said. But when he went up to the next horseman, the man drew his cloak over his face and put spur to his horse. Francis drew back and waited. The next man did not see him as Francis stood against the wall, but Francis saw his face clearly, and he wondered what a high-ranking ecclesiastic was doing in a messenger's cloak. The next man he knew, for he was one of the secretaries of the Cardinal of Ostia with whom Francis had marched in the procession into the Lateran.

At sight of Francis he drew back, and then as Francis signalled to him to wait, he bent over the pommel of his saddle and whispered, "The Pope is dying." Then, looking around as if he feared the walls might hear, he, too, rode off. But Francis went back to the great gates. Now they were flung open, and men were hurrying out, and some he noticed were carrying sacks on their shoulders.

He stopped one and asked if the Pope were dead.

"He is in his agony," said the man softly. "He will be dead before Vespers."

"It is too late for courtesy now," said Francis to himself. "I will go to one of the caves in the hills above the river, and I will pray for him. And in the morning I will come back for the Mass."

He had hardly reached the cave when he heard the vesper bell swinging slowly over the great plain, and he knelt down and began to recite the prayers for the dying.

It was dawn when Francis came back to Perugia. The gates of the Bishop's palace stood ajar, but the whole place seemed deserted. The doors of the Cathedral Church of San Lorenzo were ajar, too, and a couple of the Podestà's guard were still asleep above their weapons on the steps. Francis pushed the great door in and entered the cathedral. Enough light had come in through the high windows to pale the thicket of lights before the altar, and Francis smelt the incense. A young cleric, little more than a boy, was asleep stretched out on the marble pavement with his breviary under his head. Then through the sweetness of the incense came a curious stench.

Francis looked up to the altar and then he stood transfixed, for there on the black catafalque high under the lights, the Pope's body lay almost naked but for a scrap of linen. It lay awry, twisted as if somebody had torn the rich vestments off in haste. Of all the sumptuously embroidered brocades that must have piled that bier the night before, only a torn strip which had caught on the edge of one of the candlesticks was left. Francis looked at the face of Innocent, but the face was as still and serene as if he had been sitting fully clothed upon his throne; only there was a gray look to the frozen features, and the stench seemed to grow stronger as Francis stood there. He thought he heard a step at the door; so without thinking he untied the cord of his tunic and whipped it off and flung it over the naked body of the Pope. It was travel-stained and threadbare, but it covered that graying flesh, and for a moment it stifled the stench. Then as the steps came nearer, Francis hid behind a pillar.

When he looked around the edge of the pillar, he saw a man in clerical dress, with a traveller's cloak hanging from his shoulders, bending over the bier. "Sic transit gloria mundi," murmured the new arrival. "Nothing but a beggar's shirt to cover you, Innocent!" And Francis saw that although he spoke lightly, the newcomer was shocked; so forgetting his own nakedness, he came up to him. For a long minute the traveller looked at him and then back at the bier. "Here, beggar," he said at last, and he lifted the tunic from the body of Innocent. "I am no Martin of Tours, God knows, but my cloak will cover more of Innocent than your robe." And as he lifted off the tunic, he winced at the stench and flung his own cloak over the body of the dead Pope.

Francis huddled on his habit and ran out a side door, as he heard the voice of the newcomer raised. In the piazza the first man whom Francis met held his nose and cried out, "What carrion have you been digging up, beggar?" And Francis fled to the bridge.

7

So reminded of how fleeting is the majesty of the great world, Francis set himself afresh to the slow winning of the little world. He preached in the towns and villages around Assisi, seeking always that remnant of choice spirits that might be won, as the dead Pope had said, to mortify themselves and conform their lives to the pattern of the Crucified. His spirits rose as in village after village young men and women of all ranks flocked to him to offer themselves to the new Order. But when he preached at Cannara one day in the summer after the death of Innocent, something happened which gave even Francis pause.

He had been through Cannara often enough, for it lay halfway between the Portiuncula and Foligno. At first, in the early days of his conversion, some of the boys had run after him, and then some of the people who had friends who had heard Francis preach asked him why he always went through Cannara without stopping to preach to them, too. Finally, the village priest and several of the older men of the community came to the Portiuncula, and when he talked to them there, asked him to come and preach in their town.

"There will not be room in the church," said one of the other men; "so we will meet you in the fields outside the wall."

Cannara was a squalid, crowded little town within its ancient walls, so Francis was glad to think of preaching in the fields. He soon, however, saw that the priest did not like the idea, and as he looked at him, one of the older men noticed the priest's uneasiness, too. So they asked him if they carried an altar out into the fields would he say Mass. They would bring out the cross, and they would have a procession, and no one then could think that they had gone out to hear a heretic. Francis joined them in urging this plan with so much warmth that the priest was persuaded.

"It is a wretched little village," said Brother Bernard, "with altogether too much drinking in it, and very poor husbandry. And you cannot blame the priest if he wonders why there is this sudden passion for religion."

"But the priest seemed a dull enough fellow," said Peter, "as if he would be better at drinking with them than at preaching to them."

Francis rebuked them sharply. God had not sent them into the world to judge their betters or to tell how other men should do their jobs, but only to do the work which He had given them to do.

And so on the appointed day, Francis went to Cannara with Leo, and he asked the priest if he might serve as deacon at the Mass, and the priest agreed. Then when the Mass was over, Francis bade the people sit down on the ground outside the wall, and he began to talk to them in the plainest language he could find. He told them that he had seen the fine old painting in their church with Our Lady holding the Christ Child in her arms. Without doubt that picture had been made by a painter who had come from some great city like Rome or Constantinople because Our Lady wore a richly brocaded dress and a veil of fine silk, and she had a crown on her head like an empress, and the Child in her arms was richly dressed, too. It was proper, he told them, that they should think of Our Lady and her Child thus, as they would see them in heaven. But if one were to read the Gospel story, one would find that when Our Lady nursed her Child in this world, she wore no fine silks nor brocades nor any crown, for she was the wife of a poor carpenter, and when she first held her Child up for the kings to worship, her dress must have been very dusty from travel, and there were only a few poor rags for the Child.

And when the Child grew and walked through the fields, they were to think of them as like the fields around Cannara. Nor would you have known from the way they dressed, that Our Lady and her Son were any different from the other peasants in the Holy Land. And when Our Lord grew up and was a young man going about the countryside, helping His father and doubtless carrying his tools for him, as they saw other carpenters' sons do, if you saw them on the road, again you wouldn't know. It was only when you came to speak to them and to watch how they behaved that you would know. For thirty-three years Christ had lived this life, and for thirty of them very humbly and obscurely. It must have been very poverty-stricken and often very dull for God, who had the whole universe in which to move.

Then he asked them why they thought He had done this, and he answered that it was in order that people like the people of Cannara should live the life that men and women and children had to live in villages like Cannara in the light of the presence of God. And he went on to explain to them what that meant in patience and charity and faithful doing of the day's duty. That was why, he said, Christ had come to a place like Cannara, and it was in living that life as He lived it that they might some day come to see in heaven Our Lady, more beautiful even than the crowned Virgin above the altar in their church.

When he had finished, the whole congregation, it seemed to Francis, rushed upon him and begged him to stay with them and show them how to live or, if he would not stay with them, to let them all come with him and follow him. Francis was alarmed, for he had seen the shock on the priest's face. Hastily, he assured them that it was God's will that they stay in Cannara, that they must not leave even to join the Order. He could not abide in Cannara, for he had other places to visit, but he promised them that he would come again, and that he would remember them and pray for them, and that he would show them how they could live the life Christ wanted them to live in Cannara.

The priest, when Francis took his leave of them, had sneered at him a little. "It would tax even your ingenuity as a beggar," he said, "to feed and clothe all these people."

It was the problem of San Giorgio over again, but now in a more urgent form. As he walked back to the Portiuncula, Francis worried over his predicament, though he knew that what he should be thinking about was the approaching Chapter of the Order.

It was with mingled feelings, therefore, that when he reached the Portiuncula he found the Cardinal Ugolino waiting for him. He had not seen him since the Lateran Council in Rome; now he suddenly wondered if the great diplomat could help him with the problem of Cannara.

But the Cardinal gave him no chance. After giving Francis his blessing he began to talk quite casually, "The Bishop of Acre has been in Rome with me. He would have liked to come here, but there is trouble in his diocese, and he must hurry home."

"The Bishop of Acre?"

"Yes. You will perhaps know him as Jacques de Vitry."

"Oh," said Francis with pleasure, "the *Golden Legend.*"

"Yes. It was he who found the body of the Pope," said the Cardinal, looking at his hands, the strong hands of a man who had ridden away many of his years. "It was quite naked, the Bishop says, except for a beggar's habit on it."

"Oh," said Francis.

"A very small one. It redeems a little," said Ugolino softly, "the fact that the riffraff of the papal household began to loot and run away before the death rattle was in the Pope's throat. But," he said with an amused smile at Francis' embarrassment, "I did not come here to discuss the Golden Legend or the mystery of Rome. When do you have your meeting this year?"

"You know," said Francis apologetically, "the brethren are so busy with the Crusade and all, we're having but one Chapter this year, at Michaelmas."

"That is wise, but what plans are you making?"

"Plans?" repeated Francis. "I was thinking of that Third Order of Sister Clare."

"I don't mean," said the Cardinal, "what you will talk about. I mean what plans have you made for such plain things as housing and feeding?"

Francis gazed at his patron in astonishment, and then the astonishment sharpened to anxiety. "Housing, my lord? If the weather is fair, and it usually is at that time of year, what better housing for the Friars Minor than God's open sky?"

"And doubtless," said the Cardinal dryly, "the swallows and the ravens will bring you food. Francis, have you any idea yet how many brethren you have?"

"No. I have asked the Guardians to send me the names of the new brethren, but I suppose they are behind in some cases—months behind. They are so busy now, you know, with the Crusade."

"Crusade?"

"Yes, you remember what our father, Innocent, told us—that the Crusade would succeed only if all Christians took up their cross and mortified themselves?"

"Oh, I see," said the Cardinal. "You might be interested to know," he added presently, "that the Bishop of Acre said he had seen nothing in his journey across half Christendom to equal the stirring of life that your brethren have brought to this countryside of Umbria."

"It is the goodness of God," said Francis, shaking his head.

The Cardinal looked at him thoughtfully. "There is almost always another side to the coin of God's goodness, you know. What will you

do if three or four thousand brethren should come to your Chapter in
August?"

"Three or four thousand?"

There was no mistaking the sincerity of the wonder in Francis' voice,
and the Cardinal saw with fresh concern that the actual figures meant
nothing to Francis beyond an awe at the abundance of God's grace.
Ugolino shook his head. "It is time you began to think of it."

"But I am," said Francis. "I have asked the brethren here to pray,
and I have sent out a message to all the brethren to begin to pray for
the Chapter."

The Cardinal thought irrelevantly of the dead Pope and all his vast
plans ending in a stinking corpse, naked in a deserted cathedral, and he
shrugged his shoulders.

But Francis would not let the Cardinal go. "My lord, there is something that I have been thinking about. I have been thinking that the
great and the rich—all they have to do to receive the Pope's forgiveness
is to go on the Crusade to the Holy Land."

"All?" said the Cardinal dryly. "I would like to have some of them
hear you say that. But I know it is not of the great and the rich and
their shortcomings that you want to talk to me."

"No, but I have been thinking that all over the countryside are good
and pious men who would like to go on the Crusade if they could."

"No," said the Cardinal sharply. "We had the Children's Crusade,
and the end of that was ghastly enough. A beggar's crusade would be
even worse." And he shuddered as he saw in his mind's eye all the
beggars of Europe gathering together and sweeping like a great plague
of locusts across the cities. "You know they would never reach the holy
places anyway."

"But my lord," protested Francis, "I never thought of their going to
the holy places. What I thought was that if they could come here to
the little church of the Portiuncula and if they could get the indulgence here—" ·

"You mean," said the Cardinal, his voice deepening ominously, "the
indulgence that they would get in Jerusalem at the Sepulchre, here at
the Portiuncula?"

"Yes," said Francis. "Of course," he explained as the astonishment
deepened on the Cardinal's usually calm face, "Of course, they would
have to have confessed their sins and done whatever penance the priest

gave them, and paid their debts and composed their quarrels with their neighbors, just as if they were going on the Crusade."

The magnitude of this latest folly finally dawned on the Cardinal. He looked at the little man standing there with eyes shining and hands outstretched. "But what good would that do the Crusade or anything else?" Ugolino asked.

"My lord," said Francis reproachfully, "do you not remember what the Holy Father of blessed memory said about the sign of the Tau, and how we should never man the Crusade nor win the holy places unless the Christians at home—"

"I know," said the Cardinal. "But to whom would they give the gift, for I know that you would not allow it to stay at the Portiuncula?"

"There would be no gift, only the most precious gift of all—themselves."

"Francis, there are times when I don't know which of us is crazy."

"But you will tell Pope Honorius, will you not?" asked Francis, kneeling down and laying his hands upon the feet of the Cardinal.

"I will ask him to see you," said Ugolino, "and that is all. Even a Pope asks some modicum of sense of his counselor."

But as so often, the Cardinal of Ostia must have said more than he promised for his odd protégé, for the new Pope did see Francis before he left Perugia. From his earliest years Cencius of the Savelli had been educated in the Lateran, but even all the years of his experience in Rome had proved but a poor introduction to the concentrated course in the world's cupidity and duplicity that three or four months in the papal court in Perugia had given him. "It was the first thing anybody had asked of me," said Honorius, telling Ugolino of his interview with Francis, "that did not have a soldo anywhere between the lines. Indeed, when I bade the fellow wait till I should write out the indulgence, he told me that he did not want a parchment; the verbal permission I had given him was all he needed."

"I shall certainly be at that Chapter," said the Cardinal.

He was as good as his word. He had planned to arrive a week early with a secretary or two and go up to the abbey and catch up on his correspondence while he talked of practical plans with Bernard and Peter. But he was delayed in Rome by one of the countless emergencies of which his days were made, and though the roads out of Assisi were still thronged with brethren hastening to the Chapter, the fields and the woods around the Portiuncula were already crowded with friars when he arrived. Someone, doubtless Francis, he thought, had had the bright idea of making mats out of the rushes that grew in the river bottom, and all over the bare spaces in the fields and even in the woods, these little mats had been raised aloft on sticks, and under these the Brethren slept. They were just emerging from the mats when the Cardinal appeared at the little church. He had taken off his robes, and he had put on a pilgrim's dress as simple as the brethren's own. Now with Francis as deacon, he said the Solemn Mass. Then having laid the simple vestments of the Portiuncula aside, he had gone out with Francis to look at the Chapter.

"It is really very well organized," said Francis, and he explained how the brethren had come in together, sometimes a house, perhaps twenty or thirty or even fifty men, sometimes several houses in a district, sometimes the whole district, so that up to a hundred men had been sleeping together.

"I see," said Ugolino dryly.

"And for food, look!" said Francis. All through the fields and the orchards about them the Cardinal saw some of the younger brethren moving with their arms full of loaves of bread and with flagons of country wine and trays of country cheese, while all about the brethren were giving thanks and eating. And when he emerged from the wood, he saw that there was a steady procession of carts and of country folk with baskets on their heads bringing in provisions for the Chapter.

"Have you any idea yet how many are here?"

"Yes," said Francis triumphantly. "Bernard made a count yesterday, and he estimates that there are over three thousand."

"And you have food for that number?"

"Yes," said Francis even more triumphantly, "food, and the good country people have brought in bowls and cups, too." When presently a bell sounded and the brethren came and sat down around the church of the Portiuncula, and Francis rose to address the company, the Cardinal had to admit that here indeed was a miracle of order. Then he settled down to listen to Francis' address. It was a great thing, Francis reminded his audience, the Indulgence of the Portiuncula which the Pope had given them, for a fresh start in man's crusade against himself would be within reach of every poor man, woman, or child who came to the church on the day of its dedication. But that was only one day in the year, said Francis, and the Cardinal smiled a little as he remembered how Francis had tried to persuade the Pope to make it every day in the year, and even Honorius had held firm that one day was enough for the most extraordinary privilege in the history of the Church. He need not say anything to these his happy brethren, Francis went on, of the great blessings which they enjoyed who had taken the vows of the knights of poverty, and who with that blessed bride, My Lady Poverty, had found themselves free of the world's bondage. But there were all these men and women to whom God had not vouchsafed such high privileges, and yet they were striving to do the will of God in that state of life to which God's providence had called them, and who would say that out of the very difficulties of their way of life, God's grace might not create fresh blessings. Then he went on to tell them what Sister Clare had suggested when he had told her of these good men and women, of the warmth of whose charity most of them at some time or other had had some taste—Sister Clare had reminded him that it had been possible for the brotherhood of the Poor Penitents to found a second order for women; so why not now a third order for both men and women, who though in the world would yet in the spirit be of the brotherhood? Perhaps the Cardinal of Ostia, sitting on the steps at Francis' side, had moved a little at that point. Certainly he had looked at the Preacher hard enough, but at any rate Francis paused and added, as if he were conceding a point to an invisible opponent, that of course, there were problems and there would be difficulties, but of what of God's undertakings was that not true?

The Cardinal of Ostia looked over the company in front of him. In the front row he could see Leo, and Bernard, and Sylvester, and Peter Catanii, and a number of other clerks and scholars. Surely, they must have some idea of what the little man was undertaking, but the vast majority of the thousands before him, squatting in the dust, knew only that this was what Francis wanted and felt only the warmth of his vision. "It is another thing to worry about," thought Ugolino. And then as the session broke up in a great paean of thanksgiving, the Cardinal became aware that on the fringes of the crowd were visitors who had been watching from their horses, and who now dismounted and tying their horses to trees, came forward. To his astonishment the Cardinal saw that it was the Spaniard Dominic and a man in a doctor's robe whom he did not know. But Francis had seen the newcomers, and he went and flung his arms around Dominic and bade him welcome.

"That is a superb idea of yours, Francis," said Dominic, "this third order."

"Superb!" echoed the Cardinal, who had come up behind Francis, and as Dominic knelt to kiss his ring, the Cardinal shook his fist in his face. "You, at least, have sense enough to know what the problems are."

"Sense enough to know what the problems are," said Dominic gravely, "but it is Francis who had the idea."

Then Francis caught sight of the man who had been holding back while Dominic knelt before the Cardinal. It was Elias Bombarone. Francis embraced him, too, and then he looked at Dominic. "So he has joined you," he said happily.

But Dominic shook his head, and Elias knelt down in the dust at Francis' feet. "Francis," he said, "your father has just died up there in Assisi. I asked your brother not to trouble you until you had your Chapter under way, but before your father died he said he had been an ill father to you; and now, Francis, I ask you: do you take me to be a good son to you."

Francis gazed in astonishment at Elias, and he held him at arm's length and looked into his intensely alive face as if he would hold the heat of those burning eyes away from him. Then he shook his head. "Elias," he said, "I am a poor, simple little man, and you are a great scholar."

But for answer, Elias grasped Francis' sandalled feet and put his head in the dust between them. "I have heard the Lord's call," he said, "and I have come to follow Him with you."

Francis knelt down and took Elias' head between his hands and he traced the mystic Tau upon his forehead, and then he turned to Bernard and Leo and Peter, who had stood watching. "Brother Elias," he said simply, and as they still stood frozen in astonishment, Francis took off the cord from his own habit and tied it around the plain pilgrim tunic of Elias, and Elias burst into tears.

That afternoon Francis slipped out of the thronging Chapter, and taking Leo for his sole companion, walked through the fields towards Bevagna. Leo's heart was full of the excitement of the morning, but Francis seemed far away, as if lost in some vision of things invisible.

They were several miles from the thronging roads around the Portiuncula when suddenly they came upon a clump of trees just off their path fairly bubbling with the twittering of birds, and Leo cried out, "See what a host there is!"

Slowly Francis seemed to return to himself; then seeing that most of them were little hooded larks, he exclaimed with delight, "These larks are already suited to be friars and nuns!" As he stood there, some of the birds swooped down from the trees and hopped about his feet, and Francis lifted his hands in delight and began to talk to them. "Oh, my little sisters and my brethren, the birds! You must give thanks to God. You are free to spend all your days singing His praises. You carry your clothes on your back, and your food you may pick up in every hedge. And the dusty miles melt below the joyous beating of your wings. It would be ingratitude, indeed, if you did not use this happy freedom to please Him, to sing His praises for all of us."

It seemed to Leo that the birds listened, and Francis laughed with delight. Then he lifted his hand and made the sign of the cross, and the birds flew up in a great canopy of beating wings. For a moment they hovered above them, and then they parted into four companies forming a cross, and flew to the four ends of the earth. Francis, who watched one group of them winging over the rolling hills toward Bevagna, clapped his hands and said, "Thus will I send my friars to the four quarters of the earth that all men may have the glad tidings of their saving!"

IV: The Shadow of Success

1

As the first decade of the life of the Order drew to a close, Francis could see everywhere about him the fruit of his labors when he walked in the clearing around the Portiuncula in the evening, listening to the birds in the trees, and farther off, the quiet pattling of the river over the stones. He could have called his work good, and yet it seemed to him that it was not quite as he had dreamed. He thought there were fewer birds to sing now in the trees, for one thing, but it may only have been that the wood had been pushed back. Sometimes as he looked at the hive of low wattle-and-thatch huts, he thought wistfully of the days when one little shed held all the brotherhood. When it first became necessary to add another hut, he had insisted that it be built as close as possible to the first; and so as the flock of new arrivals made still more huts necessary, he tried to keep them together. Though Francis had been a little frightened at the way in which the settlement mush-roomed, still he could not think of a single brother whom he would have spared.

It was not Francis' way to look back, and yet there were nights when he remembered just a couple of huts in the clearing and the air sweet in the evening. On his last visit, the Cardinal of Ostia had complained of the stench, and he had pointed to the outermost hut in the fringes of the wood, and he had asked Francis, "Do you know what is going on in that house there?"

Francis had stoutly answered that the life of the Brotherhood was going on in that hut as in every hut in the Portiuncula. And the Cardinal had shrugged his shoulders. "Happy man!" he had said. But it was in that very hut that a few days later Sylvester, going to visit a sick brother, had caught a gleam of metal on a little shelf over the door and, investigating, had discovered a coin. Horrified as Francis was, however, that was only the beginning, for none of the brethren in the hut would own up to possession of the forbidden silver. In vain he reminded them of the provision of the rule that said forgiveness was always waiting to embrace the penitent, but none would confess, and presently Francis with a sigh accepted the suggestion of Bernard that perhaps after all the coin had been hidden there by somebody from another hut. But though the shadow had been lifted from that particular group of his brethren, the thought that somewhere in their midst was so shifty a traitor gnawed at the founder's heart.

When once Francis confided his worry to Peter, the latter reminded him briskly enough, "Our Lord Himself with only twelve men had one who betrayed Him. What makes you think you should be any better off than He?" And Peter went on to argue, as he had often before, that there should be some waiting time before a man was made free of the Order. But Francis would not hear of this. What was the point of embracing a new brother and then holding him at arm's length? Elias Bombarone, also, had thought that there should be some period of probation, and he had embarrassed Francis by conspicuously coming last to the church and meals until finally Francis had asked him, was he not content with what he had done? And Elias had had to yield.

In the old days, too, the brethren had sung as they worked, and had laughed and jested as they ate. But now that they were so many, the voices had fallen, and now and then Francis thought that he caught men whispering together, and sometimes the voices fell when even he came near. But suspicion was like a wraith of cloud in a clear summer sky. Even the tiniest filament disturbed Francis' clear spirit, but it blew away quickly.

Outside the settlement at the Portiuncula Francis had always been more vigilant. It was not that he watched his brethren. In the first days when one never knew when a hard word or a stone might fly, Francis had seen the familiar habit of his brotherhood at the end of an alley or coming out of a country road with a tingle of sensitiveness as if each half-seen figure were an extremity of his body, and in its well-being he rejoiced, and in its pain he suffered. Now those days were long past, and his heart warmed continually to the windows and doors that opened so readily to the Friars' salutation, "May God give you peace!" Presently he even began to worry because the housewives of Assisi were no longer getting rid of their broken scraps, but were wrapping up their finest loaves in pieces of linen for the brethren.

Of course, a good deal of the gossip of Assisi came down the road to the Portiuncula with the loaves and the meat and the wine, and when the gossip presently went from what was happening in the families of the men who had left Assisi to general scandal, Francis reminded his brethren that there were some things which the religious could contemplate only to pray over. He should not have been surprised, therefore, when one day coming from the Bishop's palace, he noticed two of his brethren chatting and laughing with a couple of women on one of the gaily-painted little balconies above a side street. "There is no harm in mirth," thought Francis to himself, and yet he was worried when he looked up at the women and saw the bold freedom of their glances. He thought that one of the brethren was a young man who had joined them recently, but the other he seemed to remember from further back. It saddened him to think that he should not know all his own brethren any more. But the bold looks of the women and the laughter haunted him, and, as so often happened, when he became first aware of something disturbing, his worries on that score soon multiplied. At first, it was stories of the new Third Order. Some foolish brethren on the road to Rome had had the idea of making a third order of beggars and had actually given the cord to a mixed lot of cheerful vagabonds, men and women alike. Francis shuddered to think how that story would echo through the whispering walls of the Cardinal of Ostia's palace.

Happily, Francis had not reckoned with the jealousy of the Third Order themselves. Solid citizens refused to see their names stained by a bunch of thieves and trollops and so frightened the poor beggars that they swore they would forget that they had ever heard the name of Francis. And this saddened Francis when he heard of it, and he found it hard to give the zealous brethren the praise they had looked for. The Cardinal's answer to the letter Francis had promptly dictated to Leo was even more chilling, for Ugolino wrote briefly that he was glad to know that Francis was listening at last to what men said of the behavior of his followers. Bernard and Peter looked thoughtfully at each other over the Cardinal's letter, but there was worse to come. A neighboring bishop complained to the Bishop of Assisi that the resort of the brethren to the Poor Ladies in his neighborhood gave their house a much-frequented air that was ill-becoming a convent of religious women. When the Bishop of Assisi passed that protest on to the head of the Order, Francis wept, and he went up to San Damiano to see Clare. Sister Clare's eyes softened at the grief in his face, but she sniffed at the bishops.

"All the Bishop has to do is to send word to the superior of that convent and to tell her that if she does not check the resort of visitors, he will ask the sisters to elect another superior—to say nothing," she added tartly, "of a word in the ear of the guardian of the brothers' house when next he comes to his palace."

Bernard and Peter were less sure. "There is something to what the Bishop says," said Peter. "It is easy to feel a rash confidence in the habit."

But Brother Juniper, who happened to be sitting on a fallen tree near them, whittling away at a wooden spoon, laughed. "What does your wisdom say?" asked Bernard, not unkindly.

"How like a theologian!" said Juniper with a smile at Brother Peter that softened the contempt of his words. "All these big words," said Brother Juniper, "for a very simple thing." And he put the wood and the knife down on the ground, and he stretched out his hands. "I work all day long," said he, "begging. And when I come back here with my arms full, what does Brother Cook say? 'Is that all you have brought me?' or 'Those cabbages have withered in the heat of the sun', or 'That meat smells already.' And then some idlers who have done nothing but doze in front of the altar all day in the cool of the chapel, they begin to laugh and they say, 'What could you expect of a clown like that?' But," said Brother Juniper, smoothing down the folds of his robe with an absurdly feminine gesture, "I take the same load of miscellaneous cast-offs of Christian charity up to Sister Portress at San Damiano, and what does she say?" And now Juniper pursed up his lips and piped like a fine lady, " 'Wonderful, Brother Juniper! How generous you are to bring us all that good food! How hot and tired you must be, poor man, tramping the streets all day in the heat, and bringing all of it to us!' " There was an indescribable little trill in the last phrase as Brother

Juniper pronounced it, so that in spite of their gravity the whole company laughed. "And then she makes me sit down in that cool little room of hers, and she bustles off to Sister Infirmarian, and she comes back with a glass of that sweet wine. What rational man, I ask you—" said Brother Juniper, and at the stress on the word *rational* there was a fresh laugh, for in the little instruction after Mass that morning Brother Sylvester had reminded his audience that though they had taken leave of the world, they had not taken leave of the obligation of every rational man to use the reason which God had given him. "What rational man, I ask you," reiterated Brother Juniper, "would not go up to San Damiano rather than here?"

But when the laughter had died down, Brother Bernard observed sadly that this was something of which they were likely to hear more. And Brother Juniper arose and with a great air of shaking the dust of the place off his already very dusty habit announced, "And this is something of which I have already heard enough!" and strode off.

"Alas," said Francis, "God has spared us wives, and here we have gotten ourselves sisters."

"Of course," Peter judiciously reminded him, "most of the sisters are a credit to us. It is a very small number who get us talked about."

And Francis admitted that for this sort of gossip it took two, at least. It was not fair to blame the sisters alone. "I am not sure," said Francis ruefully, looking first at home as was his wont for anything that had gone wrong, "I am not sure that I have been as careful as I should be."

Peter and Bernard said nothing, but Leo who had sat silent until now protested, "Whatever you and Sister Clare have said to each other could have been said before the high altar in the Cathedral. Everybody knows that."

Francis shook his head sadly. "One's shadow falls so far," he said.

Leo looked at him in alarm. "Brother Francis," he began severely.

But Brother Juniper had come back, and now out of the shadows he picked up Leo's voice, delicately mimicking its distressed severity. "Brother Francis," said he, "you are beginning to sound like the Cardinal of Ostia." And then as the little group waited, "The Cardinal of Ostia is a fine figure," said Juniper, with a large gesture sketching out the Cardinal's robes, "to grace a Chapter or a feast day; but for everyday fare, he is better off in Ostia, or wherever he disports himself when he's not here."

Francis laughed, and he bade Brother Juniper be gone; there were some things that a jest would not mend. "I shall be more reserved," said he to his old companions, and this time even Brother Leo kept still.

But he had reckoned without Sister Clare. When several weeks had passed, and he had not been up to San Damiano, the brethren who had carried supplies up to the door of the convent reported that Sister Clare was asking whether Brother Francis was ill. When the weeks grew to months, a message came to Francis which he suspected had been a little diluted. Sister Clare wanted to know what nonsense had taken possession of the Portiuncula; had Brother Francis never heard of scrupulosity? With customary discretion, Sister Clare had waited for Brother Sylvester to put this question. Sylvester had tried to take a superior line. Scrupulosity was a priest's term, he had said, and Sister Clare had looked at him.

"I'm not sure," said Brother Sylvester afterwards at the Portiuncula, "that I wouldn't rather have the Cardinal of Ostia look at me than Sister Clare." And Francis smiled. "Of course," said Brother Sylvester, with an obvious effort to be just, "the head of a convent of nuns—" Sylvester paused, and now it was Brother Leo who laughed.

"My aunt, the prioress," he said, "told me once that she had never seen a penitential book but would be improved if only the author would let a woman who'd been prioress for ten years look it over."

"A feminine penitential!" said Peter scornfully.

Francis shook his head. "After all, half of the human race is feminine, and our good Lord made it so."

"But all the doctors are agreed," said Peter, "that it is the frailer half."

But even Peter was less sure of that when another week had passed. Francis had sent a gift of especially fine white bread up to the Poor Ladies at San Damiano, and Sister Clare had bidden the carrier take it down to the leper hospital. "Tell Brother Francis that it is spiritual bread we ask of him, and not just material."

So Francis reluctantly went up to San Damiano, and he thought to himself that he would rather face the Bishop than Sister Clare. Then he remembered how when he was a boy, though his father had cuffed him often enough, the blow was soon forgotten. It was the look of distress on his mother's face that haunted him for days and made him astonish his master by the way he learned his Latin declensions. "We may be the stronger sex," said Francis doubtfully to himself.

Now Sister Clare received him with the greatest propriety with an old aunt of hers and a cousin of the Bishop there in the room, and she and her companions knelt down and asked for Francis' blessing with a decorum that would have enchanted the Cardinal of Ostia. Then when Francis was seated and one of the ladies had gone to get the cup of cold water which was all the refreshment he would ever accept at their hands, the Lady Clare came straight to the point, "What is all this nonsense about?"

For the first time, Francis did not look into Sister Clare's face, but he could still feel those clear gray eyes upon him. "There has been gossip," he said, scuffing the edge of his sandal on the tile floor, like an uneasy schoolboy under his master's eye.

"Gossip?" sniffed Clare. "There is always gossip. But has there been any gossip about this house?"

"Of course not!" said Francis, and the warmth of his indignation at the bare suggestion made Clare relax.

"You are our founder and our father—" and Clare's voice softened. "Of course, we are frail, but have you ever known us deliberately to disobey you, or to fail you?"

Then she saw Francis' face was quivering. "Forgive me," she begged. "You have so much to think of!" And a look of great compassion came into her clear eyes, and the warmth of her sympathy flowed around him, and Francis' voice steadied.

"It is the example I must think of," he said piteously.

"The example!" Clare's voice tightened again. "The example of running away for doing nothing?" she asked. "Oh, Father Francis! The example you have always given is the positive example not of fear but of the freedom of love. I will tell you what we will do, Father Francis. I and one of my sisters will come down to the Portiuncula, and we will give thanks for our foundation, and then you will ask us to sup with you."

As Clare had known he would, Francis thought of that night so long ago when she and her cousin had come to the edge of the wood and found him and his first companions waiting there for her with flaring torches, and with hymns they had led her to the little chapel. Francis' eyes gleamed.

"Do, Brother Francis!" said Clare. "Better than any words or any rules you can make, it will speak to all the Poor Ladies and the Friars of the kind of charity that is among us."

At that moment the bell sounded for Vespers, and Francis took his leave. Sister Clare and her sisters knelt down for his blessing, and as she rose, she said, "Forgive me, but do not forget what I have asked."

That night Francis consulted the oldest of his brethren on what Sister Clare had proposed. "I suppose I cannot do it," he said sadly. He thought it would be Leo who would speak first, but to his surprise it was Brother Sylvester who said, "It is only natural that she should want to see again the altar at which she took up her new life."

Brother Bernard hastened to support him. "Whatever the gossip elsewhere, the whole world knows what Sister Clare is."

"And the order she keeps in her house," added Brother Peter.

"And you, Leo?"

"The Lady Clare," said Leo, "was the first of all the women who ever came to us."

So Francis sent Brother Leo up to San Damiano to invite the Lady Clare and as many of her sisters as she should choose to come with her to sup at the Portiuncula.

"Brother Francis," said Bernard, when Leo had gone off happily, "I think you should make some plan for the Lady Clare's entertainment."

"She will not want any fuss made."

Bernard smiled at his friend. "It takes planning to avoid a fuss."

"Then do what you want," said Francis, "but all of us who were here then will come with me to meet her."

"Then," said Brother Bernard, "let us ask Brother Elias to make ready while we are gone. He will understand," Bernard added.

Francis hesitated. "I suppose," he said thoughtfully, "I should not always ask counsel of those only who were here first. I was surprised, God knows, when Brother Elias came to us, but we have never had a new man who learned so fast or understood so well." So Francis tried to explain to Brother Elias that although there had been gossip, Sister Clare had asked this thing; but Brother Elias at once answered that even the malicious could impute no scandal to anything which Sister Clare had proposed.

Francis wondered if Sister Clare would come again in the middle of the night, but she sent word that she would come before Vespers, and they would sing Vespers together in the little chapel, and then they would sup. When the day came, Brother Elias asked Francis if he would not like to know what arrangements he had made, but Francis said there was no need; he could trust him.

When they were ready to start, Bernard called Francis and showed him a clean tunic which Brother Elias had brought to his place in the dormitory. "It is only fitting," laughed Francis, "that we should go out like a bridegroom to meet the bride." But he was startled when they entered the wood to have Brother Juniper come running up with his hands full of wild flowers.

"You do not go out to meet a queen," said Brother Juniper, "without flowers to give her." And he twisted a length of vine about the stems of the flowers and thrust the bouquet into Francis' hand.

"Sister Clare will like that," said Leo.

So when Sister Clare and the sister who accompanied her rose from their knees at the edge of the wood, Francis handed the flowers to her. "This is Brother Juniper's thought," he said with a smile.

"Ah, I shall come like a bride again to the Portiuncula."

But as Francis soon noticed, they walked a little more slowly through the wood this time; yet the air was sweet, and when he looked at the face of Sister Clare, she was smiling. Back at the Portiuncula, it seemed to Francis, Brother Elias had thought of everything. He had cleared out a little reed hut just where the path from the wood emerged into the clearing, where the Lady Clare and her companion might retire. And though there was a throng of the brethren around the Portiuncula, he had a little aisle cleared and waiting for them to go into the Church.

Sister Clare wept when she saw the tapers burning on the altar. There were no golden tresses on it now, but someone had put some bright flowers there. When Vespers were sung, Clare knelt down again before Francis and, putting her hands in his, she repeated her vows. Francis said slowly, "God grant you grace to keep them all the days of your life;" then he added, "as you have always done," and Clare covered her face with her hands.

Francis was disappointed that Brother Elias had admitted to the supper in the convent only the little company that had gone to meet Clare, but Francis forgot that disappointment when he saw that Elias had served the simple repast on the ground with wooden bowls and tin cups, all spotlessly clean, and loaves of fresh bread and earthen pitchers of thin brown country wine. Sister Clare's eyes sparkled as she sat down, and when Francis had given thanks, he took the loaf of bread in front of him and broke it, and he gave a piece to her. But though she touched it to her lips and kissed it, she did not eat, for Francis had begun to speak with gratitude of the perfection with which Elias had understood the meaning of their poverty.

"He was always quick of understanding," said Peter of Catanii.

Sister Clare said nothing; only she looked thoughtfully at Elias where he stood by the door. But when he saw that all was in order, he went out and shut the door. Then Francis began to sing. It was a little hymn in honor of Our Lady Poverty which he had taught Sister Clare in those first days. Soon they were all singing with him, the men's voices ringing out clear and strong, and the women's voices embroidering them sweetly like a vine creeping with its flowers over the trunk of an oak tree. The brethren outside left their supper to stand and listen, and in the fields beyond, as the farmers made their way back home in the dusk, they stopped to listen, too, and so did the fishermen down in the reeds along the river, and some of the charcoal burners going home in the woods—and in all these places men smiled at each other and said, "The angels are singing again at Saint Mary's." And the singing continued, only a little lower, as the brethren escorted Sister Clare and her companion through the wood back to San Damiano.

2

Early that summer of 1217 Honorius the Pope came to Perugia for a rest in the hills. He was already an old man, and his years were beginning to lie heavily on his stooped shoulders. Shortly after his magnificent entourage had passed through Assisi, the Cardinal of Ostia followed to make a report on one of his unending missions. As he stopped for a night's rest at Assisi, he sent for Francis. His secretary had protested that his lordship was too weary after all the suitors he had seen along the way; but the Cardinal had reassured him with a smile, "I won't say that the little man will not bring his problems, too, but at least they will be different from those of anybody else."

"All religious orders have the same problems," said the secretary, before whose eyes the succession of suitors was beginning to blur.

"That may be, but at least the solutions which Francis tries will be different from the rest. And there are two things he will not ask for: permission to acquire another piece of land, and another relaxation of his Rule."

The Cardinal was quite right. He asked Francis the same question he had asked the long succession of abbots and priors whom he had been seeing on the way from Rome, "What is on your mind now, Brother?"

"Books," said Francis without hesitation.

The Cardinal blinked. "You mean you want some books?"

"No."

"You are the only religious superior in Italy, I believe," said the Cardinal laughing, "who would answer 'no' to that question. Have you turned against learning, Brother Francis, like some of these heretics out on the roads?" But the Cardinal ceased his teasing at the shocked look on Francis' face.

"For learning I have only the greatest respect," Francis hastened to reassure him. "But let us leave learning to the Benedictines up there," and he gestured in the direction of Monte Subasio. "We have other work to do," and he pointed down.

"Who's talking about books, then? Brother Elias?" Ugolino asked shrewdly.

Francis looked thoughtful. "No," he said, "Brother Elias is a perfect friar. He brought only his breviary with him when he came, and when he saw the Mass book and the Gospels on the altar in the church, he said that was all that a priest needed."

"Then who is it?" asked the Cardinal, noting that although Francis had leaped at once to the defense of Brother Elias, the question raised a kind of surprised uneasiness in his mind. "Or have you been luring other doctors here?"

"It is the younger brethren," Francis sighed.

"It is always the younger brethren," said the Cardinal, crossing his knees more comfortably.

"Oh, no," said Francis hastily, "they are good lads—but they are always wanting books."

"I assure you, Brother Francis"—the Cardinal suppressed a smile with some difficulty—"all the other religious superiors in Christendom would be quite content if the younger brethren were asking for nothing but books. Why should they not have books?"

"It is not their calling," said Francis stoutly.

"But they are men of education. Some of them are priests. They are going out to preach in the countryside."

Francis looked weary. "But there are breviaries enough now at the

Portiuncula, and there are several copies of the Gospels, and there is the Mass book, and the Office book—"

"What more could a man want?" Ugolino finished the sentence. "Brother Francis, has no one told you that this is a great age of learning in the church, that men are thirsting for learning as never before? Don't I hear that every variety of man now is coming to join your Order?" And then he saw how Francis' eyes flashed as he flung his arms wide.

"God has been very good to us." And then as if there had been some shadow of pride even in the thanksgiving, he hastened to add, "Men are capable of more good than people usually think."

"Yes, when you touch their imaginations," said Ugolino thoughtfully.

"The face of Lady Poverty is a beautiful one when you lift the veil."

The Cardinal sighed. It was a soft cushion in the Bishop's chair, he reflected, for which he was grateful after the day's riding. "Yes," he went on, "most of the time we ask too little of men, I suspect, less than they would give. But you haven't answered my question. What is the matter with books? I like to read myself—when I get a chance," he added ruefully.

Francis looked around the plainly furnished but very substantial-looking room in the Bishop's palace. "That is all right here," he said at last, "but books are precious things, and you cannot thrust them under the thatch, or leave them on a shelf over the door. You must erect a fine house for them, and then when you have built it, you must put a lock on the door so that thieves will not come in. Then, a man who has one book wants another, and presently you must have a scriptorium that is warm and dry where men may sit and copy books, and before you know it," said Francis, "you have two sorts of brethren. You have the brethren who sit with the books, and you must have a fire for their hands that they may not freeze, and warm robes and hoods, and even a little fur that they may be warm enough to keep awake over the books. And then they will think that they are better than the brethren in the short tunics who work outdoors in the mud and who run along the frozen roads, and who go down to the river for the water and up in the streets to beg, and then at last they will begin to think that they must have finer food."

The Cardinal raised his eyebrows. "You do sound like the heretics, Brother Francis." And then at the distress on the little man's face, he laughed, "And like Pope Innocent, too. Well, we can let all this wait until, let us say, next year. What I want to talk to you about now are your plans for this year's Chapter at St. Mary of the Angels."

"I have been thinking about that—" Francis leaned forward against the table at which they sat. "It seems to me, my lord, that everywhere we go in Italy now men are making us welcome, and they are coming to join us in greater and greater numbers."

"So!" said the Cardinal with satisfaction. "You have begun to realize that you are going to have more men than ever before for this year's Chapter."

Francis looked at the Cardinal in surprise, "But, of course, my lord, that has been true every year from the first. It is more noticeable now because we have only one Chapter a year where we used to have four." And then at the smile on Ugolino's face, he added grudgingly, "Of course, there are more friars."

"Well, what are you planning to do about it?"

"It seems to me," said Francis, "that now that people do understand us in Italy, the time has come for us to go out into foreign parts, to go over the mountains into France—" Francis' eyes shone, and then as he saw the resistance in Ugolino's face, he hastened to add, "Of course, we shall be fair to the others, too. We will go into Spain and into Germany and perhaps even"—and now awe came into his voice—"into England!"

But the Cardinal was recovering from his astonishment. "This is moonshine," he said. "Maybe all this will come true some day," he added, taking pity at the shock in Francis' face, "but not this year or next. What I am talking about is what you are going to do for that Chapter."

"But this is it, my lord."

The Cardinal was tired. Under the spell of the little man's enthusiasm he had seen that vision of the brothers of St. Francis spilling over the mountains and into all the world. How could he make him see that the problems that had not yet been solved in Italy would not be solved abroad? That would have to wait until later. How many things these days had to wait until later! And already, he knew, he was an old man. "My dear son," he said, "I was not thinking of anything that may happen in—oh, let us say—ten years." And then seeing the consternation on Francis' face, he went on inexorably, "I'm thinking of what's going to happen down at the Portiuncula in just a few weeks."

"But that is what I am going to talk about."

"Never mind what you're going to talk about," said Ugolino, and though he saw the look of relief on Francis' face, he pushed on. "It's what you're going to do that I want to know. You said you had three thousand men there last year. I thought it was closer to four thousand, and so did Bernard, my secretary, who is used to estimating crowds. But say it was three thousand. If it was, you'll certainly have four thousand men here this year. What are you going to do with them?"

"God will provide. Did he not provide last year?" And then Francis' face kindled, and he leaned forward eagerly. "My lord, did you not hear? After you and all your train had gone, we had to keep the brethren for two whole days in order that none of the good food should be wasted, and we sent every man away with bread enough for his journey, and we carried baskets up to the leper hospital and to Sister Clare."

"If you don't do something about the tangle of things that you had at the Portiuncula, people won't be able to get their carts in to bring you the food. I'll grant you," said the Cardinal magnanimously, "that they will bring in enough food for all your men, but you've got to have some way that they can get in."

"They can carry it."

"My dear friend, every parish priest knows that you have to smooth the way a little for the good intentions of Christian charity, and that stench was not the odor of sanctity, and half those buildings were falling down."

"It is not San Damiano, I grant," said Francis thoughtfully. Then there came a gleam into his eye.

"No," said the Cardinal. "God knows I wish we could ask Sister Clare and her sisters to come and clean that place up, and my palace and every other palace in Rome. I suspect that would do more for Rome than anything Innocent or any other Pope has ever dreamed up in the way of rules and regulations. But God settled that in the Garden of Eden," he said. "Now whom have you in that company of yours whom you could charge with making some rational preparations for receiving your brethren?"

"Brother Bernard is a little tired," said Francis thoughtfully, "and I have sent him up to the hermitage of the Carceri, with Brother Giles to take care of him. He will pray for us," he added hopefully.

"It will take more than prayers. Haven't you some younger brother?"

"I don't want to disturb the younger brethren." And then his face lighted—"There is Brother Elias."

"Brother Elias! Francis, he is at least as old as you are."

"He seems to understand the younger brethren," said Francis thoughtfully. "You know what you said about our giving the younger brethren more help in their first days in the Order?"

It was not quite the way the Cardinal had put it, he reflected, but it was a reasonable translation into Francis' terms, and at least the little man had heard what he had said about new recruits running wild. "I thought you were asking Brother Leo to take care of that."

"Brother Leo would do it better than anybody else," said Francis soberly. "In fact, he did do it the right way, too, taking the new brother with him everywhere, into the fields, and up into the town, and into the caves. Half a dozen, he said, was the right number, and then it was like a father with his sons. But when it came to be a dozen, he said he felt like a bishop with a lot of flunkies at his heels."

The Cardinal drew in his breath so that he almost whistled. "Brother Leo has come a long way. What did you do then?"

"I asked Brother Elias," said Francis, and the Cardinal smiled. When Elias Bombarone joined Francis at the Portiuncula, Ugolino was as astonished as Dominic and everybody else, and he used some of his agents to make inquiries for him at Bologna and Paris, and the sum of all those inquiries was what Francis had just said. For Elias was one of those men whom harassed and puzzled authority would always ask to take the responsibility it knew not how to discharge itself.

"Well," said Ugolino, "I take it that Brother Elias found a different way to do it, not like a father with six, or a bishop with twelve. How did he do it? Like a schoolmaster with forty?"

Francis looked puzzled. "I'm not sure how he did it," he said at last. "I think he put the newcomers into one hut with him and showed them how to do things, and then when they had got accustomed to our ways, he used them to help the next ones who came along. He does everything very quietly, Brother Elias." The Cardinal noticed the relief in his voice as he said it.

"He sounds like my friend Dominic," said Ugolino to himself. Then as he looked at Francis, he marvelled how the little man had penetrated the mystery of a kind of genius that was precisely opposite to his own, the genius of administration. "That is his extraordinary gift," he thought to himself, "the ability to reach the hearts of men who are totally different from himself." And the great diplomat looked at Francis with such awe that the latter became troubled.

"There is nothing wrong with that, is there?"

"No," said the Cardinal, hastily returning to his responsibilities. "You couldn't have done better."

Then said Francis, "Shall I ask Brother Elias to get Saint Mary of the Angels ready for the Chapter meeting?"

"Again, you couldn't do better."

"Then," said Francis happily, "I can go on that mission I have promised over to Cettona."

The Cardinal stared at Francis. How could a man keep such innocence so long in this world? But the Cardinal was tired. "He will find out soon enough," he said to himself.

As it happened, it turned out to be sooner than the Cardinal had expected. Francis' mission had been a joyous one, marred only by two shadows. The Franciscans in the little convent outside the town had been offered a fine stone building by the lord of Cettona. It was a plain building; actually it had been the stables for the lord's hunting lodge. Cleaned out, it would make it possible for the friars to take care of and train the brethren who were flocking to them before they sent them out to work in the fields. But Francis had been so indignant in his first reaction to this proposal that the brethren had hastily thrown themselves at his feet and asked forgiveness, and when Francis bade them go and tell the lord they would not take his stables for themselves but would use them to build a leper hospital, which everyone knew the region needed, they agreed.

Then over at Todi Francis found that the brethren were very proud of two young scholars who had left the Benedictine house and come down to join them. Now they wanted Francis' permission to send them to study at Bologna.

"What will they learn at Bologna," said Francis, "that will help them to be better servants of Poverty? Will they teach them at Bologna how to reach the hearts of the farmers in the fields or the merchants travelling along the road?"

The next day the two young brethren came and flung themselves at Francis' feet and said that they would go up into the hills and would preach to the charcoal burners, and Francis blessed them and assured them that that was a quicker way to Paradise than all the hair-splitting at Bologna. So Francis came back a little tired, perhaps—certainly not dancing along as he had when he was younger, but thinking with sober satisfaction of kneeling down and giving thanks before the altar at the Portiuncula. But just as he came to the first little clump of huts, he stood still, for there where he should have been able to look down the twisting path and see the gray walls of the Portiuncula just at the end of the path where it vanished from sight, there stood a great block of raw yellow stone in his path. For a moment he thought that he was seeing a mirage and that all his fears had taken shape and now stood in a block of delusion across his path. Then as he blinked, he saw that it was no delusion. These were the stones of reality. There was a little window, too, with a shutter.

"What robber of a lord has come and made his dwelling with us?" Francis cried out in astonishment, and then he rushed down the path and knocked with his staff at the stone. There was no mistaking its actuality. Two of the younger brethren, who had heard him cry, rushed out and knelt down at his feet for his blessing, but he pushed them aside. Then he met one of the older brethren.

"What is it?" asked Francis.

"It is a house where the brethren may register when they come in for the Chapter meeting."

"It is a house of the devil!" said Francis, and at that moment he caught sight of Brother Leo.

"I was watching for you, Francis."

"Who has done this thing?"

"Who do you think?"

Another time Francis would have stopped at this extraordinary note of bitterness in the quiet voice of Brother Leo, but he rushed on. It seemed to him as he looked about the familiar clearing around the little church that everything was changed. New paths, new timber on some of the weather-beaten walls, new thatch, golden on the roofs in the late afternoon sunshine. The sickness in his stomach had now been swept with fire, and he stood in the center of the clearing looking around as if for a fitting object which that fire might devour. It was then that Elias came and knelt down at his feet, but Francis thrust out one thin arm at the new stone building and thundered, "Who has done this?"

"My master," said Elias in a low voice, "you bade me make ready for the Chapter meeting."

"Brother Elias," said Francis, "I have commended the new brethren to you for teaching, and do you know so little of the life of poverty that you build a stone fortress here in our very sanctuary? Do you not understand that wood and mud and thatch are the stuff of which the temporary booths in the wilderness shall be made for these pilgrims who will not be at home except in eternity?"

Elias had risen to his feet, and for a moment he stood there looking at Francis uncertainly, and then he bowed his head. "What does my master bid me do?"

Suddenly the subserviency that had so disarmed Francis nauseated him, and he flung his arm out so that his knuckles were almost bruised on the stone. "Tear it down," he said, "before the lightning of God strikes us all!"

Without a word Elias went and came back with an axe, and as he flung it into the wooden door, it shattered. In spite of himself, Francis marvelled at his strength, and a little of the violence in his own breast seemed to relax, and he turned away.

"Where are you going?" asked Leo.

"I am going up to the Carceri to pray," said Francis.

When he came back three days later, Francis found the space where the yellow monster had stood quite clear. Every trace was gone, and somebody had sprinkled clean sand from the river bottom where it had stood. Elias was kneeling in that vacant space with head bowed, and Francis raised him up and embraced him, and forgot his anger and his fear, for now he was full of what he had been praying about day and night at the Carceri.

So full was he that it was not until the evening before the Chapter was going to open that he really gave any heed to what was going on around him. He had just come out of the chapel where he had lingered for a little while to pray when he met Brother Juniper coming dripping from the river. Francis stared at him but saw only the little pool of water in the sand at his feet.

"Did you fall in the river, Brother Juniper?" asked Brother Giles, who happened to be standing next to Francis.

"Of course not," said Brother Juniper with great dignity. "I am not one of these high-class contemplatives who walks into the river without looking where he is going."

The mock indignation of Juniper's voice caught Francis' ear. "What then have you been doing?"

"I have been making myself clean for the conference tomorrow.

Brother Elias says we must not offend Brother Ugolino's delicate nose."

"What is this?" asked Francis slowly.

"It is time you woke up, Francis," said Leo somberly.

"What are you talking about?"

"Brother Francis," said Juniper solemnly, "you had better look to your ways, too. Brother Elias will scratch your back more ever than the lice did if you do not clean up your ways. We shall be as tidy as the Benedictine nuns."

"But what is all this about?" asked Francis.

Giles shrugged his shoulders. "I am a plain man," he said. "Brother Leo has the words."

"I'm not sure I do," said Leo.

"But what is it?"

"To do him justice," said Leo, gulping a little, "Brother Elias has made the whole place look a lot better. But I ask you, does it look like the Portiuncula?" Then the dikes seemed to break. "Francis, he tore down that abominable stone fortress of his, but once your back is turned, there will be more. Oh, why did he not go with Brother Dominic in the first place?"

"But Leo," said Francis, "he is the perfect pattern of a friar."

"That is the trouble," said Leo bitterly. "He is the perfect pattern. But I am wrong—you have your sermon to preach tomorrow, and God knows that is more important than anything else."

"It is not more important than this murmuring and making of divisions," said Francis sadly.

But Leo shook his head. "All the divisions will be swept up together tomorrow when they listen to you."

And so it proved. The Chapter seated before him on the ground listened as if entranced when Francis spoke. He was at his very best. Indeed, he seemed to take all the vast throng to his heart as he spread his arms out over them and told them they were welcome, that they had come home to the hearth of their Order. At that, some of the younger brethren wept with excitement. Then he went on to tell of the great growth of the Order, of the wonderful outpouring of God's grace which it represented. He spoke, too, of Pope Innocent's crusade and of the mystic Tau, and of all the souls that had received that imprint since last they met, and of the great privilege it had been for the friars to be the humble instruments of God's providence. He gave thanks for the great outpouring of Christian charity manifest in the carts of supplies creaking down the path to the Portiuncula from every direction.

Indeed, he said, that was the one thing that was troubling him. There was a time when they had begged in vain, even had had stones thrown at them and been tossed into the ditches by the road; but in God's goodness, love had presently begotten love, and everywhere the miracle of God's mysterious increase was being wrought before their eyes. Now, Francis said, his only fear was that like timid children they would stay in the bosom of the family, where love cushioned their way, and they would not go out to face the world. And yet the world needed them, for there was unsuspected goodness in the hearts of all people, and it was to bring it out that God had sent the Friars Minor into the world.

At first there had been some who had laughed when he spoke of how worried he was about the easy days on which they had fallen, but Francis noticed that his oldest companions, sitting at his feet, were not laughing. Only Brother Juniper was staring at him as if he were mad. That was why, Francis went on to say, he had prayed, asking God to what end should they use the harvest which He had already given them. It had become clear to him now, he said, that the next thing for them to do was to go forth and carry their missions over the mountains into France—and here his voice rose—and even into Germany, and Spain, where men still held the battle lines against the heathen, and far-off England, which had been dear always to the hearts of the Popes. Quite literally they would go forth and carry the crusade which the great Pope Innocent had given to them to the ends of the earth.

The Brethren were now on their feet. They were cheering, and all over the vast assembly rose the cry, "Send me! Send me!" and even the crusading cry, "God wills it!" But at that Francis shrank back for a moment, and then he raised his arms, and he cried out, "Peace! Peace!" And when the tumult of their enthusiasm had died down, Francis resumed his speaking. They must not forget, he said, that they would be going among strange peoples whose languages and customs they did not know, and there would be hardship, and there would be misunderstanding, and there might even be danger. He would not send them where he feared to go himself; so he would lead one of the missions. He would lead the mission to France. And then he chanced to look down and saw that the face of Leo was shining, and the grave eyes of Bernard were fixed upon his face with a deep content, and Giles could hardly stay on the ground in his place; but when he looked at the face of Brother Elias, he wondered where he had seen that look before, and then he remembered that he had seen it in the eyes of a hawk that had been hooded too long. Francis knelt down and bade them all pray with him for God's blessing on the missions. As he stepped down from the little platform before the church, Brother Leo smiled to find that he was humming an old French hymn, the prayer for divine help of the knight setting out on his quest.

The Cardinal of Ostia had not been able to arrive at the Chapter until the last session, but he had already heard on the way of Francis' sermon on the missions. He had been shocked and thoroughly alarmed. "Someday that fanatic will decide that the Judgment Day is tomorrow," he said in exasperation to the chaplain who was riding with him. But the next day when he heard that the great meeting was proceeding with charity and enthusiasm to a peaceful close, the Cardinal had second thoughts, "For all his innocence he is a shrewd strategist sometimes, this Francis of ours. It is not the first time that the ruler of a faction-torn kingdom has pulled his forces together for a foreign adventure." So he went on to preside over the closing Vespers and give the Pope's blessing.

At supper that night the Cardinal heard the guardians of various houses asking Brother Elias if they could not give him their names at once for the missions, and he heard Brother Elias say that word would be sent to them at the proper time. Then he explained to the Cardinal, "If I let them enlist now, the French mission would have them all."

"Why the French mission?"

"That is the one that Brother Francis is leading."

Ugolino noted the matter-of-fact way in which Brother Elias spoke, and he decided to say nothing for the present, but after supper he drew Francis aside. "You must understand," said he, "that someone else must go with the mission to France." And then as Francis' face fell, he spoke more gently, "God has wrought miraculously in the number of friends he has given you, but you know that not every bishop or secular lord in Umbria is convinced of the soundness of your Rule, and there are reservations in Rome of which you know nothing. I can protect you better against—not your enemies, but, let us say, against those who are doubtful and skeptical if you are here where I can put my hands on you." He saw the disappointment in Francis' face. "You see, I am not asking you to depart from anything in your Rule, or to give up your basic mission."

"That is true," said Francis. "I will obey you as I promised my lord, Innocent, I would."

As Francis went out sadly, Ugolino bade one of his chaplains bring Brother Elias to him. "I want to thank him," he said, "for the fine service he has done in planning for this Chapter." But when Elias knelt down in front of him, the Cardinal said nothing for a minute. Then he bade him arise. "You know," he began, "that you have done an admirable job in organizing this Chapter."

"My lord," began Elias, his dark face flushing a little.

"What I want to make sure you know, however, is that it is not your planning that has sent your brethren home in such astonishing agreement. That is the work of Francis." Ugolino paid no attention to the distress in Elias' face. "I have heard of, let us say, disagreements," the Cardinal went on quietly. "They are what one must expect when one is dealing with many men, and you and I can plan for them. That is the gift of the rulers of this world. But neither you nor I could ever have brought those men together here in the first place. Only Francis could do that, and only Francis will keep them coming. Don't you ever forget that, Elias Bombarone." Then before Elias could speak, he raised his ringed hand in blessing and dismissed him.

3

For the next year and a half Francis lived through an agony of disappointment. There had hardly been time for the missions to get across the mountains when the reports of disaster began to drift back. The missionaries had starved on their long marches over mountains, and they had nearly died in a sudden late snowfall. They had all but perished of thirst in desert places; they had nearly drowned on storm-tossed rivers and lakes. But worst of all was what they had suffered at the hands of their fellow Christians. They had been beaten by robbers and stoned by farmers. They had been dragged into bishops' courts, and thrown into local lords' dungeons, and tossed into village ditches. In Portugal royal caprice had flung them from princely table into princely dungeon because a loyal friar had refused to become a part of a royal household. French authority had taken the trouble to consult Rome, but by the time official reassurance arrived, the brethren were weary, and authority was wearier still, and those to whom they had hoped to preach were quite indifferent. In Germany the violence was worst of all, for peasants and mobs of suspicious villagers had beaten them up before authority, a little tardy, could intervene.

At first Francis had taken all these rumors and reports cheerfully. He had reminded his brethren that this was the way in which God always marked His own, and he chided them with having become so used to ease and favor in their own comfortable Umbria that they had forgotten that they were called to martyrdom. And when the first stragglers came back, Francis received them and gave them a martyrs' welcome, and the brethren at home listened with wide eyes to the tales of their hardships. "This will bring us fresh life," said Francis cheerfully; "we will make ready for another mission."

But the really bad news from Francis' point of view was the news which Brother Pacifico brought back just before the second annual Chapter after the missions had begun. Of all the leaders of the new enterprise, Brother Pacifico was the one of whom Francis had had the highest hopes. He had been a famous troubadour whom the Emperor had crowned as the king of poets; and then, with all of Rome crowding around him and begging for his songs, he had gone one day to a little convent of friars outside of Rome to find out about the man who had started it all, and he had told the brethren that the man—Francis— seemed to him like another kind of troubadour. The brethren had rather resented the comparison, and that night the troubadour had dreamed of the man Francis, and he had seen him standing with light about him and a pair of crossed swords behind him. In the morning he told his hosts, "I am wasting my time making love songs. I am going to find your little man Francis and join his crusade." He had come in a great heat of resolution, quite prepared never to sing again, and he had been surprised almost to ecstasy when Francis had embraced him and assured him that the gift of song was one of God's finest gifts, and it was the use to which one put it that made it good or ill.

Now it was Brother Pacifico who brought the worst news of all, that half a dozen of the younger brethren had stayed at Paris. "No," he said to Francis, "they have not deserted the Order. They are living in a little house next to the house of the followers of Dominic, and they are keeping the Rule there."

"But what are they doing?" asked Francis sharply.

"They are going to the lectures."

"They will want to be doctors." Francis shuddered.

"They say they must know the ideas which they are supposed to meet and to refute."

"Ideas to meet and to refute!" said Francis scornfully. "What have they to do with that? Our business is to live as Our Lord lived, and to preach penance and love and freedom from the world's bondage."

"If only," said Brother Pacifico, "they would let you and me go and do it, Brother Francis, like a pair of troubadours singing songs and getting the people to sing with us, the language wouldn't matter so much. It is when you go like preachers that the language makes such a difference!"

But Francis made no answer, for he knew only too sadly that it was precisely here that he could not convince his brethren. When the Chapter met, the first thing which the guardians began to talk about was the failure of the missions. The idea was like all Brother Francis' ideas, an inspiration from heaven, said Brother Elias. Francis had seen the suspicion on Leo's face when Brother Elias rose to speak, and he thought it unjust, for Elias never spoke without first saying that nothing they did had any meaning, or would have ever existed, without Brother Francis. Indeed, sometimes Francis wished that he would say less of him. "For if it all depends on so little a thing as me," he thought, "how shall it last?"

Then Brother Elias had gone on to say that the difficulty was in the lack of planning. They should have thought of language, and they should have waited to get permission from the proper authorities. Brother Juniper, sitting on the other side of Francis, shook his head. "We would be waiting yet," he said. "No one would even die, if he waited for permission from the proper authorities." But Francis bade him hush. There was worse to come, however, for Brother Elias was followed by others who said it was not a matter of waiting for permission from ecclesiastical authorities in the countries to which their missions went; it was a matter of having the proper licenses and privileges before they ever started out. The Pope had approved their crusade. Let them have, as other ecclesiastical bodies had, the proper papers, and they would have none of these troubles.

Francis was on his feet. At first he tried to control the passion of indignation that burned through his frail body. "No papers!" he cried sharply. "No papers, my brethren. We shall spend our days in the courts of bishops and cardinals, seeking out ever fresh privileges. And then we shall be asking for houses in which we may keep our privileges. They will be worse even than the books. And how then shall we preach of poverty who have made ourselves rich, and of poverty's freedom who have put ourselves in bondage to papers?" And then as murmurs rose all over, Francis shouted, "You can do it, but you will regret it, and you will find it impossible to undo it. You will become like everybody else," he said, "and what point then will there be in your being at all?"

But at that point Cardinal Ugolino rose. The session had grown long, he said, and no one could deny that Brother Francis was right when he said if they sought privileges, they would only be like the rest. "If the salt have lost its savor," said the Cardinal, and he gave his blessing, and all those who had been shouting to make themselves heard went off, nodding their heads together. But Ugolino detained Francis. "Surely," said he, "this is not all you have to say."

"Of course, not," said Francis, who was beginning to feel ashamed. "I should have known how to restore brotherly charity."

"I will not ask you," said Ugolino, "what it is that you have on your mind, but I think whatever it is, you'd better talk to them about it the first thing in the morning before any more of this bickering breaks out."

So in the morning Francis arose, and this time he began with the old greeting, "May God give you peace!" And then he went on to say, "We have Our Lord's example here. If the children of the house will not listen, then the bread of the word shall be carried to strangers. We have tried to make our fellow Christians understand, and the time has not yet come. So now let us go to the heathen." There was no murmuring now. Most of the audience were aghast, and Francis lifted his hands. "All men know that the armies of Christendom are gathering in Egypt, and the armies of the heathen are drawn up there. The great Pope Innocent, who launched this crusade, knew that arms in the hands are powerless without the arms of the spirit. And what good will it do if we slay the bodies of the heathen, and their souls have known nothing of the light of God's truth?"

Cardinal Ugolino held his breath. He had found urgent messages from Rome at his lodging the night before, but he had said that he must stay until he heard what Francis had to say. "It is better to get it straight from him than twisting through the rumors of others."

"The great Pope Innocent knew in his wisdom," Francis went on, "that the two crusades must go hand in hand. Again and again, we have said that we would carry the Gospel to the heathen, but we have let ourselves be turned back. It isn't safe, it isn't the time. But now is the time. If our armies are victorious, we shall need the healing balm of Christ's love and charity. And if, God forbid, our armies are thrown back, this may be our last chance to let the fresh air of God's truth blow over those desert sands." Ugolino listened with the deepest interest. Francis, he knew, had quite forgotten his presence, and like the breeze of his figure, his spirit was blowing through the hearts of those before him. And when Francis said, "This time I will lead the mission. Who will go?" all over the vast assembly rose the cry, "I will go with you!" It seemed to Ugolino that for the first time in that Chapter, the whole group had been pulled by Francis into one mind. As he hurried back to Rome, he thought, "I wonder if I will ever see the little man again."

But the old joy had come back to Francis. Elias and half of the new leaders crowded around him. Only Brother Pacifico and Brother Juniper held back.

"Do you not want martyrdom, Brother Juniper?" asked Francis that night at supper.

"I'm as ready for martyrdom," said Brother Juniper, "as most men. Not as ready as you or Brother Elias, of course," he added with a great air of judiciousness. Elias blushed, but Francis laughed. "And why are we so ready for martyrdom, do you think?"

"You are always inviting people to walk over you," said Brother Juniper, "and Brother Elias is always inviting people to walk into him." Then as he saw the distress on Francis' face, he went on, "But no matter what you men of action do, you need a few of us contemplatives to stay at home and pray for you." There was a hearty roar of laughter at Brother Juniper in the contemplative role.

"That is true," said Francis. "We do need prayers. I shall send you, Brother Juniper, up to ask Sister Clare to pray for us. Now, Brother Pacifico, why are you not coming with us?"

But Brother Pacifico looked so distressed that Francis' heart went out to him. "What would you do with a troubadour in Egypt?" asked Brother Pacifico. "Would you send him to jingle at the Soldan?"

Francis' face sobered. "I might do worse," he said. "Brother Pacifico, you shall be my first choice."

"Then," said Brother Juniper with an injured air, "I shall be second."

"No," said Francis gently. "I must leave somebody to cheer up Sister Clare and her ladies."

It seemed as if a full quarter of the Chapter trailed after Francis down to the port of Ancona. In vain Brother Elias asked for time to send word to their friends that they might have proper supplies. Francis rebuked him sharply, "That would be tempting providence to express such doubt of God's mercy at the start." So Brother Elias bowed his head and silently followed Francis down to Ancona.

There Francis found a messenger from Ugolino. He had received a petition from some of the lords of the castles in Syria. There were many Christians in that land now, and Ugolino thought that there might be a chance for a few missionaries there. So Francis bade Brother Elias take whom he wished and go to Syria. Then he bade Brother Giles and Brother Bernard go and look for shipping. But when they found a ship ready to go to Egypt, there was room for only a dozen men, and the captain assured Brother Bernard, who seemed to him— as Brother Bernard always seemed to men of affairs—a knowledgeable person, that there was no hope of more space for the next couple of months. The Cardinal Pelagio had taken all the available vessels to carry supplies for the reinforcements he had just taken to Damietta.

"It is as well," said Francis. "We've always done best with a handful."

"But how," asked Brother Peter, "will you choose among so many?"

"I will let God do that." So he sent word that all the brethren were to assemble at the quay, and when they were all there, he made a little speech to them. He said that from the beginning he had always meant that every brother should find an equal place in his love, and that no brother should ever wonder about any difference of degree in his affection; so now he would not keep one brother and send another away, but he would let God choose.

Almost at his feet there was a ragged child playing with a mangy-looking kitten. Francis called the child to him, and lifting him up in his arms, he bade him pick out the men who would go on the big boat. Solemnly the child looked over the throng about him. Brother Pacifico was smiling at the picture of the dirty little urchin with his grimy hand around St. Francis' neck. The child pointed to him, and Francis patted him in approval. Then the child picked out eleven others including, to Francis' delight, Peter Catanii and another of his first companions, Brother Barbaro, and two young knights who had recently joined the order, Illuminato and Leonardo. "It is enough," said Francis. "It is one more than the captain allowed us. We will not mind crowding a little." And he kissed the child and set him down.

Once aboard, Francis set himself in the old way to preparing his brethren for their mission, talking joyously of the love of God and of Christ's purpose in coming into the world, and of God's purpose that all men should live in charity and peace. So they came ashore at Damietta singing, and Brother Pacifico smiled, for Francis was singing a crusading song in French.

But the quay of Damietta was crowded with great sacks and bales and boxes, and thronged with such a host of soldiers, merchants, merchants' servants, and wharfside riffraff, pushing and stumbling and hauling and shouting, that Francis had a hard time getting the attention of anyone. He had stopped several passers-by before he found one who could understand even Brother Pacifico's very good French. And when they did finally reach Cardinal Pelagio's headquarters, in an old stone building that looked as if it had once been a merchants' warehouse, Francis was appalled to find that it was quite as thronged as the dockside and by a company as varied. When he told Brother Pacifico this, the latter laughed. "It is the generals here," he said judiciously, "where it was the common soldiers on the quay, and the merchants themselves where it was their servants. But I doubt if the interests are very different." So it was only after a long day's waiting that Francis and his companions were able to reach even the Cardinal's antechamber.

"I have seen the Pope himself with less trouble," said Francis to one of the Cardinal's servants.

"But this isn't the Lateran," said the man wearily. "Or if it is, it is the Lateran and the Emperor's palace all rolled together in a field headquarters. Have you not heard? Everything was in such confusion here when the Cardinal arrived that he had to take control."

The Cardinal, when Francis finally reached his feet, certainly looked like a man who had had to take control of more than he had bargained for. He was a younger man than Ugolino, but he had the same air of quiet competence, or, Francis suspected, would normally have had it in his palace in Rome. Here he looked at Francis as if the sight of these dusty friars were the final straw.

"Look here," he said, "pilgrimages are all right, but we're getting ready for a battle."

"That is what we have come to help with," said Francis quietly. He thrust out his empty hand, and the Cardinal, looking at it, laughed. As he laughed, he relaxed a little. Then he looked again at Francis. "Oh," he said, sitting down and motioning to the others to sit on the stools scattered around the room, "you are Ugolino's little man. He told me you were coming, and that I wouldn't need to worry about what to do with you." As he said that, he looked doubtfully at the little company.

"We will not bother you," said Francis. "We will pray for you. Brother Pacifico here will even sing for you."

"When we win the battle," said the Cardinal, "I will be glad to hear your song." And then, remembering that of all the host who had come to see him this day, these only had asked no favor of him, he blessed them, and he sent for the messenger who was to leave for Rome in the morning and bade him tell the Cardinal Ugolino that, madman or saint, his little man was the most refreshing visitor he had had that day. "But who," he said to his secretary, "will listen to him in this mad-house, I cannot imagine."

Cardinal Pelagio would have been surprised if he had known that that was precisely what Francis was thinking the next morning. "While the rest of you beg for our supper for tonight, Brother Pacifico and I will go and stand on the road between the wharf and the Cardinal's headquarters."

"And who do you think will hear you there?" asked Brother Barbaro good-naturedly.

"We shall sing, Brother Pacifico and I," said Francis, "and they will hear us. We shall sing under the din," he explained. And so Francis and Pacifico took up their post in the dust at the side of the road, and they began to sing a little French hymn in praise of Our Lady. It was a hymn that Francis had heard sung when he was a child journeying with his father to the great silk market in Champagne. Some men-at-arms going down to the quay to guard a shipment of arms for their lord heard the song, and it brought back to them the evening in their village with the girls singing on their balconies, and they lingered. Brother Pacifico, Francis thought with admiration, had lost nothing of the fine person and the beautiful voice that had carried him to fame as a troubadour. But it was of the little man that the soldiers and the merchants had heard rumor, and while Pacifico sang, they looked at him curiously. So the throng grew until presently some of the stewards down at the docks came up to see what had happened, and the servants came out of the Cardinal's house to know why things were not arriving. When the servants threatened to arrest the two singers as vagabonds, the entire crowd protested, and the servants went back to the Cardinal to report what had happened: all the preparations for the attack held up by two vagabonds singing hymns. The Cardinal Pelagio had not won his place in the world without some sense of humor. He laughed now at the absurdity. Then with that habit of facing facts and finding a realistic solution for them that had brought him to the top of the world's heap, he told the servants to offer the friars his own chapel, a simple enough wooden structure as befitted an army in the field, but hung with fine tapestries inside. They could stand by the door, he said, and it would do no harm if some of the audience were moved to go into the chapel.

The Cardinal had just appointed a young cousin of his as chaplain and put him in charge of his improvised chapel. The young Giulio frowned at the thought of the crowd making a din outside of the sacred precincts of his new realm; but when the first day, some of the delighted listeners not only came into the church to pray, but asked to make their confessions, the new chaplain was reconciled; and as the little trickle swelled, and all sorts of men seemed to be reminded of the religious duties they had so easily let slip, the young chaplain began to remember the time when he had thought he would be a village priest, and like Christ and His disciples go through the fields seeking out the lost sheep. It was an odd thing to have had to come so far to return to his beginnings. But a week later he had gone so far as to follow Francis and Pacifico down to the ancient pilgrims' hostel where they were lodging.

Brother Peter wondered if Francis would not do well to see the Cardinal before they accepted the young chaplain into the Order, but Francis said, no. He had shown that he already belonged to them; why should they delay in embracing him and clothing him in the habit, girded with rope, that would preach to everybody who knew him more eloquently than any words he could speak?

But though the Cardinal was busier than ever as the time of the assault drew near, he yet found time to send for Francis. "This camp," he said, fixing the little man with a glance that had made hardened Syrian traders, embracing a heaven-sent opportunity for profiteering, quail, "is full of the greatest assortment of thieves and vagabonds and sheer adventurers that you can find in any comparable area of Christendom. You have brands here that you could snatch from the very jaws of hell and decorate your missionary priests' sermons for years to come with the tale of their rescue. The Bishop of Acre's *Golden Legend* would seem as tame as a post-lenten sermon when you begin to tell the stories of these converts; and then you go and take one of my priests, a kinsman of mine, who was likely to have a very distinguished career in the Church once he could get over his family's nagging about preferment."

"But, your lordship," said Francis, "Brother Giulio is now free of not only his family's nagging, but all his own nagging about preferment. He is one of the Friars Minor now, and he will never in this world have to think of preferment again."

"But the work I need him for?" said the Cardinal sharply.

"At this moment," said Francis, "he is doing his Father's work. It is long past sundown, and he is still hearing confessions in the chapel there."

The Cardinal flung up his hands.

"He is a great prince," said Francis thoughtfully as he went out of the old warehouse with Pacifico. "But he hasn't thought of what is needed most of all if the assault on Damietta is to succeed."

It was night now, and across the sands they could already see the watchfires of the enemy. There was a turn in the breeze, and they heard a bell ringing. "Maybe," he said, "their heathen priests are calling them to prayer. And who knows but they may outdo us in prayer, even to a heathen god."

"It would be worse than heresy to think that," said Brother Pacifico, and Francis said no more. But that night as Francis slept, he dreamed that he was in the middle of a great fight. As so often in dreams, he was not quite sure as to where it was. Sometimes he thought the fighting was on the sands between the lines of the Muslim and the Christian watchfires, as he had seen them the night before. And sometimes it seemed to him it was on the ancient bridge between Assisi and Perugia. And he was sore afraid. And then the voice which he had heard so many years ago at Spoleto and again in Rome went like fire through all his being. "Stop the fighting, Francis. The time is not yet come for the city to fall."

Francis raised himself on his pallet, but all about he heard the even breathing of his brethren in the stifling night. "If I wake them, they will not sleep again," he said, "and they are all weary with the labor in the heat." He thought of the cool dawns in Umbria. "We do not thank God enough for his blessings," he said ruefully, and he lay awake and tried to think. But when he heard Brother Peter rise to make ready to serve Mass at the chapel, he stopped him and told him of his dream. Peter awakened the other brothers, and they went out of the great pilgrim dormitory together, and they stood in a cluster near a little shed so they would not wake the others who were sleeping.

It was Brother Giulio who spoke first. "You should let me tell the Cardinal," he said.

"No," said Francis. "If we tell him, he will say, 'This is a madman. Why should we listen to his dreams?'"

"But," said the young priest, "if my cousin hears that you had a prophecy, and you let him go out to battle and did nothing, what do you think he will say then?"

But Brother Peter interrupted him sharply. "It will not matter what he says, but what will Christ say when He has warned you?"

"I will tell the Cardinal," said Francis simply.

"Let me go with you," insisted the young priest.

Peter thought it would be better if Francis went alone without any reminder to the Cardinal of his loss, but the young priest warned Francis of the difficulty of reaching the Cardinal at all. So Francis was persuaded to accept his help.

The Cardinal was only breaking his fast when the two brethren stood before him. "You again," he said sourly, looking at Francis, and studiously avoiding the sight of his young cousin.

Francis lost no time in trying to appease his ill-humor, but told him simply of his dream and of the voice that had spoken. The Cardinal smote his ringed hand on the table so that the wine glasses rang.

"I am getting ready for a battle, little man," he said, "and you come to worry me with dreams and portents. Ugolino says you are not mad, but I think it is charitable to think you are," and then he turned angrily away.

The young man sprang hotly to his feet, but Francis seized his arm and dragged him away. "We have done our duty as God's messengers. It is out of our hands now." And as they went along, he told the young man that they should tell no one, and they should go on as the Cardinal certainly would, as if nothing had happened. But when they came to the chapel, Francis found that he could not join Brother Pacifico in singing the pleasant little hymn which he was singing to a gathering crowd.

"What shall we sing now?" said Brother Pacifico when he had finished, and Francis began to sing one of the hymns from the office for the dead. All the company stood still, but to Francis' relief, at that moment messengers began to come from the Cardinal to bid all the idlers get to their posts. If they wanted to go in and make their confession, it would be all right; but otherwise, each man to his post.

"You have heard the Cardinal's command," said Francis. "We shall go to our post in the old chapel at the hostel and pray."

When they arrived there, Pacifico asked, "For whom shall we pray?"

"We shall pray for those who are about to die."

Next morning Francis rose before dawn, and he sent Brother Giulio, the priest, to the camp to hear the last-minute confessions, and Brother Barbaro with him to bring him any news. But he himself went straight to the little stone chapel attached to the hostel. There he flung himself on the steps before the altar and confessed himself an unprofitable servant.

He was still lying there when Barbaro came back to say that they were going to make the assault before the sun rose. Even as he spoke, the trumpet sounded. So Francis sent him back with instructions to watch the fighting from a prudent distance. Then he knelt down again, and this time he looked at the crucifix above the altar. As in the crucifix at San Damiano, there was the same look of long patience in the eyes of the Christ, and Francis prayed again. This time he prayed for forgiveness, for here he was grief-stricken because he had spoken and not been heeded, when all through these centuries Christ had spoken and most men had not even listened. It was a long time before Barbaro came again to report that he had stayed in hopes that he might see the issue of the fighting; but the sand had risen from the floor of the desert and covered the struggling armies, and no man could tell yet what the outcome would be. Francis sent him back, but before he could kneel to pray again, he heard a voice speaking. The light was beginning to fade, but as he came down to the door, he saw that it was a man in a bishop's dress.

"I thought it was you when I heard the story," said the Bishop. Francis recognized the voice of the traveler who had come to Pope Innocent's bier in the cathedral at Perugia. Then the Bishop of Acre's voice fell. "It would take more than your little robe to cover the nakedness of those who have fallen today. And some of them were great lords, too."

"And the end of it?"

"That is what I have come to ask you," said the Bishop.

"What do you mean?"

"I have seen the Cardinal's young cousin, and I asked him where you were, and he said you were praying in the chapel here."

At that moment Barbaro came in. He had been running, and he was weeping. "The assault has failed completely," he said, "and only the night will keep the Saracens from following us here into our camp."

"Then I shall stay here and pray for the dead."

But Barbaro shook his head. "I just outran a whole crowd," he said. "They will be here."

"What are they coming for?" But before Barbaro could answer, the young Giulio pushed his way into the chapel.

"Brother Francis," he said, "they are all coming here, and they are crying 'The Prophet! The Prophet!' "

"They must have been frightened out of their wits to take up the heathen cry!"

"No," said the young priest, "it is you they want."

Now the Bishop stepped forward. "Francis, it is all over the camp. The Cardinal himself said this afternoon when the battle began to turn, 'If only I had listened to what the little madman said!' "

"What shall I do?" asked Francis as the cries broke in on them, "The Prophet! The Prophet!"

"Nothing that I could tell you," said the Bishop humbly. "You have better counsel than mine."

Francis went out and stood on the step in front of the old hostel, and as the first of the fugitives fell at his feet, he lifted his hands and said, "Come to me, all you that labor, and are burdened, and I will refresh you," and he pointed to the open door of the pilgrims' chapel.

4

The day was well advanced before Francis had finished with the crowd outside the hostel chapel. Many were simply frightened, anxious in their terror to come under the wing of one who obviously stood closer than they did to the divine protection. Some were wounded, or thought they were wounded. It was a curious thing, Francis reflected, that on the eve of battle there had been a great pressure to receive the sacraments; but now that they had escaped there was little thought of making their peace with Heaven. A few did come into the chapel to offer thanks for their survival, but Francis noted that they were few, indeed.

Then came the messenger from the Cardinal. Pelagio had gone with his men to the battle, and he was worn out. But more than that he was disgusted with himself, and with Francis, too. "The next time you know what's going to happen, don't let me brush you aside."

Francis smiled.

"Yes, I know," said the Cardinal angrily. "You did tell me and I did not believe you."

"That is not why I was smiling," Francis hastened to explain. "It is easier to be rebuked, my lord—" Francis hesitated—how can one say that one has heard people murmur "Saint" all day and, in spite of one's best efforts, felt them kiss one's hands? But Francis guessed that to the Cardinal a reputed saint was all in the day's work. Usually there was nothing to it, and it cluttered the way; but there was something to this prophecy, and Pelagio knew it.

"If you want anything," he said quietly, "just tell me. I know a fact when I see it."

"There is something I want to do"—Francis held his breath for a moment—"I want to go over to the Soldan's camp."

"You mean you want to go through the lines?"

As he saw the astonishment on the Cardinal's face, Francis knew he must try to explain. "They will have won. They will be feeling more generous."

"Generous? Have you not heard that the Soldan gives a gold bezant for the head of every Christian?"

"He will not think that I look worth a bezant."

The Cardinal looked at him more keenly. "Whom are you taking with you?"

"I will take one of my brethren, Illuminato. He is a very pleasant-looking young man," he added humorously.

The Cardinal considered. "I ought to forbid you to go. You understand that if you get yourself killed, I will have to answer for my judgment in Rome?"

"Cardinal Ugolino will defend you."

Now for the first time, Cardinal Pelagio relaxed and smiled. "He will say he knows how hard you are to stop, you mean?"

"Something like that."

The Cardinal made up his mind. "Of course, I can't give you permission or anything like that; I simply won't forbid you to go."

"That is quite enough."

"One thing only I will beg you. Don't get yourself killed if you can help it." And characteristically, now that the decision was made, the Cardinal was ready to get on with it. "When are you going?"

"Just before sundown. They will be less likely to think it an attack then."

The Cardinal smiled again. "Ugolino always said that you were not anywhere nearly as big a fool as you looked." And he waved the little man aside.

As he made his way back to the chapel, hearing the soldiers carousing on every side, Francis thought to himself that it was no wonder that Pelagio must be about his business. Presently, he noticed that several knights in chain mail with their squires were making their way down the path toward the Cardinal's residence. When Francis told Brother Illuminato what he proposed to do, the young man's face blanched. Then he recovered himself as Francis had felt sure he would. "Let me go with you."

"I had hoped you would say that. I am asking you to come at once, because I think that if the other brethren knew—"

"They would all want to come, too."

"Yes, and I think it is better if just two men go alone."

The color of the sky over the sands had softened, and Francis pointed out to Brother Illuminato how gently the sun was setting over the scene of yesterday's battle. Then as he saw that the young friar was not looking at the sky but at the bushes and trees ahead of him, he began to chant the Psalm, "The Lord is my shepherd." Presently Illuminato's voice joined his a little uncertainly, and then it steadied.

There was a slight movement behind some bushes ahead of them that startled both men, and then Francis pointed out that it was only two sheep browsing on dusty herbage. "The Lord is taking care of those two sheep," said Francis. "How much more will He take care of us!"

After that there seemed no motion, no life. And then suddenly from a little hollow in front of them, half-screened by low bushes, a number of Saracens rode up on their graceful horses with silken scarves fluttering in the light evening breeze. Before Francis could speak, they had seized both of the friars. Brother Illuminato struggled, but Francis bade him go along quietly, and as the men saw them relax, Francis cried out, "Soldan! Soldan!" The Saracens looked at each other, and then they thrust one of their number forward, and in the French language he asked them what they wanted.

"We wish to see the Soldan," said Francis.

"They are messengers," said the French-speaking Saracen, and he spoke to his comrades in a language Francis had never heard. Francis was wondering if perhaps he were not acting a lie, but when they presently reached the nearest tents of the Saracen army, a couple of men came out with chains and bound Illuminato and Francis so that they could barely walk together.

"We have come," protested Francis, "to do good to the Soldan and not to hurt him."

The French-speaking Saracen apparently translated this into the unknown tongue. But the leader of the group that had seized them only shrugged his shoulders, and when Francis asked when they might hope to meet the Soldan, the interpreter laughed at him and said, "Do you think the Soldan has nothing else to do but keep watch?"

"Let us sing a hymn," said Francis to Illuminato.

But when he raised his voice in a hymn of thanksgiving for the goodness of God, his guard bade him be still. "There is racket enough over there behind your disorderly lines."

So Francis and Illuminato prayed silently. Presently Francis fell asleep, but the younger friar watched the Saracens come and go all night, some of them coming over to look at them, others whispering and shaking their heads. Once in the middle of the night, Francis awoke, and for a little while he watched the Saracen soldiers, too. They were talking quietly now. "At least they are not drinking the night away," he said to Brother Illuminato. When in the morning word came that the Soldan would see them, Francis reminded the young friar that if they could convert the Soldan, they would have won the Crusade, and if they failed, what finer thing than the martyr's crown could man aspire to?

Neither of the friars had ever seen anything quite like the brightly colored arches in the courtyard of the Soldan's palace. Then they came into a large and beautifully tiled room that looked as if it were walled with precious stones. The room seemed to be all a rustle with the soft movement of the bright silk robes and many-colored turbans. It was not hard to find the Soldan, for he was sitting on his throne, leaning forward and looking curiously at the intruders. Francis bowed courteously to him, and only then did he notice that between his feet and the Soldan's throne stretched a bright blue carpet, studded with gold crosses. He looked up from the crosses at the Soldan, and he saw that he was smiling at him. It was not, he thought, a cruel smile; rather it was quizzical, as if he had set a puzzle for his guest and wondered how he would solve it.

Francis smiled, too. "Soldan, there were three crosses on the hill of Calvary. On one Our Lord hung, and on the other two, thieves. The true cross I carry here"—and he put his hand to his heart—"and these crosses that are put here to trick me, they are the thieves' crosses, and I do not fear to walk on them." He went boldly across the carpet, while the Soldan's eyes lighted with pleasure.

"You're an ingenious fellow, at least," said the Soldan, and a ripple of laughter ran around the room as somebody repeated the friar's French for the benefit of the audience.

But Francis went on as if the Soldan had not interrupted, "One of those two thieves recognized Christ on the cross, and though he had been an evil man all the days of his life, Our Blessed Lord promised him that that night he would walk with him in Paradise."

"So you want to bring me to your paradise," said the Soldan. At Francis' answer several of the bystanders had started toward him, but the Soldan stopped them with a glance. "What sort of paradise is it," he asked, "and how will this Christ of yours help me to come there?"

Francis began to explain to the Soldan the whole story of Christ's coming for man's redemption. The Soldan listened, and as Francis spoke, simply and earnestly, with all his body coming into play so that the movement of a hand or a foot emphasized a point, the room grew still.

"You do believe it, don't you?" said the Soldan.

"I believe it so much that I want all men to have the joy of believing it." And then Francis stretched out his hands to the Soldan, and he besought him to let him but talk with him and pray with him for a little.

The Soldan looked around his company, and he said, "I do not know when, my friends, we shall have so good a chance again to try our Muslim arguments against the Christian."

"But it isn't of arguments that I am talking," protested Francis. "It is of faith."

"That is harder to measure," said the Soldan quietly, and he looked around his company with lifted brows.

"Listen to me, Soldan," pleaded Francis. "Build a great fire in front of your palace here, and I will take the cross of Christ, and I will pass through that fire, if some of your priests will do so, too. And whichever one of us emerges unscathed from that fire, I shall ask only that you accept his faith for the truth."

Again, somebody spoke aloud in the strange tongue, and the whole room grew very still. Then the Soldan shook his head. "There are several of my priests here; yet there are no volunteers for your challenge. But I shall ask you to wait. Your co-religionists are not idle, and I am afraid they are more practical than you. So come tomorrow, and I will talk with you."

The next day when Francis went into the Soldan's presence, he was no longer in his throne room but in a little room with a balcony. He took Francis out on the balcony so that he could look down on the crowd in the street. "Little man, I think you have the faith to go through that fire, and I feel quite sure that none of my priests has. And may I say that I don't think any of those high priests of yours over there behind us would go into the fire either. But have you thought of this"—he pointed to the crowd below—"if I should change my faith, what do you think those men below would do?"

"Would they not obey you?"

The Soldan smiled. "If they saw you lift that cross of yours and strike me with it, they would scale the balcony and tear you to pieces. But if they were to see me kneel down in front of it, they would also scale the balcony, but it would be me whom they would tear to pieces. Power has its chains, my little friend."

"That is why I have come to bring you freedom."

"Have you thought of bringing freedom to your Emperor or your Pope?"

Francis stiffened. "For the Emperor, I can say nothing, for I am a poor religious; but the Pope is a holy old man, who lives very simply in all his splendor."

"It is pleasant to hear of power simple in its splendor," said the Soldan. "Come, let us not talk of kneeling down before crosses, or fires to test our faith, but rather let us talk of these things like two intelligent men. I will give you and that pleasant-looking young companion of yours rooms here in my palace, and we will talk of these things together."

"I do not want quarters in your palace."

"You are more practical then? Some of my men tell me that your young brother says you were a rich merchant once. I will give you silks that have come over the great highway which men call the Silk Road, and amber which men have brought from those ancient roads to the Baltic, which you have made it so hard for us to reach. And there are gems from India. You will have a generous reward for your time."

"There is only one reward I want," said Francis, "and that is you."

"You think I am more precious than all my gifts, then?"

"Any man's soul is more precious."

"You lower the price," said the Soldan with a sigh, "but at least you do not put my gifts above me, and I assure you I see few men of whom that could be said; and I suspect there are not so many over there where you come from that they would gladly lose you. So will you not take the gift as a substitute?"

"No, gold and silver I have nothing to do with."

"It is not only a strong faith, yours," said the Soldan, "but a very odd one. Come. Will you take no token of my goodwill with you? It is poor courtesy to refuse all tokens of friendship."

Francis looked around, and his eyes fell on a horn on the railing of the balcony. "That?" he asked.

"Oh, it is the horn of an odd kind of deer whom they hunt in the mountains of Persia."

"What do you do with it?"

"The Muezzin uses it when we are in battle to call our men to the hour of prayer."

"Then that I will take," said Francis, "and I will use it to call our men to sermon."

"When you do, pray for me," said the Soldan, "that I may know what the true faith is."

As Francis took up the horn, he looked over the balcony at the crowd below. "Why don't you let me talk to them?" he asked.

The Soldan laughed. "No, little man, they would kill you, and I should be sorry for that, for if I cannot let my people hear the things you have been saying to me, I should very much like to have those crusaders of yours over there hear them. I think it would be better for all of us."

"I shall hope to come again," said Francis.

The Soldan smiled. "Whatever paradise it is that you are in, Brother Francis, there would I, also, like to be. Do not forget to pray for me." Then the Soldan called some of his guards, and he said, "Take them through the lines, and tell the men at watch that I will strangle with my own bowstring anybody who lets an arrow fly after them."

Francis and Illuminato must have been seen crossing the stretch of desert, for there was a great host waiting for them when they came through the crusading lines, and it seemed as if everyone cried out, "What is the Soldan like?"

"He is a very courteous gentleman," replied Francis, and there was a roar of laughter.

"What gifts did he give you?" cried another.

Francis lifted the horn. "It is the Muezzin's horn and I shall use it to call you to sermon." The laughter redoubled.

Then Brother Barbaro and Brother Peter pushed their way to Francis, and they embraced joyously. "Thank God, you are here. They have been holding the attack until you should be back."

In the early hours of the next day a messenger from the Cardinal awakened Francis and asked him if he had had any more dreams. "I have not dreamt this night," he replied.

"Then," said the messenger, "I can tell the Cardinal that he may look for victory."

Francis had been sleepy when the man first spoke to him, but now his brain began to clear, and he said with great sadness, "I wish we could win the Soldan without all this fighting." The messenger listened to him in astonishment; then he turned and ran out of the dark dormitory. As he was reporting to his master that the madman was as mad as ever, Francis went into the chapel to pray.

"Do you think we will win?" asked Illuminato.

"It depends on what you mean by 'win,' " said Francis. "I think we will take Damietta, but I don't think we'll convert the Soldan."

Twice Illuminato came back to report on the progress of the battle as he watched it from the ramparts above the hostel. The third time he came in and knelt down beside Francis before the crucifix.

"Is it over?"

"It depends on what you mean," said the young friar with a sigh. "They haven't taken the city yet."

And then Brother Giulio came in.

"Have they taken the city?"

"Oh, yes," said the young priest. And as Francis watched him, the young man shrugged his shoulders. "The whole town is pouring out across the sand. The whole waterfront—"

"Should we go, too?" asked Francis.

The young man shrugged his shoulders again, and with an attempted lightness which the sick eyes belied, he answered, "Dagger, lance, sword, mace, fist, fire, bare hands—take your choice. You would die the first move you made to stop one of them."

"But won't the Cardinal try to stop it?"

"He will try to stop it tomorrow morning," said Giulio, suddenly looking old. "Brother Francis, you have seen the night of a defeat. Have you never seen the night of a victory?"

"It is no way to convert the Soldan," said Francis.

"Oh, the Soldan is many miles south of Damietta now. He will not be surprised at what he hears in a few days; he has taken towns himself."

"But these are Christians!"

The young priest sat down on the steps of the altar and put his long hands around his knees. "When I think of tonight," he said, "I wonder. Tomorrow, perhaps—" And then he looked at the great crucifix above his head, and he asked Francis, "Do you suppose He is waiting for tomorrow, too?"

Francis shook his head. "Innocent was right. Even winning the battle will not matter if—"

But a familiar voice rang out in the little church. "I thought I would find you here." It was the Bishop of Acre again. When Francis and the young men had kissed his ring, he came and sat down with them on the steps of the altar. "You know, we are pretty nearly the only men except the wounded and the ill left in this town tonight." And as he noted the sick look on Francis' face, his voice recovered its brisk note. "Nothing we can do over there tonight—or tomorrow for that matter. You might not guess it," he said companionably to Francis, "but the Cardinal, when he is sufficiently indignant, can preach a blistering sermon. Some of the lords will even be thinking of a visit to the holy places when he is through. I have a ship here, my friend; we can land in Syria, and then we can see what the chances are of you getting to Jerusalem."

Francis stood up and faced the Bishop. "You think there is nothing more for us to do here?"

"Oh, you might perform a miracle or two," said Jacques de Vitry cheerfully. "But don't you think you'd better take a chance for the great pilgrimage when you have it?"

Francis' eyes gleamed, and then the light died. "My lord, there are all these new brethren of ours."

"Yes," said the Bishop. "I heard the Cardinal say this morning that he had lost more men to you, Francis, than to the Soldan."

"He is exaggerating."

But the Bishop shook his head. "I think his young cousin, Giulio, will tell you that he is only a little; besides, the ones you have taken are the very ones he wanted to keep."

"But can we take the new brethren with us?" persisted Francis.

"No," said the Bishop. "I'm sorry," he added as Francis' face fell, "but I think the Cardinal will find a boat to send some of them to Elias in Syria, and the rest he will take back with him to Rome. I don't honestly think, Francis, there's anything better you can do than a pilgrimage now."

"No," said Francis, and as he spoke, he rubbed his hands across his eyes. The sand of the desert still clung to them, and he was so weary now that one moment he wondered if he had a fever, and the next he was shaking with the chill of the night. "I will come with you," he said to the Bishop, "as a pilgrim."

5

"I never did justice to Jonah before," said Francis when his host, the Bishop of Acre, asked him how he did that early summer evening in 1220.

"The doctor is right that you are better," said the Bishop, settling himself on the rampart and gazing down affectionately at the little gray figure on the pallet. "I did not think either that we would get you to land."

Francis shook his head sadly. "I am afraid that I lost hold of my faith in the depths of the great waters."

"Nonsense," said the Bishop. "The doctor on the boat and the doctors here all agree that it is the fever which has laid low so many, even some of those blonde giants from the north."

"What a poor figure I should have made before St. Peter, reeling and retching!"

"I was not worried about the figure you would make before St. Peter," said the Bishop dryly, "but the figure I should make before all your brethren if I did not bring at least some relic of you ashore."

At first Francis was shocked, and then he remembered that saints and relics were the literary trade of Jacques de Vitry, and what would have been blasphemous absurdity in another man was only a professional jest in him. That anybody should think of this wasted carcass of his! Then he looked out over the sea. With his usual imaginativeness, the Bishop of Acre had had Francis' pallet laid on trestles so that he could look out over the rampart of the half-fortress, half-palace, and watch the great bay. It was evening now, and the tide was coming in softly in an opalescent shimmer, pale gold and rose, as the sun was sinking behind the low hills, and the whole bay was flowering with the sails of the little boats hurrying in to anchorage before the darkness should fall.

"It is hard to believe it is the same sea, isn't it?" said the Bishop.

"The world is like that," said Francis thoughtfully. "When we are in the middle of it, we are so tossed, so frightened, that we can see only its terror. And then when we have escaped from it and have come up to a high place, lo, it is as fair and as still as a dream."

"Enjoy the dream while you may, Brother Francis," said the Bishop, dropping with a light sigh from the parapet. "And as you do, say a prayer for me."

"How selfish I have been! That is real sickness when one is so absorbed in his own wretchedness that he does not think even of the kindness of a host who has so many burdens."

"A great burden!" laughed the Bishop. "A heap of straw in the corner of a little closet. That was the first thing, Francis, that gave me hope that you might live—when you would not let us put you into a bed but demanded a pallet on the floor."

"I have forgotten."

The Bishop smiled. "You know what the doctors say? When a man is poised like you, half between this world and the next, it is what he cares about most that comes out when he can no longer think about it."

"It is time I were thinking," said Francis, stirring weakly. "Do you suppose tomorrow I could be carried down to the chapel?"

"Wait a day or two. When the doctors give us their permission, I will say Mass for you myself. And how are your eyes?" he asked, as he lingered for a moment on the battlement.

"I can't look at the light long," said Francis in a puzzled fashion. "I do not know whether it is faintness of the eyes or of the heart."

"We'll let the doctors worry about the eyes," said the Bishop cheerfully. "As for the heart, that is my province, and I can assure you there is nothing wrong there."

"What did I tell you?" cried the Bishop a couple of days later when finally Francis managed, leaning on the arm of Brother Illuminato, to come to the chapel. "Is it not a strange chapel?" he asked when he had finished Mass and had come to sit down by Francis on the step of the altar, where he had finally yielded to the persuasions of Brother Illuminato and accepted gratefully the support of the cool stone.

"It looks a little like the Soldan's palace," said Francis, "the same coolness and airiness, and the arches. It isn't at all like the rest of the fortress."

"No, I thought the chapel at least should not look like a fortress; so I got some of their native workmen here, and I told them to build as they liked. The altar would make it a church." And then he turned to one of his acolytes. "I have a little wine here to give you strength before you try to go back to your chamber."

As the wine tingled through Francis' body, the Bishop watched him. "Some of your brethren are waiting for you," he said at length. "I have had a hard time keeping them from you and letting them look at you only in your sleep."

"What is it?" said Francis, and then he looked more closely at his host. "Is it bad news? I can face it now."

"I'm not sure," said the Bishop, "that you will call it bad news, though your brethren feared to tell you."

"What is it?" There was something Francis seemed to remember before they took ship, something that had taken the heart out of him before ever he fell into the grip of the sea.

"You remember your brethren who went out on the mission?"

"Yes," said Francis. "I think even in my fever I remembered to pray for them, though their names and their faces kept slipping away. There were the brethren who went to France and to Germany and to Spain," said Francis with a sudden access of memory. "Yes, and some of those last to Morocco!"

"It is they, the ones who went to Morocco. They are in heaven, Francis," said the Bishop, watching him anxiously.

"But surely," said Francis, "there is nothing in that for which we can say anything but 'Thanks be to God.'"

"I knew you would say that."

"But how came they by so high a promotion?"

"You have been reading that book of mine these last days," said Jacques de Vitry with a smile, "or rather Brother Illuminato has been reading it to you. I need not remind you, Brother Francis, need I, that it is often by a very narrow and painful gate that we come to the throne of God."

"They are martyrs!" said Francis, and a great joy lighted his face. "Tell me!"

"I will let your brethren tell that," said the Bishop. "But before they do, let me remind you that many of these martyr stories are much the same. I will not say that they rushed upon death, but I think they could have saved themselves if they had been willing to hold back."

"But why were the others afraid to tell me? Surely they did not think—"

"What they were afraid of," said the Bishop slowly, "was not your grief, but they said 'Maybe he will want to make haste to join them and not stay with us who need him so.'"

Only after Francis had helped the Bishop sing the Te Deum of thanksgiving for the new martyrs did he have time to think about what was happening to the Order in Italy, whence those who brought the news had come. But before he could ask them any questions, the Bishop returned to Francis with Brother Elias. At sight of Brother Elias the brethren from Italy drew back, and Elias was so full of his story that Francis could think of nothing else. Elias had heard of the Moroccan martyrs before Francis had, and he had lost no time putting all of the missions in Syria in order against the renewal of attacks from the heathen who had been driven back in Egypt. Francis was shocked at the look of weariness that came over the faces of the brethren from Italy as Elias reported this, the latest example of his extraordinary readiness to make the most of every occasion.

"That is well done," said Francis gravely. But the look on the faces of the brethren from Italy haunted him even after they had excused themselves. "Are the new missions keeping the Rule?" he asked when Elias had at last finished the extraordinary tale of new brethren received and organized into fresh mission bands.

"They are keeping the Rule."

"And not accepting any gifts of houses?" Francis persisted.

"No," said Elias, "I have not forgotten." Elias' had been a tale of triumph, but now his face sobered, and Francis hastened to add, "I was sure you would not, my son."

But he pressed again, "Are they living in wooden and straw and thatched huts?"

"In this land?" said Elias, and he looked around the cool stone room in which they were sitting talking.

"That is true." And then as Elias said nothing, Francis went on, "My weakness has betrayed me. But now the example of our glorious brethren and these heartening tidings which you have brought us, they have made me strong again. Now you must let me come with you and see these brethren whom you have won for us."

But the Bishop and his doctors were adamant. The kind of visitation which Francis proposed in this country with its climate and the uncertainty of travel would only hasten Francis' leaving of this world. Brother Elias hastened to support the argument of the doctors and the Bishop. "We need you," he said anxiously. So for a compromise it was agreed that Francis would content himself with travelling slowly to Bethlehem and to Jerusalem; and then if the sight of the holy places had restored him, they would consider a visitation of the new houses.

"Never fear," said Francis happily. "On that earth where Our Blessed Lord has walked, I cannot fail to grow strong in spirit, and where the spirit is strong, the donkey that carries it will not dare to lag."

But whether it was the fever that every so often returned to him, or the chills that followed the fever, or the soreness of his eyes from which the Egyptian sand seemed never to have been completely washed out, Francis failed to find the renewal of spirit on which he had counted. At first it was a little worry, like a wraith of dust on the highway in the distance. The brethren from Italy had looked disappointed when he went off with Elias, and Francis had wondered too late if, weak as he was, he should have managed to see them alone before he went. But Brother Elias was such a perfection of care and attention on the journey that Francis presently forgot even the faces of the brethren from Italy.

When he was not pointing out places of interest, Brother Elias rode with lax rein, always ready to chant a psalm with Francis, or to make the responses for the prayers. Yet he had the gift of silence, too. He would ride for an hour, seemingly absorbed in mental prayer, and then when Francis began to tire, Elias would suggest that they break their journey.

His tact never failed, either. He was always careful to choose an old deserted church, or a small convent, or an ancient pilgrim hostel. A few times on the road they came upon people who knew Elias and begged him to come with them and sojourn in their castles. But always Elias declined. Never once, either, did he even hint at the identity of the tired little man riding on a mule behind him. "He is a perfect model of a friar," said Francis to himself. Then with a flick of pain he remembered the distaste on Leo's face as he repeated Francis' praise. And again he was torn unhappily between his trust in his old friend and the desire to be just to his new brother.

That sense of some discord at the very heart of things was sharpened when they reached Bethlehem. Francis was already tired when they came to the foot of the hill that led to the church, for they had been on the road since early morning, and now it was approaching dusk. But Francis could not rest so close to the place where Our Saviour's manger had stood. "We will just go and kneel down for a moment in the cave," he pleaded.

But Elias was worried. "It is not exactly a cave any more. You know they have built a church over it."

"Of course," Francis tried to reassure him. But when they went down into the lower church, Francis was appalled. For this was no cave, but a great basilica with richly carved lamps swinging from long chains, and jewelled mosaics, wherever one turned. Only a gold star in the pavement marked the spot where the manger had stood, but over against it somebody had set a golden manger, rich enough to hold an emperor's son. "It was here," said Francis, kneeling down and kissing the star in the pavement, "and that is what I must think of. It is here," he said, and he shut his eyes so that he would not see the golden crib.

That night as they looked out over the flat roofs of Bethlehem from the roof of the pilgrim hostel and saw the moon rising over the plain,

Francis thought, "This is as it was that night." And when one star deepened in brilliance as the sky darkened, he thought of that other star. "If only men could leave the earth alone like the sky, which God has put out of reach of their meddling hands," he sighed. Then as the noise of the little town subsided and all was still in the night air, Francis thought again, "What a blessed thing we are bound to this earth and cannot trouble the ancient peace of the stars, for they keep clean and plain the memory of what they have shone on here."

Brother Elias was so distressed, however, when the next morning Francis proposed that they should go on at once, that out of compassion he relented and agreed to look at the church again. But going in from the sunlight he had more than ever the sense that out of the original cave men had made only a splendid dungeon, and then they had jewelled the walls, and plastered over even the jewels with the tokens of their own mortality. One only of these tablets interested Francis. That was the tablet which Jerome had put up above the grave of a woman, Paula. "He must have loved that woman," said Francis when Brother Elias had translated the sonorous tribute of Jerome, "with a pure and holy love," he added at the look of surprise on Elias' face. Sister Clare at San Damiano would have understood about the star in the pavement and the stars in the sky.

That day Francis was so weary when he went back to the pilgrim hostel that he allowed Brother Elias to persuade him that he should rest. The next morning as they ate before beginning the day's journey, Francis asked, "Brother Elias, have they put a lot of stone over the sepulchre, too?"

Elias looked thoughtfully at Francis, and he smiled that faint smile that made Francis wonder what went on behind those firmly controlled features of his. And then, as so often happened, Elias seemed with that extraordinarily prehensile intelligence of his to have reached out and to have grasped the thought which was hardly formulated in Francis' own mind. "You will like the garden of Our Lord's agony," he said. "They can have done very little to that, although of course, the olive trees are older now."

"The garden of Our Lord's agony," Francis repeated the words slowly.

But as it turned out, the time for that had not yet come. They were almost ready to start on the journey to Jerusalem when a new pilgrim arrived at the hostel and asked for Brother Francis. When he was told that there was no Brother Francis there, only Brother Elias and a company of his friars on pilgrimage, the newcomer insisted that he must then see Brother Elias. Elias looked annoyed, but even as he hesitated, a ragged pilgrim came through the door into the yard and looked around him. He paid no attention to Brother Elias, but when he saw Francis, he came and knelt down and clasped his feet.

"What do you want, fellow?" asked Elias sharply.

But Francis had taken the pilgrim's head in his hands. "It is Brother Stefano!" he cried with delight, and he slid off the mule and embraced him. Brother Stefano was one of the earliest of Francis' brethren. He had been a well-known merchant whom Francis had met in his father's house once or twice only, for he had the name of being a little tricky, not the kind of man with whom Peter Bernardone and his friends cared to deal. But when Francis had finally convinced him that he was wasting all his cleverness on things of little value, he had made a very good friar—a little literal-minded, perhaps, but devoted and as ingenious in meeting the emergencies of a vagabond life as he had been in his trading.

"How did you find us?" asked Elias. Francis was surprised at the insistence in his voice, as if anybody should ever ask how a friar had found his father.

But Stefano seemed completely unaware of Elias' very presence. So Francis took his hand and drew him aside into a little room off the courtyard. "It is a long journey and a hard journey," he began. "Did you come alone?"

"I had to come alone," said Brother Stefano. "The others were too cowardly."

But at that moment Brother Peter broke in, "Brother Francis, Brother Elias says that so long as we have been detained, we might as well have our dinner here."

"Brother Elias is right," said Francis. "After dinner it will be easier for Brother Stefano to tell us what it is all about."

But they had barely said grace, and the meat had just been put on the table when Brother Stefano cried out, "You must not eat that."

Francis stared at him. "Why not? Is it not good meat, this which the custodian of the hostel has provided?"

"But the new rule says that we should not eat meat today."

Francis turned to Peter Catanii. "Brother Peter, you always keep the calendar in mind. Today is not Friday, is it? Nor one of the universal fast days?"

"None that I have ever heard of."

"Then," said Francis, "let us eat what God has given to us." And when they had eaten the meat, Francis looked at Brother Stefano and said, "Brother Stefano, who made this rule you talk about?"

"The two brethren whom you left for vicars."

"But they swore before the altar that they would keep the Rule, and they would not think up any new ways to get around it."

"But what, precisely, have they done?" asked Peter, frowning at Stefano.

"They have put forth some new 'constitutions,' they call them."

When they first saw him, Brother Stefano had been half-starved and frightened, but now that he had eaten meat, and above all now that he had found the object of his search, he seemed for the first time to be able to look at the matter reasonably. "You have been gone so long, Brother Francis," he said, "and again and again the story has come that you were dead."

"Dead?"

"Yes, that the Soldan had killed you, and then that you were lost at sea; and the last one was that you had died of the fever."

"Nearer the truth than most rumors, at that," said Brother Peter, looking at Brother Stefano thoughtfully.

Francis had to admit that he was not a prepossessing object of contemplation. His tunic was soiled and torn; his beard and his hair needed cutting. Hunger and fear had given his eyes a wild glitter, and yet there was a certain shrewd intelligence in the look with which he faced Elias that Francis saw had convinced Elias that here was a man whose testimony was not to be dismissed lightly.

"What did they do to you?" Elias asked.

The glitter in Stefano's eyes hardened. "They tied me up and put me in the cellar of one of their houses!"

"Their houses?" exclaimed Francis.

"Their houses! They are building stone houses again, and they have taken a house at Bologna."

"A house at Bologna?" Francis' words were a cry.

A cunning look came into the eyes of the man in front of him. "Ah, you have been away a long time, Brother Francis! These days it is study they talk about and not prayer."

But Elias was not to be deflected from his course. "Why did they put you in prison?" he asked.

Stefano shrugged his shoulders. "There were some people over beyond Perugia whom I had promised to preach to at harvest time. I had been there before."

"That is true," said Francis. "I sent you the first time."

"But now, you know, you must get permission from the guardian of the house before you do any travelling."

"That is something, you remember, that the bishops have always wanted," Peter reminded Francis.

But Francis shook his head. "Why should we have all this formality?"

"And then," said Stefano, "when I asked the guardian's permission, he asked me what I was going to do, and I told him I was going to preach to the farmers there in the field. And he said I was not the man to go; they would send one of the learned brethren." A note of mockery came into Stefano's voice. "They sent the learned brother," said Stefano, "but I went, too, for I had promised. I found the learned brother talking to the people, and some of them were asleep, and some of them had wandered off already when I arrived. The learned brother was angry, but, Brother Francis, he was not even talking the dialect of the people in that part of the country."

"What did you do?" asked Francis.

"I remembered you, Brother Francis," said Brother Stefano humbly, "and I went up and called out to the people, and those who were leaving stopped, for they knew me. And they shook those who were asleep awake, and I told them they had done wrong not to listen to Brother, for he was a son of Brother Francis, and he brought them the word of God, and they should listen. I talked to them like a plain man," said Brother Stefano, "and they listened. But the learned brother was angry, and when we got back, he complained to the guardian, and I was thrown in the cellar."

"But how came you here then?" Elias was frowning.

"The rats gnawed through one of the ropes, and I managed to break the rest. I waited until they were all busy with a feast which they were making for a lord who had come to visit."

"A feast for a lord?" said Francis sharply.

"Yes."

"But how did you get out?" persisted Elias.

"There was a window high up in the cellar, and I climbed out of that. Then I set out to find you, Brother Francis."

"But how did you know I would not be dead as they said?"

"No," said Brother Stefano. "I was sure you were not dead, for I had asked some of the brethren at the Portiuncula whether you had been seen there in the night, or anybody had dreamed of you. And they said, no, had I gone quite mad; but I knew then that you were not dead, for I knew that you would not have gone to Paradise, Father Francis, without stopping there to see how it was with the rest of us."

Francis shook his head. "I have been away too long, and men have forgotten."

"No," said Brother Peter. "There have always been those who wanted to make our order more like the others, and now they have dared to speak up."

Elias said nothing but seemed to be waiting.

"Were there none to oppose them?" asked Francis.

"Oh, yes," said Brother Stefano. "Some they have beaten, and some they have given many prayers to say, and some they have put fasting on bread and water, and some they have locked up. And some of these brethren have run away and are hiding up in the old caves on the mountain. But," said Brother Stefano with a gleam in his eye, "when they hear that you are not dead, they will come down, and then they will speak out."

"I will go back with you at once," said Francis.

"You are still too frail," protested Elias.

"I am not dead."

"But won't you go first to Jerusalem to see the garden of Our Lord's agony?"

Francis shook his head. "If I do not get back to the Portiuncula soon, there will be no need of my going so far as Jerusalem for that."

6

When the little party from the Holy Land landed in Venice, Francis astonished his companions by announcing that he would not go directly to the Portiuncula himself, but that he would send Peter and Elias with the other brethren to escort them, and he himself would keep only Brother Leonardo with him. Elias at once protested that Francis was really too ill to journey with one brother alone. Suppose he should have a return of the fever? But Francis said stoutly that God had protected him so far, and He would not fail him now.

"What shall we do at the Portiuncula without you?" asked Peter.

"You will speak for me," said Francis. "You will tell those two faithless Vicars that they are deposed, and you, Peter, will be Vicar until I can come. And you, Elias, will help him."

"But when will you come?" asked Elias, obviously already looking ahead to the next business in hand.

"I will be there as soon as I can," Francis replied. "I am going first to Rome."

Elias was evidently puzzled, Francis saw, but Peter Catanii understood. He had remembered those other times when Francis had gone to Rome to ask for the approval and the confirmation of their Rule. He nodded. One concession only Francis would make to Elias' worries about his health, and that was the acceptance of the loan of an ass. So humming a little Umbrian folk tune, Francis set off with Brother Leonardo leading the ass.

The road into the country led through a pleasant stretch of woodland where the birds were singing cheerfully in the trees above them. "We have not said our office today, Brother Leonardo," said Francis; so they started, Francis saying the prayers and Brother Leonardo making the responses. But the birds' song seemed to rise above their voices. "They are the birds of our own land, making us welcome," said Francis happily; then with affectionate severity he raised his voice, "Oh, little sisters, you have had your chance now to say your office, and sweet is your praise in God's presence. But do you keep still now and let us say ours."

It seemed to Brother Leonardo that the birds fell silent, and only the two friars' voices rose, his own strong with the freshness of his youth, and Francis' still sweet but frail. Then they continued along the road in silence, and the dust and the heat of the day arose about them, and slackening his grip on the ass, Francis now and then slept a little. Brother Leonardo, unaccustomed from the long days at sea to trudging along in the dust, grew tired. Presently he said to Francis, "Should we not perhaps rest here a while?"

But Francis said, "No, for we have work to do, and we must be about it." So they went on, Francis out of exhaustion lapsing into silence, and the young man growing wearier and wearier.

"What a queer thing it is," he mused presently. "Here am I a lord's son, trudging along in the dust like a peasant, and this son of a merchant is riding like a lord."

He was sure he had said nothing, but in a moment he heard the voice of Francis, quick and eager, as if he were no longer ill, "It is not right, Brother Leonardo, that you who were of so much higher rank in the world than I should walk in the dust, and I who came of much humbler stock should ride here on the ass. Let us stop, and we will change places." But when Francis had with some difficulty dismounted from the ass, Brother Leonardo stood there holding its bridle and making no effort to move. Then, as Francis came toward him, Brother Leonardo cast himself at his feet weeping, and he begged Francis to forgive him. But Francis only thanked him for speaking like a true brother.

Then when they had resumed their journey, Brother Leonardo asked Francis whether they needed to go to Rome, but Francis' face hardened.

"You are thinking of coming home to the Portiuncula, Brother Leonardo."

"No," said Brother Leonardo, "I am thinking of seeing you come home to the Portiuncula, and all your enemies flying at the sight of your face."

But Francis rebuked him and said that one brother should never use the word "enemy" of another. That night they had lodged in a convent of the Cistercians in a room which was reserved for poor pilgrims, but the next morning they had hardly taken to the road again when they met a beggar. Francis was delighted, but when he came close to them, they saw it was one of Francis' first brethren. Indeed, it was the one whom Francis had put in charge of the convent at Bologna when it was founded. Francis embraced him joyously and he bade Brother Leonardo look upon this true model of a guardian of the Friars Minor who had come out to them in the dress and with the look of a beggar to greet them. But the friar shook his head, and though he had been weeping with joy at seeing Francis again, he now laughed scornfully.

"Do you think Peter of Stacia would walk the road in these rags?" he asked. "At this moment he is sitting like a lord in his doctor's gown by a fire."

"A fire?"

"It is only the first chill of autumn, but it is cold enough for Peter of Stacia."

"But why do we talk of Peter of Stacia?" asked Francis in puzzlement.

"He is the guardian of the house at Bologna."

"Of the house at Bologna? And what are you?" asked Francis.

"I would not agree that they should buy a house." And at the astonishment on Francis' face, he repeated the word. "Yes, buy a house! Of course, the excuse was that our scholars would be better supervised if they lived in our own house at the university."

"Our scholars?" said Francis. "Are we Benedictines and Brothers of Dominic? And who put Peter of Stacia in your place?"

"The new brethren," said the old brother shamefacedly. "They said times had changed, and I could not change with them."

Brother Leonardo was shocked to see how grimly the face of Francis hardened. "We will go to this house of Peter of Stacia," he said.

It was a fine stone house, close to the university, and there was a bell which the old brother went up and rang triumphantly. The porter put his head out and said, "You vagabond, going off without permission of your superior!"

"I went out to meet my superior," said the friar, and then he stepped aside so as to reveal Francis with a triumphant gesture.

The porter recoiled as if he had seen a ghost, and then he ran into the house, and still triumphant, the deposed superior pushed the door open and bade Francis welcome. As he had said, Peter of Stacia was sitting comfortably by a fire reading a book. Francis came in and snatched the book from him and flung it on the floor, and when the astonished Peter went down on his knees, Francis turned his back upon him and strode from the room as if anger had given him wings. He went into the refectory, and now the word seemed to have run through the house, for all the brethren were crowding around and falling on their knees, some crying with joy and some staring as if they had seen an apparition which they could yet hardly believe. One of the brethren whom Francis did not recognize said, "Welcome to your house."

Francis looked at him as they knelt before him. "Every one of you," he began quietly, "knows that you have sworn to own nothing either individually or collectively. What is this house you have bought like the traitors you are?"

Peter of Stacia had apparently recovered from his shock, for now he stood in the doorway. "It is a house of studies, Brother Francis."

"It is a house of damnation," Francis' voice rose. "It is a house that has been bought by traitors and perjurers. It is a house which every true brother of the Friars Minor will flee from for peril of his soul." Already Francis could see one or two of the brethren trying to speak, and yet not knowing quite how to begin.

One of them spoke up at last. "What do you wish us to do, Brother Francis?"

"I order every one of you who remembers his vow of obedience to leave this house instantly!"

Several of the brethren went out at once, and Francis saw the others look at each other. Then more went out, and then some of the first came back, carrying books or clothes.

"So you have been collecting books and extra habits and mantles as well as houses," Francis shouted, and the guilty friars shrank from his scorn. "If it is the Gospels, if it is your breviary or your Psalter, and you are priests, take it. If it is any book of fine-spun casuistry that will gloss the meaning of words so that a man may break his oath, leave it here with the father of lies to whom this house belongs."

"But," said Peter of Stacia, "some of our brethren are old, and some are sick."

"It were better for them," said Francis, "to fall in the ditch and to be covered by the dust of the passing traffic than to abide an hour longer in this house!" And now Brother Leonardo saw that some of the brethren were hesitating, looking from Francis to Peter of Stacia.

The face of the latter was white and rigid. "This is God's work," he said, "and I, at least, will not give it up."

"Then, Peter of Stacia," said Francis, "I consign you to the father of lies to whom you have dedicated yourself. You are anathema, and all who shall cleave to you; and the house in which you have put your faith will fall about your ears." And as the brethren shrank away, Francis turned upon them. "Any of you who wish to be saved within the Order of the Friars Minor will follow me to the road!" And so most of them came, one or two limping on the arms of their brethren, one or two still clutching their precious books. As Brother Leonardo turned at the door, he saw that there were only a couple of the younger brethren who remained with Peter of Stacia. He stood still in the doorway as if frozen in horror, and even as they stood with him, the younger brethren shrank against the wall. But Francis never looked back. He led them to some caves in the wood outside Bologna. They were made of great blocks of stone, and as they came near, one of the younger brethren called out, "Brother Francis, these are the tombs of old heathen, and the peasants have reported ghosts here!"

"You are safer with the dead," said Francis, "than with the living heathen." And so they settled for the night, gathering leaves and fallen branches for a little softening of the hard ground and a fire to keep off the night chill. Leonardo saw that Francis was very tired. It was as if the flame of his wrath had died down and left him a frail little man, huddling in his hood from the cold. And Brother Leonardo went out, and in a field nearby he found some straw, and he brought it back and made a bed for Francis, and then he lay down on the earth beside him. When the younger man awoke in the night, he heard the voice of Francis praying, and he was afraid to ask him if he were well; but in the morning Francis told Brother Leonardo of the dream that had wakened him.

"I dreamed," he said, "that I was a little black hen, and I spread my wings, and so many little chickens ran under them for shelter that I knew that I was not big enough to cover them. It is a bigger wing than mine that is needed." And so he addressed the brethren, and he bade them build a little shelter for themselves out of fallen boughs, for the autumn winds had already been through the woods, and to go out and beg for bread, and those who were able, to help the farmers in the gleaning of the fields, and those who were not strong enough to beg or to work, then let them say their office, and pray for the other brethren as good friars should.

"But what will become of us?" asked one of the older brethren of Brother Leonardo.

"We are going to Rome," said Brother Leonardo; "to see the Pope," he added. And although he knew it was foolish, he was pleased at the awe in the older brother's face.

But when they reached Rome, Francis refused to let Brother Leonardo ask the porter at the gate of the Lateran to let them in.

"The Pope is too busy to be troubled by such as us," said Francis. "We will sit here, and we will wait."

But presently there was a great excitement at the door, and a couple of the papal servants came out, then a couple of clerics. Francis stood up. And then a little old man in a white mantle came out, and Francis, recognizing the Pope, flung himself at his feet.

"It is you, Francis!" said Honorius, gesturing his guards back.

"They told me you were dead." And then he spoke to the priests around him, and he said, "Do you go along to the Cardinal's supper. I will see Francis first." He sat down in the courtyard on the foundation of a pillar, and he bade Francis sit at his feet. Brother Leonardo stood and watched. "He is a simple man," he thought to himself with wonder, "and he really wants to know what Brother Francis has to tell him." And a great awe came into the soul of Brother Leonardo, for he saw the Pope was listening as a man to a man.

"I did not think you would like what they are doing," said Honorius, with the simplicity of the very old, who, standing on the shore of eternity, find already that the noises behind them are growing a little dim. "They told me you were dead, and this was a new time, and new men must carry on. They are always saying that to me, Brother Francis."

Francis thought of his dream, and the old man looked so kind that he told him of the little black hen and all the chickens his wings would not cover. Honorius chuckled sympathetically, and he said, "Brother Francis, you sound like a pope." But what Francis saw was the body of the great Pope Innocent, lying too long for his short, gray habit. So he turned to the living Pope and he said, "Holy Father, I need someone who will give me not privileges or indulgences, but somebody who will give me counsel where a wiser head than mine is needed."

"Again you sound like a pope. But all the religious orders have their protectors. Whom do you want?"

"The Cardinal of Ostia has always been kind to us, even to laying aside his robes and putting on our habit to come to our Chapter."

"Then," said the Pope, "I will appoint the Cardinal of Ostia your protector." And he called one of his secretaries to him and he bade him make out the letter to the Cardinal of Ostia. Francis did not wait for the parchment, but as if suddenly he had found all his strength again, he took Brother Leonardo's hand, and he hurried to Ugolino's palace.

When the Cardinal saw who it was who had pushed into his presence, he said, "It is a joy to see you, Francis, but you know too much of this world to need me to tell you that when the dead revisit their houses, it is a mixed welcome they find."

"But I shall have the benefit of your wisdom now," said Francis, "for the Pope has given you to us for our protector and our adviser."

Again, the Cardinal shook his head, and this time he smiled. "Oh, Brother Francis, I have been adviser to too many men too long not to know that when a man asks for advice, he wants to be told that he is right, and that he should do what he wants to do. And now tell me, Francis, what would you do?"

"The will of God," said Francis, "wholly and perfectly."

The Cardinal looked at him with that long, quiet look that Francis had always found more challenging than any objection. "That is a large order," he said. "Are you sure you know what the will of God is?"

Francis looked astonished, and then he remembered that the Cardinal of Ostia, who gave counsel to the aging Pope, must have many things on his mind; so he smiled deprecatingly, "For the world, or the Church, no," he answered, "but for myself and for those whom God has confided to my care, I am sure."

"Then," said the Cardinal, "let us call a Chapter at the Portiuncula without delay, and do you set down in a new rule what it is you think that will is."

"A rule?" said Francis doubtfully.

"A rule," said the Cardinal firmly. "With all these new constitutions and all these arguments as to what the Rule means, we need to have something clear to present to the Chapter that all the men who are arguing may know where they stand."

So Francis set about making the new rule at once. At first he worked very swiftly with a little preamble in which he renewed the dedication of his brethren to poverty and the direct realization of Christ's gospel among the poor. But when, later in the day, one of the Cardinal's secretaries brought in to him a copy of the Constitutions which the Vicars had promulgated while he was away, he grew first so angry and then so weary that the Cardinal commanded him to give up the attempt for the present and to come with him for a rest. It was to the little hermitage of Fonte-Colombo that the Cardinal took his troubled guest, high up in the mountains above the valley of Rieti, with only the cries of the birds and the chanting of the Office to break the stillness. Here Ugolino stayed for a few days in a room as bare and plain as Francis' own. And when Francis told him that he could make no sense of these Constitutions, that he could see no way in which he could bring them into relationship with his rule, the Cardinal sympathetically suggested that Francis take the next month or so for rest and prayer and then try again, with any of the brethren whom he wished to help him with his task.

"Of course, I should like Leo best," said Francis.

But the Cardinal shook his head. "From what I have heard, he would not find it any easier than you to make any sense of what has happened. How about Peter Catanii?"

"He would know what they are talking about, I suppose," said Francis.

But by the time the Cardinal's message could reach the Portiuncula, Peter Catanii was dying, and everybody had agreed to obey Elias. The latter reminded the Cardinal that there was a young convert of his whom Francis knew and liked for his modesty, whom he would be glad to send to Francis to see if he might help. The Cardinal had liked the young man when Elias brought him to see him on his way to Syria. Elias had said that Caesar of Speyer was the most promising young friar he had seen in a long time, and the Cardinal had agreed with him. Francis had liked him in Syria, too. He had been modest and tireless, though he had clung to Elias like a shadow, and made Francis yearn for the primitive freedom of the young man. Now when he sat down with the Constitutions and the Rule, he was quick enough to disentangle the issues, and it seemed to Francis that he saw through all the subterfuges and the equivocations and the evasions. But it seemed to Francis, also, that he was timid when it came to meeting the issues, and then too late Francis remembered something else which Elias had told him: he had been a very powerful preacher for one so young, Elias had said, and he had preached the Crusade in Germany with great effectiveness. When he heard that, Francis had been frightened, and then seeing the young man come and report humbly on an errand on which Elias had sent him, Francis was reassured. "He seems content to keep silent here," he said.

"Yes," said Elias. "He is a child whose fingers have been burnt by the fire." Elias had gone on to explain what he meant. Men said that the voice of Caesar of Speyer as he called upon the throngs crowding his pulpit to foresake the world and to redeem themselves in rescuing the holy places had run like fire through dry stubble, and great hosts, particularly of the young, had taken the cross from his hands.

At that Francis had shaken his head with pity. "It is hard for the great preacher not to be moved to vanity."

"It was not that. It was something very different." Caesar had never lost his head, but when one boatload containing some of the young men of the noblest families in Germany was at sea off Venice, slavers had waylaid it, and seized the boat, and sold these young men in the slave markets on the inaccessible Arabian peninsula. Another boat had been wrecked in a storm and all lost. And another boatload had arrived just in time for a Saracen assault on the port, and many had been killed. The great lords who had been loath enough to see their heirs march off to glory were mad with anger and grief at this series of disasters, and Caesar had had to flee for his life. It was then that Elias had met him, and the Order of the Friars Minor had seemed a refuge from a world in which he could hope to do no more. So now it seemed to Francis that although he saw the issues clearly enough, he was loath to meet them directly. He was quite willing to put into the rule the Scriptural direction against taking purse or scrip for a journey, but he was unwilling to put in the definitive gloss that this meant that no friar could ever have money or any provisions of food and clothing beyond the immediate need. Furthermore it seemed to Francis that he was always trying to reconcile what could not be reconciled, and that the end would be a statement which different men could take in different ways, with each claiming the authority of the Rule.

But when Francis confided his fears to Ugolino, the latter reminded him of the time when he had wanted no rule whatever in order that the movement of the spirit might be free and unconfined. Then Francis, in his turn, reminded the Cardinal that that was a time long before any evil spirits had got into the Order, and one could trust the spirit. Then the Cardinal asked him if that was not true of the Gospels in general. At that, Francis looked so discouraged that Ugolino repented and admitted at once that although this was a difficulty which men had faced for centuries, it did not mean that they gave up the attempt to realize the Gospel pattern of life.

So Francis tried again to make Caesar of Speyer understand that the men who had written the Constitutions were actually confining the free spirit of love of poverty and were making the life of the Friars Minor something narrower and more restricted with petty rules. But soon he saw that although Caesar understood all this, it did not seem to him important; so Francis gave up the battle. He was weary again, and he was homesick for the Portiuncula. Surely there, he thought wistfully, there will be men who will know what I mean without my having to explain it. And here to his relief both Caesar and Ugolino agreed. What they had, said the Cardinal, was clear enough, and what was needed by the Friars was the influence of Francis, his presence among them. And Caesar seconded this, adding that the younger brethren, who had never had a chance to see Francis, would feel when they looked on his face that they had, indeed, seen at last the meaning of what they had undertaken.

When they were as yet some miles from the Portiuncula, Leo and Giles came out to meet them, and Caesar, with the quickness of perception even of what he did not always understand, which had astonished Francis, hastened to say that he would go ahead and help Brother Elias make ready for Francis. Francis saw the cloud come over the faces of Leo and Giles at the mention of Brother Elias' name, but they were obviously relieved to see Caesar go, taking Brother Illuminato with him. Happily, Brother Giles took the bridle of the ass on which Francis rode, and Brother Leo walked at his side. "Brother Elias," said Leo stiffly, "charged me to convey to you his regret that business would not let him come out to meet you."

"Business!" repeated Francis with distaste, and then he smiled at Leo. "At least it leaves us free for a visit with good conscience."

"I bring you greetings, too, from Sister Clare," said Leo, and now the cloud lifted from his face. "There at San Damiano, Francis, you will find all things as you would have them. It is as if time had stood still."

"And Brother Peter?" asked Francis. But he knew the answer from the look on Brother Leo's face, and he reached for his hand. Presently Leo could speak, "They have buried him there, close to the wall of the church, and Elias has put up a stone above him."

"Brother Elias still likes stones, doesn't he?" And then seeing the scowl return to Leo's usually serene face, Francis put his hand on the arm that held the bridle. "Let us give thanks that Brother Peter completed his life as a true brother should."

"It is very wonderful," said Leo, some of the old light coming back to his face, "in spite of Elias' stone. The sick come there, and they kneel down, and they pray."

"No offerings!" said Francis sharply.

Brother Leo smiled. "Only flowers and berries, and the things country people bring. Sometimes the grave is heaped high with berries, and the birds come and peck at them. One day a squirrel was on top of the stone when Brother Elias was passing by, and I heard him say that they must move the grave inside the church when they had room."

"Brother Peter would not like that."

"A lot Brother Elias would care!" said Leo somberly. "It will heal many sore hearts to see you, Francis."

"I know," said Francis, "I have been away too long. But hasn't Brother Elias begun to repair the damage and cleanse the temple?"

"Brother Peter had begun to do that," said Leo, "as fast as Brother Elias would let him, that is. But now that Elias has things in his own hands . . ."

"But surely he will do as he promised me."

Brother Leo shrugged his shoulders, and he looked with pity at his friend. For the first time Brother Giles spoke. "Brother Elias has certainly taken everything into his hands."

But Leo shook his head. "Those who are faithful to you, Brother Francis, they tremble before the face of Elias. He has said nothing yet," he added, "that one can point to and say 'This is a betrayal,' but good men are fearful. And those who would destroy all, they walk with ever more confidence."

"He will prove a proud man in the end," said Giles.

"God only knows what any of us will prove in the end," said Francis sadly, and both men fell silent at his rebuke. But it went to Francis' heart that these two old friends of his had suffered such worry because of him. Then he bade them stop. "I must not come riding into the Portiuncula as if I were a bishop. So, Brother Giles," he said, "you take the ass on to rest it for Ugolino's next messenger, and I will come back with Brother Leo as a good friar should, on my feet." And this he insisted on doing in spite of all the protests of his companions.

Then when Giles had gone on, Francis laughed and patted the arm which Leo had insisted he take. "How often have we taken this road, weary and hungry?"

"I should have brought food," said Leo, "but I was so excited at the thought of seeing you."

"You came out without provision as a good friar should," said Francis, "and in that is happiness beyond anything that the others can ever know."

"It is joy simply to see your face again," said Leo.

For answer, Francis pressed the arm on which he was leaning. Then he asked soberly, "But tell me, Brother Leo, what would be perfect joy?"

"Perfect joy," answered Leo at once, "would be to have all the brethren come out in peace and in one mind and fall down on their knees before you and promise that never will they again depart from what you have taught them."

"That would be a great joy," said Francis soberly, "more even than I think we have any right to ask. But there is a joy greater than that, Brother Leo. Can you not guess it?"

"When all this is over," said Brother Leo thoughtfully, "and we have all met together in heaven—if we all get to heaven," he added.

"That," said Francis sharply, "is for the next world. But for this?"

"For this," said Leo wonderingly, "what would be greater than that things should be as they were when you and I in the old days came home along this road?"

"No, there is a greater joy," said Francis, "and I will tell you that, little lamb of God." At the old jest on his name, Leo smiled wistfully. "I will tell you, Brother Leo, what would be perfect joy. If we two, weary and dusty and hungry, and not too sure of the welcome we shall have from all our brethren, should come up to the Portiuncula and should knock at the door and the porter should say 'Who are you? I know you not,' and then when we ask him to go and find somebody who knows us, he should begin to beat us and to call us vile names. And then when the others come they should look upon us, and say, 'They are but disturbers of our peace, these two,' and should beat us and throw us out into the cold of the night, hungry, then little brother Lion of God," said Francis, and as he paused, Leo looked at him in bewilderment, "oh, then, if we should kneel down in the dust of the road and lift up our cold hands and our famished voices and give thanks to God for all this we have received, for the vile names and the buffeting and the refusal of the fellowship of our brethren. If then we should give thanks to God and say that all this is well because it could only have happened with His will, that, Oh, Brother Leo, would be perfect joy!"

For a moment Leo stood there, looking at him. Then he dropped Francis' arm, and he knelt down in the dust, and he clung to his feet, and, weeping, he cried, "Forgive me, Francis, for I, too, have betrayed you!"

But Francis embraced him, weeping happily, and he said, "This, too, is perfect joy, when we kneel down and tell God that of ourselves we are nothing, and one thing only matters: that His will should be wholly fulfilled in us."

V: The Wounds of Christ

"**A** dead man does not resist," said Francis to Leo. Outside the door of the hermitage of the Carceri, the Cardinal of Ostia's messenger was waiting, and the Cardinal's letter lay on the table before them. It was March now, and there was little enough time, as the Cardinal's letter pointed out, if they were to have the Rule ready for the Chapter in May. Leo watched Francis. "Another rule!" he had said scornfully when Francis had shown him Ugolino's letter.

"Another rule," Francis had repeated wearily.

"You are too ill to make that long journey to Rome."

But Francis shook his head. "You can draw a dead man by the heels, and he will not cry out. You can set him in a chair, and he will not arise and leave—such is the obedience a man owes to his superior." And the heart of Leo sickened, for he could still hear the voice of the young Francis, crying out joyously, "Obedience is love's free offering, and it frees love's heart."

But Francis went to the door of the cave, and he looked out over the plain. The spring was coming now. The fields were green, and there was a gash of white blossom in the soft gray-green of the olives on the hills opposite. And there was the freshness of the spring in the breeze, and in the sound of the little waterfall behind him, and in the light on the river below. But it was not just the pain in his eyes that lay like a film over it all; it was the emptiness within him. "The beauty of the world is ashes between my teeth," he said to himself. He was not only dead, but he was empty, and he could not remember any longer how it felt to thrill to the world's awakening.

It would be two years in August since the world had died for him. He had known it when he came back to the Portiuncula, and the brethren came out with lights to meet him, and knelt down and kissed his hands, and sang the *Te Deum* in the little church, and then all stood around, waiting. There were so many of them, he thought, but it seemed to him that when he looked into their faces, most of them were quite empty. And it seemed to him that the emptiness of those faces was the echo of the emptiness within his own heart as he looked upon them.

When the Chapter met, Brother Elias had knelt down and had asked him to address the Chapter, and he could not find the voice. It was not the chill that came after the fever, the weakness that unstrung his limbs; rather it was that there was no fire within him. His chest and his throat were dry like a bellows that had collapsed and stuck with the dust of the rotten leather. So he had sat at Elias' feet, and he had listened to the reading of the new rule which he had brought from Rome. When, now and then, the tense voices broke through the veil that now seemed to lie over his ears as well as his eyes, the voices that said that times are not now as they were, and you cannot govern ten thousand men as you did ten, and this is the way the other orders do it, Francis would twitch Brother Elias' robe, and no matter what he was saying or doing, Brother Elias would stop, and he would put his head down to Brother Francis, and he would listen to his hoarse whispering, and then he would arise, and he would shout, "Thus Brother Francis would say." No one could have been more faithful than Brother Elias in repeating what Francis had said to him, but he always shouted so that what had Francis spoken would have blown like a breeze through the vast audience before them, moving all hearts, now seemed rather like a stone hurled against an absolutely unyielding wall. Presently, Francis grew too tired to follow all the entanglements of the argument.

In the end they agreed to adopt the new rule, but to Francis the final vote seemed merely an empty formality. The brethren like Leo who remained faithful would rejoice in the reiteration of the injunctions of poverty, and the other brethren would return to devising fresh methods of circumvention. Francis was tired, and he knew he was tired, but he was not prepared to find, as he did, that when he turned from the rule-making and the reorganization to plans for the future, there was no return of the old warmth of anticipation. The Chapter had approved his rule for the Third Order. The expected objections had been raised. There were bishops who said that lay people were lay people, and they should not try to live like monks in the state to which God had called them. There were lords who had objected that to release the Tertiaries from the oath to their lord, if the lord should bid them fight against the Pope and against their consciences, was to dissolve the bonds of society. There were even one or two in the front rows before Francis who muttered, "Rome certainly knew what they were doing there!" But they had approved the rule in the end, and the promise that Francis had made long ago to the people of Cannara—that if they remained quietly in their village and performed their accustomed duty, he would make provision for them, too—was discharged. And Luchesio spoke eloquently of how the Third Order was spreading all over Italy, with whole villages living as if it were the time of the Apostles again, and the bystanders saying again, "How they love one another!"

But the future was taken away from Francis, and though Luchesio and his wife came up and kissed his hands with shining eyes, Francis could hardly bring to his lips the smile that once, it seemed, never left them. Then he had allowed Leo and Giles and Sister Clare to persuade him that he was ill, and he had gone off to one of the little hermitages in the mountains. But it seemed to him that though his lips moved, the prayer never came from the heart, and that answering fire never warmed the chill. And when some of his old brethren came to him to complain of their sufferings and to tell him of the evil done by the fallen-away and to beg him to lead them out of the Order that they might live apart, Francis was too horrified and too exhausted even to argue with them. So he fled with Leo and Giles to another hermitage higher up in the mountains and more difficult to reach. But from himself he could not flee, and from the despair that lay heavier than any mountain on his whole being.

Now the return of the spring mocked him, for there was no spring, no burgeoning in his heart. The beauty of the world reproached him, for he had had a life in his hands, the gift of God, and he had flung it away, and the end had been nothingness. Then it seemed to him as if his whole being were falling apart. There was no purpose to his desolate days, nor could he remember that there had ever been. True, he pulled himself together to listen to the complaints of his brethren. But he had nothing to say to them; all he could do was shudder at the horror of what they suggested. Now came the voice of authority. It seemed to him that if he did not answer, he would be blown away as one who had never really been. So he bade Leo write simply that he would obey.

But not even Rome could stir the ashes of desolation within his spirit. The pilgrims were still coming singing into the city, but Francis felt that he was a leaf borne along on a stream over which he had no control. So when he sat down to work on the Rule in the chamber which Ugolino had given him in his own palace, he turned to the Gospels. "There is no good thing in me," he said to Leo. "And a father cannot give his children a stone for bread; so let us turn to where we know the good wheat is." And leafing through the Gospels, he bade Leo write as he read. "For if they will not listen to me," he said, "they may perhaps listen to Christ."

But when he handed his work to the Cardinal, Ugolino shook his head and said, "This is no rule. This is just a collection of texts of Scripture, and they will say, 'We have heard all that before. It is read in the Gospel in every parish church in Christendom.'"

"They hear, but do they listen?"

"You . . . need no doctor to answer that question."

So Francis sat down again with Brother Leo. "I will make them listen," he said, and now he began to dictate, his breath coming fast. He told the brethren that these were the words of life, and the soul and heart of them was love, God's love; that it was that love that had created the universe and kept it alive. And that love was what warmed and filled the heart of men, and all the material things to which men trusted in their folly were powerless to touch that heart; but where love was, the ample road opened to paradise, no matter how straitened or dusty the path. For the first time in months it seemed to Francis that his spirit had taken wing again. Though the sweat gleamed on the brow of Leo as he strove to keep up with him, there was a light in his eye as he looked to him for the next word.

But Ugolino threw up his hands in despair when he read the result. "This," said he, "is poetry. You may give it to the brethren to sing in their choir like a canticle, but when men say, 'This is according to the Rule, and this is against the Rule, and do you judge between us,' what is there here that I can point to?"

The fire died down in the embers of Francis' heart, and the bitterness deepened in the face of Leo, and Ugolino said, "Let me have that copy of the Rule of two years ago, and I will see what I can do with it."

A couple of days later the Cardinal sent for Francis and Leo. "You will see," he said, spreading the parchment out for Brother Leo to read, since Francis' eyes were bothering him sorely these days, "you will see that I have kept the gist of what you want, but, of course, I've had to cut down on the text, and this is not poetry. This is law."

"Which the canon lawyers may take and twist to suit their intentions," said Leo bitterly, when the Cardinal had left them. But Francis rebuked him and bade him read. There was nothing to which Francis could object in what Ugolino had written, but he had left out all the spirit of it, so that what he read was as empty of all light and color as the heart of Francis himself. Leo looked imploringly at him when he had finished, but Francis said simply, "We will go back to the Portiuncula." And it seemed to Leo that Francis said this as if returning to that loved home were going to the Judgment.

But when they came to Assisi, Francis insisted that they turn aside from the road that led down to the Portiuncula in the plain, and take the road to San Damiano. The old church was quite empty when they reached it, and Francis and Leo went in and knelt down in front of the crucifix, and Francis thought to himself, "Here is where God spoke to me, and here I shall ask Him for help that what I began here may be completed." And then he thought of the Chapter that would begin in a week, and of the Rule that he must deliver to Elias that night, and the face of Elias rose, inscrutable as always, before his eyes. Then deep within his spirit a voice spoke, not the voice that he had heard at San Damiano, and not the voice that he had heard in Rome. It was a quieter voice, low within the depths of his own spirit. "Francis, why are you so troubled about your Order? Have you forgotten who is its head?" And Francis stood up, and he looked at Leo, and he said, "I shall give the Order back to God, and I will concern myself no more with any rule. I shall only pray. I shall attempt nothing but what I can do by prayer and by example."

But Leo looked so desolate at his words that Francis yearned to say something that would give him comfort, and he could not. In his great helplessness he knelt down again, and he looked up at the face on the crucifix, and it seemed to him that it was incredibly remote, farther away even than the youth he had been when he had looked up at it first, and he fell on his face before the crucifix, and he stretched out his hands, and he gave up every effort even at prayer. And then the voice spoke clearly within his spirit, "Oh, Francis, little man of little faith, if you had but the faith of a grain of mustard seed, you could lift even this mountain from your heart."

"What is this mountain?"

And the voice said, "It is the mount of temptation."

Francis looked up at the remote sadness of the crucifix, and he said very simply, "Lord, let it be as You will." Then he arose, and he smiled at Leo, and he said, "Little lamb, little lion, of God, let us go and see what the Gospels have to say to us." So Francis opened the book of the Gospels on the altar, and Leo read the text, "My Father, if it be possible, let this chalice pass from me. Nevertheless not as I will, but as Thou wilt." And again Francis opened the book and again Leo read, "My God, my God, why hast thou forsaken me?" And for a third time Francis opened and Leo read, "And Jesus, crying with a loud voice, said: Father, into Thy hands I commend my spirit. And saying this, he gave up the ghost." Then Francis kissed the book of the Gospels, and he laid it back on the altar, and taking Brother Leo's hand, asked him, "Is the servant greater than the master? Should we who are the heirs of Christ's passion ask for anything but His prayer, that the will of God may be wholly fulfilled in us?" And for the first time in many months, he began to sing softly as they went out into the falling dusk.

2

At first Brother Leo and Brother Bernard and the rest of Francis' oldest companions were in despair because Francis paid so little attention to the discussion of the Rule at that Chapter of May, 1223. They knew he was ill, too ill much of the time to follow the arguments, too weary even to pay much attention to what the brethren who crowded around him for his blessing said to him. But it was not that which troubled them. It was that Francis made so little of all the proceedings. It seemed to Brother Leo and Brother Bernard that the Rule was being gutted by the amendments and the glosses which friar after friar proposed. And yet when they spoke to Francis about it, he seemed quite indifferent, as if all this were basically irrelevant to any purpose of his. They were thankful that his despair had lifted, but they could not understand the composure with which he seemed to contemplate the wreckage of all that he had labored for. Once Brother Leo tried to put something of this into words, but Francis only smiled at him. "It is in the hands of God," he said. "In what better hands could it be, little Brother Lion?"

Leo was forced to leave it at that, but when the summer heat had yielded to the autumn chill, and Francis seemed to have recovered something of his strength, Leo asked him if he had thought what message he should give for the brethren who were going to see Ugolino at Rome about the revised rule.

Francis seemed surprised. "But I am taking it to Rome, myself." And when Leo exclaimed in surprise, he explained, "Brother Elias told me that he wished me to do it."

On the journey to Rome Brother Leo and Brother Bernard again tried to talk to Francis about the Rule, but he shook his head, and with something like his old smile, he asked, "Have you forgotten, my brethren, how little Christ Our Lord talked of rules? It was what He did that tells us His intention." And then he added, as if the idea had come to him for the first time, "And it was the stories He told, those halfway houses between theory and action in which so many of our preachers take up their dwelling. It takes more than a rule to bring Him in our midst and to make people see Him in action among them."

With that they had to be content. But Ugolino was surprised, too. He had looked over the Rule, and its lack of any structure bothered him.

"It is like that medley of huts of yours at the Portiuncula," he had said to Francis.

"That medley of huts," began Brother Leo angrily, but Francis smiled at Ugolino.

"That medley of huts, my lord, I've heard you yourself say, houses the nearest thing in Umbria to the life of Our Lord on earth."

"And that I still say," said Ugolino. "But that has nothing to do with a rule that will tell men how they may build that life in all sorts of very different places."

"Or how they may tear it down," said Leo bitterly.

"Men die in huts," said Francis, stubbornly, "unless there is air in them."

"Do you think," said Ugolino, "I would have taken all this trouble

if I had not known that?" And Francis said no more. He made no
protest either when Ugolino told him that there was a chamber in
his palace for him and his brethren, and a place for them at his own
table. Bernard and Leo looked at each other, but they said nothing.

"How silent we are becoming!" said Leo to himself, and he was
astonished to find that Francis was humming one of his little French
tunes as he went out the door. "He has quite given up the fight," said
Leo to Bernard, and Bernard shrugged his shoulders helplessly. But
the next morning neither Bernard nor Leo could find Francis. They
even went into the Lateran Church and then to St. Peter's, but he
was not there. They were surprised, therefore, when Ugolino and his
guests had taken their places at the long table for dinner to see Francis
come in the door. It happened that a couple of the Cardinal's most
distinguished guests, an ambassador from the King of Aragon and an
ambassador from the Emperor, were sitting opposite the door, and
one of them recognized Francis, and they rose and beckoned to him
to come and sit with them. Again, his old friends were astonished that
Francis made no objection; but with a polite bow to the Cardinal at
the head of the table and a bow to them, he came and sat down between the great men, while the servants ran to get him food.

Leo and Bernard looked at each other, and then, Leo looked back
in time to see Francis take from his dusty frock, which made him look
like a real beggar among the fine woolens and silks of his companions,
something he could not see, and put it on the table. Bernard and Leo
were sitting far down the table, but even so Leo, standing up for a
moment, could see that it was some crusts of black bread that Francis
had laid on the table. "He is going to eat them and not the fine food
they are bringing," said Leo with excitement. And then his heart
leaped up, for Francis with grave courtesy was offering his crusts of
bread to the great men around him. Bernard stood up to see, too, and
as he did so, others rose until the whole table was watching, but the
great men to whom Francis offered the crusts of hard black peasant
bread accepted them gravely, and broke off pieces and began to eat
them. Astonished, Leo watched them, but Francis solemnly said grace
over his share of the fragments and then began to eat. The servants
stood behind him holding a silver dish, not knowing what to do.
Francis felt them behind him, and he turned and looked, and then he
pushed his scraps to the edge of the linen cloth in front of him so
that they might set the dish on the table. He made no effort to touch

it but went on talking in perfect ease with the great men beside him, and the whole table resumed eating. Leo stood still, however, and watched, and now he saw that the men with whom Francis was talking had quietly put the scraps of bread away in their purses as if they were something precious.

"They will keep them as relics of him," thought Leo, and he sat down with a strange sense of reassurance.

But at the end of the meal Cardinal Ugolino came up to Francis. "Brother Francis, you have shamed me before all my guests. Did you mean to say that you could not trust me to find you the food you needed in this big house of mine?"

But Francis shook his head. "No, my lord. You know I would never intentionally cast any shame on your hospitality, which all men know is free. But my brethren, too many of them, have grown too proud to beg, and they say My Lady Courtesy will not allow them to turn away from the banquets of the rich. I am a poor unlettered man, my lord. No one knows better than you how rude an answer I should make when the doctors at Paris and Bologna speak. But I can show them what I do not want them to forget, and men remember the gesture when they have forgotten the words."

For a moment Ugolino stood there looking at him. Then he said, "You know what you have to do. Far be it from me ever to tell you that."

Before they left Rome, Francis reminded him of that. Ugolino had offered him the Rule a little apologetically. "It isn't so much that I have changed it," he said, "as that I have tied up some of the loose ends." Ugolino saw the faces of Leo and Bernard tighten, but Francis seemed uninterested.

"It is not of that, my lord, that I want to speak before I leave, or perhaps rather it is of that. In the beginning you remember what I told you: that it seemed to me the thing the world most needed was to see Christ come again, here and now, in Umbria, and even here in Rome."

"You need hardly remind me of that, Brother Francis," said the Cardinal. "That is the heart of what we are all about."

"Yes, but so much of what we do veils it, I think." And then he told the Cardinal of the church at Bethlehem and the golden crib.

"How long do you think a wooden stall would stand?" asked Ugolino when he had finished.

Francis corrected him hastily. "It isn't the church that I object to," he said, "in itself, nor even the golden crib. But it does not remind men of what they forget so easily: that Our Lord came into the cold and hunger and pain of our human frailty when He came to Bethlehem."

"How do you propose to do it?"

And then Francis told him. The Cardinal looked at him thoughtfully. "You would not do this instead of the Christmas Mass?"

"Of course not," said Francis. "The Christmas Mass does it more directly; it does it over again. This is just to remind people of what they have seen."

"I can see no harm in it," said Ugolino. "I am sure the Pope will not."

"Then that is settled," said Francis, and Ugolino smiled with affectionate amusement. This was one of the easy things about dealing with Francis. You need never worry about his pestering you for a parchment with a heavy seal to exhibit in the treasure of his house like most of the ecclesiastical officials with whom Ugolino dealt. Now he even declined a copy of the Rule which Ugolino had approved.

"You can give it to one of your men," he said, "to take to the Portiuncula when next you send somebody to Assisi."

Leo and Bernard said nothing to that until they had passed the northern gate of Rome. Then Bernard seized Francis' arm. "If not to the Portiuncula, then where do we go?"

Francis stopped and faced his companions.

"Bernard, do you remember Giovanni Velita, the Lord of Greccio?"

Bernard blinked. He had been too much absorbed in thinking of Elias and the others at the Portiuncula. "It was a long time ago—" he fenced for time to remember.

"You remember," said Francis, "he was a great knight, and he threw his arms away to do penance for his violence."

"There were so many in those days," said Leo with a sigh.

"There are even more now," said Bernard; "that is the trouble."

But Francis shook his head. "He has proved a good brother of ours."

"Oh, I know now," said Leo. "He wanted to build the brethren a house, and all the town applauded, and said they would have the house in the middle of the town that they might not forget, and you said, 'Let God decide.' And they gave a child a torch to fling, and it winged clear over the valley and fell on the hillside opposite the town, up on the bare rocks where they had to hollow out the hillside to get a perch."

"We will go there," said Francis. "There we shall keep Christmas."

It was a steep climb, Brother Leo thought, for a sick man. But Francis' eyes were shining, and Brother Leo knew that now he had found something that was his to do.

When they reached the collection of huts clinging to the bare stone hillside, Francis told the Lord of Greccio, who was now the guardian of the little convent, that he wished him to build a shelter of boughs in the clearing among the oaks and the ilex trees above their house. And when the shelter of boughs was built, Francis asked him to get a wooden manger from one of the farmers, and an ox and an ass to place there with straw in a corner of the shelter, and then to take there the portable altar from the chapel, and let the people of the neighborhood know that the Christmas Mass would be said on the mountain.

"It is a steep way for some of them to come," said the friar who had been Lord of Greccio, doubtfully.

"They are good people. They will come," said Francis. "They will know that the old Christmas carols that they sing in their village will lighten their climb."

At first that night Brother Leo thought that a swarm of fireflies was dancing up the winter mountainside, and then he saw the flashes lengthen into flares, and he heard the voices of the people coming up the mountainside and through the wood singing. When they reached the mountain top, it was as light as day, and the gold embroidery on the white vestments of the priest shone in the light. The former chaplain of the Lord of Greccio was a large man and a splendid figure in the festal robes of Christmas, so that Francis serving as deacon looked very small and frail beside him—much like the tiny ass beside the great ox which had been tethered in the corner of the shed with the hay and the manger between. All through the Christmas Mass the ox watched the lights with its large limpid eyes and the ass with its gleaming teeth, and then at the end of the Mass Francis read in the dialect of the countryside the Gospel of the Mass. His voice rang out sweet and strong, and its tenderness glowed through all the assembly. It seemed to Leo and to Bernard that he was young once more, as he told the congregation that it was on just such a night as this in just such a simple and everyday setting among people like themselves that the Creator of the whole universe had laid aside His majesty for the weakness of a child. And His mother brought him forth, "even as many of you have brought forth your first-born child, and she laid Him there in the straw in the manger with only the breath of the ox and the ass to keep Him warm, and her love." And as he spoke, Francis turned to the manger, and he knelt down beside it and cried out with a voice that went like a bell through the whole audience, "My little Lord, and my God!" And all down the mountain side, voices cried, "The Christ Child is there, and He smiled at Francis!"

The next day all the country was full of the wonder, for now many of those who had gone painfully limping up the mountainside, and even some of those who had been carried on the backs of their kinsfolk, threw away their canes, and walked whole and well in the village square of Greccio for all the world to see. And some of the farmers came and took some of the straw from the manger, and they gave it to their sick cattle, and they, too, were made whole and well. And the people from one end of the district to the other said to each other, "Christ has really come to us!" And from all over, came the parish priests with their parishioners, begging Francis to come and talk to them in their villages, and it seemed to Leo and Bernard that Francis' strength had been miraculously renewed. Many pilgrims came to Greccio and climbed up to the little convent on the cliffs, and finally when Easter time came, the Minister of the Province sent word that he was coming to see for himself all the marvels that were being wrought at Greccio.

So the brethren in the little convent at Greccio made ready the Easter feast. The grateful villagers sent up provisions, and the lady of the castle which the Lord of Greccio's brother now held, sent up some of her servants with fine linen and crystal glasses and silver. But when it was time for them to go in to the feast, Francis was nowhere to be found. They had gone all over the immediate neighborhood, looking in the caves and under the trees and in the bare space where the manger had stood, and where now was a little wooden shrine, and had found no sign of him. So they sat down to the table before the good meat should spoil. But they were barely seated when a little beggar with a tattered hat pulled down over his face and a ragged scarf about his mouth came in, and in a high-pitched voice cried, "For the love of the risen Christ give food to the hungry!" A little chill went through the brethren, and the Lord of Greccio rose, and took a plate and put some of the meat on it and handed it to the little beggar, and the little beggar said, "God bless you and reward you, for even in your pride you have not forgotten His charity."

And then as the Lord of Greccio stood in his place, uncertain as to what had happened, two of the brethren rose and said, "There is room for you here at the board." But the little man had gone over and sat down in the ashes at the edge of the hearth, and now he set the plate in the ashes while they all watched him. Then he loosened the scarf, and he took off his hat, and he said, "Lo, this is the place where a poor beggar of a friar should be eating the meat God has given him!" And they all stood aghast, for it was Francis. But he began to eat, and he said, as if he were tasting the food critically, like an epicure, "It is good meat, worthy even of the fine lords you have become. Indeed, I am not sure that it is not too fine for a poor beggar," and he took a little of the ashes and sprinkled them lightly on the meat. And when he ate, they heard his jaws crunch on the grit.

Then the Lord of Greccio ran to Francis, and he knelt down beside him, and he began to weep. And all the brethren, including the Minister of the Province, followed his example. And Francis said softly, "You remember, you asked me to preach an Easter sermon for the people."

The Lord of Greccio choked as he said, "And you said that the people of Greccio did not need your sermon; that you would preach where the sermon was most needed." And Francis stood up and embraced him. Already two of the brethren had begun to roll the fine linen from the table, and Brother Giles took one of the fine glasses and dashed it to the pavement. But Francis put out a hand—"The glasses are not yours. Restore them whole to him from whom you had them." And then all the brethren sat down on the floor of the refectory, but they ate very little.

When grace had been said, the Minister came and knelt down before Francis and asked his blessing, saying "I have seen all I came to see," and then he turned to the brethren and he said, "You have no need of me, who have the best preacher of all among you." And he went out. And though the brethren had asked many of their friends to come up to the chapel to hear the Minister preach that afternoon, no one made any effort to stop him.

3

It seemed to Francis that in those quiet months at Greccio he had recovered a good deal of his strength, and even his old freshness of energy. So he had agreed that in June he would go to the Chapter of 1224.

But when the time came, it was already hot in the plain, and the fever returned to him, and in the clouds of dust on the roads, his eyes stung. Before ever he reached the Portiuncula, he was a frail old man again, and when he arrived there, he knew that he need never have come. For the very look of the leaders of the friars now pouring into the little settlement told Francis that this was a quite different world from that in which he had recently been living. These men coming with their large companies of brethren were as different from Francis and his old companions as anybody could imagine. Looking at them, Francis saw that they might well be devout and earnest men, but they were men of power. Many of them were physically taller and handsomer than their fellows. They walked not like Brother Giles, as if they were ashamed of their strength, but rather as if they took it for granted that the whole world would recognize its potency. And even if they did not wear the gowns of doctors, Francis knew that many of them might have. There was a neatness, too, about the habits of these new brethren, dusty though they might be from the road. Moreover, many of them had mules and asses with them, carrying supplies. Francis had no doubt that these were gifts, but, far from the spontaneous offerings of the poor, they were the well-considered largesse of the rich and powerful.

When the sessions opened, it was no longer the details of the Rule that engaged them, but the establishment of a house of studies at Paris, and still another at Bologna, and the organization of missions, and the training of friars for other new ventures. And the brethren who took the lead in these discussions spoke with the assurance of men who were quite aware that they were the leaders in a very great enterprise. Francis did not attempt to speak. He was too exhausted, and he was quite sure that nothing he could say would have commanded any hearing. There was no bitterness now in this realization of his. Every time he appeared at a session all of these strong men crowded around him and knelt down for his blessing, and kissed his hand, but he knew that the dry whispering of his voice brushed by them like the infrequent breeze.

Meanwhile, Brother Leo had gone up to San Damiano to see Sister Clare. Sitting there in the coolness of the little room with the low voice of Sister Clare in his ears, Leo thought to himself, "Only Sister Clare does not change. This quiet of hers is as fresh and as invigorating as the breeze in the hemlocks above San Damiano." Of the sickness and the pain of Brother Francis, Leo said little, but he told her of how still he sat beneath all the turmoil of the Chapter, and of how easily the great doctors who had knelt down to kiss his hand forgot him.

"Of course," said Sister Clare, "they only think they forget him."

But Brother Leo shook his head, and that evening he went back to the Portiuncula, and he told Francis that Sister Clare was praying for them. For the first time that day, Francis smiled. "How much alike," he said, "are all of us sons of men. I had forgotten that. And did she send me no other message?"

"Only this," said Leo. " 'Having dismissed the multitude, he went up into a mountain alone to pray.' "

"As always, she is right, Brother Leo. There is no color in the painting unless the sunlight of God falls on it," responded Francis.

He rested for a few weeks after the Chapter was over. Then he summoned Brother Giles, and he told him that he wished him to gather together a few of his oldest friends and to go up with him to the little convent on the Mount of La Verna. When Elias would have escorted him, he declined with thanks, saying that the Guardian of the whole Order could not occupy himself with one poor brother. Even when Elias offered him an ass, Francis also declined, and pointing down to his own feet said, "Brother Ass here has long carried me safely, and will not fail me this time."

But when they had gone only a small portion of the journey, Francis staggered, and Brother Leo, who had been watching him, caught him, and sent Brother Giles to a friend's house for the loan of an ass. One of the peasants on the friend's estate soon brought the animal. He was a short, stocky block of a fellow, and when Francis was mounted on the ass, he looked at him curiously.

"Are you that Francis of whom they tell so many stories?" he asked.

Tired as he was, Francis laughed. "I suppose," he said, "they do tell a good many stories, and the stories grow the way stories do."

But the peasant was perfectly serious. "You had better take care," he said soberly, "to be as good as men say you are, for it would be a disappointment to many men if you were not."

Brother Leo, who had been standing at Francis' side, frowned, but Francis slipped, with astonishing speed for his infirmity, from the ass to the ground, and he knelt down in front of the peasant, and he said, "Thank you, brother, for reminding me of my responsibility when I was forgetting it. Do you pray for me," said he earnestly. The astonished peasant nodded his head, and then slowly he sank down to Francis' feet, and Francis embraced him.

After that, Francis seemed stronger, and presently he asked Leo if he remembered the day when they had first seen the Count Orlando of Chiusi, to whom they owed the gift of La Verna. Leo smiled, "I remember how worried he looked, this handsome young man in his rich robes, as he came out from the feast for his brother's knighting."

"Yes, and he told me he would like nothing better than to put off his robe and take on mine, but there was the brother who had just been knighted, and the wife who was waiting for him so anxiously under her crown of flowers, and the son with his nurse up in the high castle behind. So I told him that the will of God might be fulfilled in a good lord as well as in a friar."

"He has been a good lord, too," said Brother Bernard, who had just come up; "all men agree on that. It is a sweet house there on that hillside, and with the winds that blow on those rocks, you will forget the summer fever."

When they reached the hermitage of La Verna, Count Orlando came to tell Francis that he had heard of his coming and that his men were ready to do his bidding.

"There is a point high above us," said Francis, "where across a chasm there is a level place in the shelter of a great beech tree. If you will build me a little hut of reeds there, you will do me a great service."

The Count Orlando replied that he not only would do that, but would also have his men build a proper bridge across the chasm. But Francis said it would take too long, for he wished to fast there from the Assumption of Our Lady to the Feast of St. Michael. A little foot bridge of saplings to hold the weight of two men would be all that would be needed.

So while the Count Orlando went off to give his orders, Francis told Brother Leo what he wanted, "Let all the rest of the brethren remain here, and here in the woods let them pray. It is a holy place, this, where the great chasms in the rocks and the overhanging cliffs speak to us eloquently of the dangers of this world, and the sunlight falling over the plain beneath, and the birds singing above our heads remind us of the sweetness of God's providence. Brother Leo, we have thought too much of what we can and cannot do. We have not listened enough to what God has to say to us." Then he went on to explain to Leo what he would have him in particular do. Twice a day he would come across the little bridge: once in the morning to bring him bread and water, and once before midnight that Francis might say the office of Matins with him, as a good friar should. "When you bring the bread, there is no need of words," said Francis. "You may leave it there. But when it comes to Matins, do you say the first line, 'Domine, labia mea aperies,' and I will answer you, 'Et os meum annuntiabit laudem tuam,' and then you will come over. But if I do not answer you, then go back."

"But if you are ill?"

"What a timid lamb you have grown, my lion!" Francis laughed at him affectionately. "God will have me in His keeping, and what suffering of mine is to be thought of in the contemplation of His Passion?"

"We shall pray for you," said Leo, "and I shall ask one of the brethren to go and ask Sister Clare to pray, too."

"That is not necessary. She will have heard we have come here, and she will know the rest."

So with the help of the Count Orlando and Brother Leo, the simple arrangements Francis wanted were completed. The first night when Leo and Francis had finished the morning office, Leo begged him to let him stay, for it seemed to him that Francis was very ill, but Francis bade him go back across the bridge.

The days that followed brought Leo times of almost unbearable anxiety. Sometimes Francis would come out and bless him when he set the bread and the water in the appointed place under the shade of the beech tree. But sometimes Leo would only hear him praying in the depths of the cave behind the little hut, and sometimes he would not hear any sound at all. One day, Francis had apparently forgotten to scatter the remains of the bread for the birds; so, overcome with anxiety, Leo crept back before sunset that he might look across to the rock and see if he could find any sign of Francis. Fortunately, he looked first through the bushes at the end of the bridge, and saw Francis sitting in front of the cave gazing afar off as if he were completely absorbed in the vast panorama which, Leo knew, was visible from that point. The faithful brother crept back, reassured.

Some days later, Francis seemed to have become aware at last of Leo's anxiety, for when they had finished reciting Matins, he stood in the starlight before the cave, with the soft radiance of the moon over the valley below and the dark shadows of the rocks looming with fantastic magnitude above them, and he talked a little with Leo of what had been happening to him. "It seemed to me that my heart was as thin and as dried out as the leaves that the winds rattle against the rock. Then," he said, "I heard a single strain of music, as if an angel had drawn his bow across a viol. It was so sweet that I wept with joy, and I waited to hear that strain again." Francis paused.

"Did it come?" asked Brother Leo, softly.

"No, and then I knew that if it had, my ravished spirit would have left the body entirely."

Another time when he had not answered Leo's greeting in the night, he waited for him when he brought his bread the next day. "You must not worry," he told Leo, seeing his face so white in the sunlight. "There is a falcon here that comes to visit me, each night just before time for Matins, and again at dawn he wakens me that I may praise God. But sometimes when I am very tired or sick, I think he knows it, and he does not disturb me."

Now Leo was ashamed of his anxiety, but when a few nights later for the second time he had called out in the night, "Domine, labia mea aperies," and there had not been even a whisper from the other side, Leo crossed the little bridge very softly, carrying his sandals in his hand. When he was in the middle, he saw a light ahead, and he was astonished, for Francis had no candles with him. Then he realized that this was not the light of a candle; it was like the after-glow of a great light, and then it was dark again. Leo heard the voice of Francis, "Who art thou? What art thou? My God, that Thou dost stoop so low as to speak to this worm in the dust!"

Leo realized that this was no ordinary praying, but rather as if Francis were speaking to an invisible visitor. Frightened at his own disobedience and intrusion, Leo hurried back across the bridge. The saplings swayed and grated a little against the rocks, and he was still more frightened and thrust himself among the bushes so that they rattled about him.

Francis called out to him, "Come here, little sheep! Why have you disobeyed me?" And as Leo flung himself on his knees before him, Francis asked him sharply, "Did you hear anything?"

"I heard you talking," and as Francis waited for something else, he added, "you were talking to somebody."

"And did you hear the other voice?"

"No."

"I was talking with Christ, Our Lord. I had shut my eyes praying here, and suddenly a light fell on them, and I opened them to see the whole place alight." And as in the darkness Francis felt the stillness and awe of Leo, he bade him say nothing of this to his comrades.

But when Leo got back to the hermitage dormitory, Brother Bernard raised himself on his straw and asked, "Is Francis all right?"

"Yes," said Leo. "Why are you not asleep?"

Bernard answered in a low voice, "When we came out of the oratory after we had said Matins, we saw a light on the mountain, and then it faded." And at that moment from out of the darkness of the dormitory came the voices of all Francis' brethren, "We saw it, too."

But Leo without saying anything lay down in his place.

Another night, when Francis had been so frail that it was only in a whisper that he finished Matins, Leo again begged him to let him stay with him. But Francis said, no, Christ had spoken to him again, and He had promised him that something wonderful was going to happen on the mountain. "I am sure," said Francis, "He will give me strength enough to stay for that."

So they came to the Feast of the Exaltation of the Cross. When they had completed Matins that morning, Leo was loath to leave Francis, for it seemed to him that it was only the strength of his spirit that had kept the frail voice answering. When Leo begged him to let him stay, Francis told him not to worry, but Leo persisted, "I hate to leave you here alone for fear you would die with no one to help you."

But Francis' voice was now much firmer and clearer. "There is no need to worry, for I know now what to ask of God, and when a man knows that, he has accomplished the purpose of his life on earth."

Now Leo was even more afraid, and he said, "Can you not tell me before I go?" And the hunger in Leo's voice was so sharp that Francis hesitated.

Then he said, "I shall ask God for two things"—and now his voice was low with awe as if he were praying—"I shall ask Him that I may understand the depths and the heights of His suffering in His Passion, and then I shall ask Him that I may know for Him a little of that love for me which made Him submit Himself to such pain."

Leo was frightened. "Do you know what you have asked, Francis?"

But Francis bade him go at once. Leo thought to himself, "I have been the voice of the tempter to him," and, weeping, he stumbled back across the bridge. When he reached the little hermitage of La Verna and saw the low building shouldering up out of the darkness, he did not go in, but he went beyond to a little clearing in the wood from which he could see in the moonlight the precipice where he had left Francis, and he waited there until the moon had set, and all around him the night darkened. Now he could not see even the fading stars, but he was not sure that it was not his weeping that had veiled his sight. Then suddenly he saw a great flash of light hurl itself against the rock of the mountainside. As he looked, there was a moment when he thought he saw Francis kneeling with upraised hands and lifted head clear against the black screen of the rock. Then it seemed to him that like a bolt of lightning the flying torch of light dashed itself against the rock just where Francis had been kneeling. Then everything was darkness again, and in his terror Leo fainted.

The pale light of dawn had washed over the wooded precipice, and the birds were chattering when Leo recovered his senses. Shivering with cold, he crept into the dormitory and lay down in his place near the door. But when the brethren awakened and asked him when he had come in, for they had all been anxious and had lain awake for him, he could not speak. All morning he kept seeing that bolt of light hurling itself against the wall of the mountainside. If it were not a dream, if he had really seen it, it would have burned Francis into the rock and left him a cinder. Sick with fear, he crept to the bridge and left the bread and water in the accustomed place. There was no sign of Francis, but neither was there any sign of fire anywhere on the mountainside. And his fear was for the moment allayed, and when he got back to the convent, and his brethren crowded around him, asking "Is he all right?" Leo reported that there was no sign that everything was not as usual.

Then he went into the little oratory to pray until the time should come to go back for Matins. But it seemed to him that there was nothing he could say, for when he tried to pray, he saw the bolt hurling itself against the mountain, and for that he could find no words even in thought. So long were the hours of that afternoon and that evening that although Leo knew he was ahead of time, he hurried to the bridge, and his voice shook as he called out the opening words of the Office. He thought there was no answer. Then just as he was about to start across the bridge, he heard the voice of Francis. It was weak and a little choked, as if it were a long time since he had used it. In his relief Leo dashed across the little bridge so that it swung as if it would tear itself from the cords of its mooring.

Francis was sitting on the earth under the beech tree. He made no effort to rise when Leo knelt down. There was only the pale moonlight

and Francis' face white, with the eyes glittering. He had his arms
wrapped in his sleeves and clasped over his heart, but when Leo began
to ask him how he was, Francis went on with the Office, and not until
it was completed, did he speak to Leo. Then he said only, "It is finished." And when Leo lingered for more, Francis told him to be gone
that he might sleep.

The next day when Leo came with the bread and water, he saw that
Francis was still sitting in the same place. "Like a wounded man,"
thought Leo, "unable to move from where he has fallen." But when
Leo started across the bridge, Francis bade him be gone sharply. So he
went back, shaking his head in bewilderment. The next night, Francis
did not answer Leo's greeting at all, and he went across the bridge to
find him huddled in the same place. The night was so still that Leo
heard his breathing, and reassured that at least he was alive, he crept
back.

The next day, there was no sign of Francis when Leo came, and that
night when Francis answered his greeting, and Leo came across the
bridge, Francis was kneeling with his hands clasped before him. When
they had finished the Office, Francis asked Leo to bring some fresh
linen with him when he came again, but when Leo asked him if he were
hurt, he made no answer. The day after that when he brought bread
and water, Leo saw a piece of linen hanging on a bush as if it had been
washed and put there to dry; so that night he brought more fresh linen.

So with Leo's curiosity becoming almost unbearable, they came to
the end of the appointed fast, and the Lord of La Verna sent word that
he would have an ass ready for Francis to come down the mountainside. The night before they were to come down, Leo found Francis
weaker than he had yet been, and after they had finally with great
effort finished Matins, Leo asked Francis if there was anything he could
do for him. At first, Francis made no answer. Then he reached for Leo's
hand, and he said, "Brother Leo, you have been so faithful a lamb in
tending me and so valiant a lion in leashing your curiosity that I will
ask you to do one thing more for me and still ask no questions." So
he bade Leo take off his tunic, and when Leo touched the tunic, he felt
the cloth stiff under his fingers as if it had been wet and dried in the
sun. But when he lifted it, his hands struck moisture, and then Francis
said, "It is beneath the heart. Take the linen and wash."

Leo's fingers trembled as he felt the ooze under them and knew it was blood. Then he remembered the bolt of light. "You are wounded," he cried in horror.

"It is Love's wound," said Francis. "It is nothing to be afraid of. And," he added sharply, "nothing to talk about."

When Leo had finished washing the wound and put fresh linen over it, binding it about the thin ribs, he put Francis' tunic back, and as he did so, his hand brushed Francis' hand, and Leo felt what seemed to be the edge of a stick in it. But though Francis winced in pain, he refused to let Leo look at his hand and bade him be gone and tell no one. "So the bolt did hit him," said Leo to himself, and a great desolation came over him, for Francis had deliberately shut him out of this strange thing.

In the morning as soon as the Count Orlando's servants had brought the ass, Leo took it up and tethered it at the end of the bridge, and crossed to find Francis kneeling with his hands folded in his sleeves. When he heard Leo, he kissed the ground, and then he stumbled awkwardly to his feet, wincing with pain. Clutching Leo's arm, he went over to the rock, and he kissed it too, and looking at the countryside spread out below them, he said to Leo, "This is a most holy place. Let none but those who will understand ever come here." Then he staggered across the bridge, and Leo lifted him onto the ass, and as he did so, he saw the back of one of Francis' hands. Protruding from it was something which looked like a large thorn, but even as Francis caught him looking at it, he slipped the hem of his sleeve over it. Then Leo looked down to help Francis arrange his feet, and he saw that his sandals were stuffed with straw. But Francis met his astonishment serenely, saying "We have accomplished all we came to do, Brother Leo. Let us go back."

But Leo hesitated. "Are you sure you are able? Let me get you food and a cloak and make you comfortable here."

Francis shook his head. "I have been up on the Mount of Contemplation, and now I must come down and be about My Father's work." And for the rest of the journey he said nothing but seemed to be lost in thought even where the path narrowed between the rocks, and Leo feared that the ass might slip on the moss and the ferns. Even when his brethren came out to meet him, Francis still seemed wrapped in the contemplation of some wonder afar-off, and returned their greeting as if he had only half heard them. And though he made no objection when they all went into the oratory to give thanks for his return, he seemed hardly to be aware of their presence. Then as he suddenly noticed that the brethren were staring at his straw-stuffed sandals, Francis asked Leo to get him a pair of woolen stockings. When he brought them, he bade Leo go apart with him out to the spring behind the hermitage, and there Leo again washed the wound below the heart and put fresh linen on it. Then Francis bade him wash his feet, and Leo saw to his horror that there was blood on the straw, and on both feet the same kind of large thorn. Leo bandaged the feet and put the stockings on them and eased them back into the sandals, and then he looked at Francis, and threw himself at his feet, saying, "They are the wounds of Our Lord."

"Tell no man," said Francis. But that night at supper he himself asked his brethren, "When God does a marvel to a poor sinner, a creature completely and totally unworthy, is it not a blasphemy to speak of what should be hidden?" All the brethren sat silent, and Leo thought, "If only Brother Peter were here to advise us."

But young Brother Illuminato spoke out when his elders were silent. He said, "There is no blasphemy in telling of the wondrous works of God, for in them speaks His grace and not our unworthiness."

Now Francis for the first time seemed to come from afar off, and he looked directly at the young man. Then he turned to Leo and the others. "Do you agree with what the youngest of us has said?" And for the first time he smiled a little—"Out of the mouths of babes and sucklings . . ." and Illuminato blushed. But they all agreed that what God gave should be shared. "And yet," said Francis, his voice warmed as he thought for the first time in many weeks of the Lady Pica, " 'Mary kept all these words, pondering them in her heart.' "

Bernard answered this time. "These were the things that had been promised and had not yet come to pass."

Francis said no more that night until after Matins, and then he asked Leo to wait outside the dormitory with him, and they stood there where Leo had stood when he saw the bolt of light. And gently leaning on Leo, as he so often did these days, Francis asked him, "Did you never look back again at the mountain all those nights?"

"Yes, one night."

"When?"

"I turned and stood here in the hour before dawn."

"What did you see?" Francis drew his breath sharply.

"I saw a great light hurl itself upon the mountain wall like a bolt.

Before it struck, I saw you in its path." And Leo flung himself at Francis' feet, crying, "My lord and master, do not thrust me into outer darkness!"

But Francis lifted him up, and he said sharply, "Foolish little lamb! Those are words you say only to Christ, and not to a poor fellow-sinner." Then as he felt Leo trembling, he went on more gently, "I have not spoken, Leo, not because I was ashamed that God should stoop so low, for all His grace to us is a touching of the dust, even as was our making in the beginning—but, my brother, I could not find any words for it. I have seen such things as I cannot tell. But of the thing you saw, I can tell you this. You remember my prayer?" And when Leo had steadied himself enough to reply, Francis continued, "It was answered. And I hid my face, and when I lifted my head to give thanks for what I in no way deserved, then I saw"—and he paused as if even the memory of that vision still awed him to silence—"I saw a great bird of fire come toward me out of the most high heavens. Then as it came nearer, I saw that it was a seraph such as Isaiah"—and he repeated the words of Isaiah as if here were something he could cling to. "Then as he came nearer—Oh, Leo, it takes me so long to tell what came in a flash,"—and then his voice sank to a whisper—"I saw the face and the body of the seraph between the wings, and it was a Man hanging on a cross. It was like the crucifix at San Damiano, only it was not a painting nor a sculpture—" and he paused, and Leo shook with fear that he had said all he could. But Francis went on, his voice rising with excitement, "The great flaming seraph came toward me and struck me and passed through me, and as I burned in every nerve, I felt it dash upon the rock behind me, and then it was darkness, and I fell upon my face."

"And then—" said Leo. But Francis was standing rigid in Leo's arms, and the moonlight was too dim for Leo to see his face.

Then Francis shivered a little, and he clutched Leo and said, "I am here." Leo felt the thorns in his hands, as Francis said, "Tell no one."

And Leo said nothing, though all his brethren looked curiously at him the next day. But after supper Francis said, "We have lingered here long enough. Tomorrow morning let us go back where we belong." So early the next morning Francis took leave of the brethren at the hermitage, and with his hands wrapped in his sleeves he went out, with the companions who had brought him there.

Off they all went in silence down the road until they reached the turn from which they could see the whole mountain before them.

There Francis knelt down, and he blessed the mountain, "Farewell, Mount La Verna. I shall never come here again, nor see you more. Let only those who can understand your wonder come here, and for them let it be a holy place forever." He remained kneeling there so long that Leo touched his arm. Like a man in a dream, Francis rose and mounted his ass, but none of the brethren said anything. And Leo thought to himself, "I have not said anything, and yet they know something has happened." And the word must have reached the village, because when they came to the highway, people were waiting to kneel down and ask for Francis' blessing. And again, when they came to the little town of Borgo San Sepolcro, the people pressed about Francis in the marketplace, and like a man in a trance, over and over again he repeated the words of blessing, "May God give you peace."

They were long past the little town of Borgo San Sepolcro when Francis seemed to come to himself, scanning the fields on either side of the road. Then he turned to Leo. "When do we come to Borgo San Sepolcro?" he asked. When Leo did not answer, Francis looked at Brother Giles, who was the leader of their company, and Brother Giles looked at Leo. Then Francis understood, and quietly as if he were thinking of nothing more than the journey on the road, he said, "Let us sing a hymn of thanksgiving to God for His surpassing goodness."

4

"In my end is my beginning," said Francis one day early that winter when Leo had pleaded with him to spare himself. "I had once thought to be a knight and to do great deeds and to win glory for them. Now, I am Christ's knight, and I have taken up my quest and put on the livery of His pain. And of that there is no fame or glory, but only something that speaks to the common heart of man."

Leo and the rest besought him to stay at the Portiuncula and rest for the winter months at least, but Francis scoffed, "What a poor knight should I be to spend the winter mured up in a castle?" And when Sister Clare sent him a pair of soft leather shoes to cushion the pain in his feet, Francis kissed them and said, "Though she came after us, Sister Clare in her watchtower at San Damiano is often the first to see the road ahead."

He put the shoes on, and then he insisted that he must go out into the villages. "I have something to tell them," he said, and when his brethren tried to persuade him that one who suffered as he suffered should save all his strength for his own health, Francis rebuked them, and reminded them of the fable of the pelican, who out of the tearing of its own breast found the life-restoring blood for its young.

Francis saw Leo and Giles wince when he could not hide the twinge of pain as his hand brushed the saddle, or his feet touched the ground. He would smile slowly to reassure them, but the sun on the snow burned his eyes, and in the depths of his being the never-ending pain gnawed unceasingly at his vitals. Sometimes it was the blood of hemorrhage that betrayed him, and sometimes his voice failed him. And when Leo protested that he could not long endure the weary days and the sleepless nights, Francis reminded him that he was but studying the theme on which he was to preach.

For when he spoke in the little churches, or the village squares, or along the road to chance pilgrims, or peasants plodding to market, his theme was always of God's love, of the love that made Him come on earth and share the pain of man's sin-sprung existence, and by the fullness of His sinless suffering, redeem it. Francis spoke so sweetly that everywhere he went it was as if ordinary human life flowered at his touch. He no longer worried about the talk of miracles that brought the crowds thronging to his feet. "It is nothing of me," he said when Leo told him of the wounded boy who had been made whole by the touch of his hand, of the possessed woman who had been freed by the kissing of his pierced feet.

But when the brethren asked him if they might see the wounds, he refused, and always he bade Leo be sure the door was shut when he bathed them and changed the bandages. But when the woman nearly mad with pain in her head asked him to put his hand upon her forehead, he did so; and the shivering peasant who brought a fresh ass, he warmed with the touch of his hand, and changed his grumbling to praise of God's mercy. Sometimes he seemed quite unaware of what he was doing, but once when Leo spoke to him of the marvelous healings, he bade him remember that they were not his, that it was what God had wrought in his flesh, and he was but the maidservant who carried the bread to the table that the hungry might be fed. All of God's gifts were free to the need of the least, and so long as those who received gave thanks to God, it mattered not how the gifts were given.

So troubled were Francis' companions at his wasting away that they sent word to Elias at the Portiuncula and to Ugolino in Rome. Elias came at once, and he overtook Francis in the little house at Foligno. At first Francis was angry with his brethren that they should have turned from him to a man whom they had never trusted, and whom he had so often to defend against their suspicions.

But Elias said nothing of obedience or of authority. He sat down by Francis' bed, and he told him that he had had a dream of him, and in his dream he had seen Francis walking down a road with his back to him, but he had known who it was. He paused, and Francis was amused to think that Elias hesitated to tell him that he had recognized his figure because it was so small and frail. But it was not that. For Elias went on to say that in his dream he had also seen coming down the road a friar whose features he could not make out. The friar embraced Francis, and Elias heard him say, "I will be waiting." Francis went on, and then Elias saw the face of the friar, and it was Peter Catanii. And Peter smiled at Elias and said, "It will only be a couple of years now." Then Elias awoke.

But Francis said, "It is the more urgent then that I do all that can be done in the time I have." Elias, however, begged him to think of the brethren who would be left forlorn, like sons bereft of their father. But Francis shook his head. "A good father knows always that he leaves his sons to God when he leaves them in God's service." So Elias bowed his head and said no more.

Then came word from Ugolino at Rieti, where the friars' messengers had overtaken him. He wrote that Pope Honorius was taking refuge from the rebellious Romans in that city, and since his age was now lying heavily on him, his Saracen physician Tabald was with him. So Ugolino bade Francis come at once and consult that most learned of doctors. And when Francis answered by Leo's hand that he would in no way seek to flee the pain which was God's final gift to him, Ugolino wrote back at once to remind him that the herbs of the earth, and the skill of the physicians who knew how to use them, were also the gifts of God, and it was no honor to their Giver to scorn their help. Ugolino did not scruple, either, to use the authority which Elias had not dared to invoke, for he bade Francis on his obedience to go to Rieti.

"I will go," said Francis to Leo, "and the obedience will be the purer because I know it is in vain. And I shall pray that it may be an example to the lawless brethren."

But Leo reminded him that it would be a poor return to Sister

Clare for all her prayers to go without taking leave of her. And here again it seemed to Francis that Sister Clare had, as so often, been ahead of him. For she welcomed him at the door of her convent with such joy that Francis felt all his being renewed, and then she led him into the garden and showed him a little hut of reeds which she had made ready, with a bed of fresh straw in it. When Francis had knelt before the crucifix at San Damiano, he had not been able, with the darkness and the pain in his eyes, to see the face of the Christ on it, and for a moment he had wept. But now at the sound of the fresh, sweet voice of Clare, it seemed to him that all the years between had fallen away, and he was again a young man starting out on the unknown quest with all the wonder of it before him.

He repeated to Clare what he had said to Leo, "In my end is my beginning." And Clare answered, "That is, I think, the greatest of all God's wonders, that in Him all things are made new." And they sat in Clare's little garden in the evening, sweet with the scent of her roses, and Francis felt the breeze blow in across the great plain he could not see below, and he was content. But that night he could not sleep for the rustling of the mice in the reeds, and their rattling against his straw. And as he tried to frighten them away, Francis reminded himself that though he had this evening been given a foretaste of heaven, he had not yet earned his rest, and these were like the twinges of a too complacent conscience. But presently the annoyance passed beyond the bounds of reminder, and as he tossed, it seemed to Francis that the twinges within his body had taken on an external embodiment, so that the gnawing of the pain within was now all about him. It seemed as if the night would never end, and he thought of the apostles who slept in the garden of the agony, which he had not stopped to enter when he was in the Holy Land, and of Christ's words to Peter, "Could you not watch one hour with me?"

And then he reminded himself of all the joys he had known here at San Damiano, and of the promise of Christ to the thief on the cross that he would walk with Him in paradise. And he thought to himself, "It is a generous meal which God has given to us here on this earth, and before we leave, it is fitting that we say grace." So when in the morning his companions came to see if he was any stronger, he said only a word of the troubled night, and then, sitting up in his bed, he bade Leo fetch his writing materials. "I have a new song," he said. "It is the praise of all created things, for they are the witnesses of God's goodness to us, and the pledge of what He has in store for us." And he began to sing his song praising God for all the creatures he had made. And then he went on to praise God in the sun, in the moon, in the wind and in the air, and all the varied faces of the weather, and for water and fire and the earth, the mother of all things created, which nourished and gladdened the life of man. And as he sang, his voice swelled, and he made his brethren learn the verses and sing them with him so that Sister Clare came into the garden and laughed with joy to find Francis so happy.

"Some poor men at the gate," she told him, "hearing your singing said, 'They are the angels who used to sing at the Portiuncula. It is a long time since they have sung there, and now they have come to San Damiano.' "

So Francis taught Sister Clare, also, the verses, and he listened with delight as she and her sisters sang them by a window opening on the garden. He said that he thought it was thus that the choir of heaven would sound when it welcomed them to the Blessed. And he sent one of the brethren down to the Portiuncula to bring up Brother Pacifico and some of his choristers, for now that he sang no more songs of earthly love or knightly prowess, the old Troubadour was spending his days training some of the younger brethren to sing the church services as they should be sung. Brother Pacifico and his choir sang so sweetly in the garden at San Damiano that Francis swore that he would send them forth to sing his song to the whole world. Sister Clare laughed with delight to see how gaily Francis' imagination was soaring over the future as it used to in his youth.

"I will send you, Brother Pacifico," said Francis, "back to Rome where the Emperor crowned you, and you will sing this song to those riotous Romans who have driven the Pope out, and you will subdue all hearts to the love of God."

Brother Juniper had insisted on coming up with them to see Francis, because he said, "For all your singing you will not know how to make him laugh. It is laughter he needs." And they had let him come on condition that he would not do anything to spoil their singing. Now that they had sung, Brother Juniper shrugged his shoulders. "I don't see why you wait for Rome," he said, "when always you have right here at hand Assisi, and not even the Romans can match the strife between the civil and the religious authorities here."

And Francis' joy had sunk like a fire into its ashes. "Here in Assisi?" he asked unhappily.

"If you have not heard, you are the only man for miles around who has not," said Juniper. "The Podestà insulted the Bishop, and the Bishop excommunicated the Podestà, and now the Podestà will not let any of the civil officials go near the church, nor near the Bishop. And the whole town is embroiled between them, and some of the old nobility have sworn that they will go across the bridge to Perugia and bring the Perugians in."

"But," said Francis with horror, "that would be treason."

"I don't know what you call it," said Juniper, shrugging his shoulders as if the question were an academic one. "I shall leave that to the brethren from Bologna and Paris. But if you want to try out the effect of Brother Pacifico and his singing boys, I can't think of a better test than the Podestà and the Bishop."

"Be quiet, fool," said Brother Pacifico.

But Francis raised himself on his elbow and looked at Brother Juniper. "I have always said you were the wisest friar of all."

The whole company laughed. But Juniper bowed gravely. "No one has better appreciated my talent, Brother Francis, except always Sister Clare." And the laughter filled the little garden.

But Francis looked thoughtful. Presently, he turned to Brother Pacifico, and said, "Here is another strophe to add to the song." And he sang to the same melody a strophe giving thanks for all those who forgive each other for the love of God, and who patiently bear the weakness and the suffering of this life. When the choristers had learned it, Francis asked Brother Pacifico to go up to the Palace of the Commune and invite the Podestà to come to the Bishop's palace and hear the song which Brother Francis had made.

At first, the Podestà refused to listen to Brother Pacifico, reminding him fiercely that he had forbidden all his servants to have anything to do with the Bishop or to go near his palace. But Brother Pacifico did not hesitate to tell him that Francis was dying, and that if he refused to go, he might find that he had denied the last request of a dying man. The Podestà blanched at that prospect, and he said he would go if Brother Pacifico would guarantee that he would not be turned away. That Brother Pacifico promised with confidence, and then he went to the Bishop and told him what he had promised. But the Bishop told him that he had excommunicated the Podestà, and asked how could he himself receive an excommunicated man. Then Brother Pacifico reminded him that the man who had asked him to do this was the man who bore in his members the impress of the wounds of Christ; so the Bishop bowed his head.

When the word flew through the city that the Podestà was going to the Bishop's that afternoon, a great crowd of the citizens of Assisi gathered before the Bishop's palace. Some were supporters of the Bishop, and some were supporters of the Podestà, each party eager to hold up the arm of their champion, but many went simply to see what would happen.

When Brother Pacifico and his young men began to sing Francis' canticle, the Podestà was so moved that he stood in his place and listened with deep attention. Presently, his eyes were seen to be glistening with tears. At that, people turned to where the Bishop sat in his chair, and they saw that his head was bowed. Presently he lifted his ringed hand to his eyes, and all the great throng listened with delight as the beautiful voices swelled through the Bishop's palace. But when Brother Pacifico and his choir had sung the strophe of praise for those who forgive and who patiently bear what must be borne, the Podestà went over to where the Bishop sat, and he fell on his knees before him. Stretching out his hands to the Bishop, he told him that he was ready to give him whatever satisfaction he could ask for. Then the Bishop lifted him up, and he said, aloud so that everybody could hear, "I have been at fault, too, and for your pardon I ask pardon of you." And he embraced him with tears, and all around them the partisans of the erstwhile enemies embraced each other, and even those who had come simply to see the fun, wept.

When Brother Pacifico returned to San Damiano, he found that Francis was sick again with the fever; so he and his young men went into the garden and sang softly the Canticle of the Sun. It seemed to those who were watching Francis that the music flowed like cool water over his fevered limbs, and his tossing ceased, and he lay still. And when they had finished singing, he asked Brother Pacifico what had happened.

When Brother Pacifico told him of the miracle of peace that had been vouchsafed in the Bishop's palace, Francis raised his hands in thanksgiving, and he prayed aloud, "Now Thou dost dismiss Thy servant, O Lord, according to Thy word in peace," and he fell asleep with a smile on his lips.

5

When Francis sent word to Ugolino that he would obey him, he thought it would be simply a matter of going to Rieti and letting the Pope's physician examine him. It would be a troublesome thing, one more thing to be done, before his Master relieved him at his post, but after all it would be a simple matter. He and his companions would go to the Franciscan house beyond Rieti, and there they would wait for the doctor to come. So, the decision having been made, Francis relaxed and, again, the curtain of pain went down between him and the external world.

It lifted a little when Brother Elias came in to kneel down at his bedside, and Leo and Bernard closed in as if to protect him. Francis half opened his eyes to see the face of Elias, inscrutable as always, but with a look of unmistakable concern in the grave eyes. Then the walls of pain closed in, and Francis relaxed in the prayer that was the very texture of his consciousness these days, "Not my will but Thine."

When Leo asked him if he could bear to have a heavier tunic put on for the road, Francis protested feebly, and Leo said they would get a mantle to wrap him in.

At first the motion of the ass was torture; then in the unexpected sweetness of the fresh air, the curtain of pain lifted, and though Francis could see but dimly, there was a pleasant sense of the shadows of the trees, and the shimmering of the wind coming through them as they went along the road. Leo and Bernard began talking to him where they watched on either side of his steed lest he fall off. "We shall be at Rieti tonight, and the Cardinal Ugolino will lodge us in the Bishop's palace where he is staying." Francis tried to tell Leo and Bernard that he did not want to go to the Bishop's palace, that he wanted to go to the little house of the Friars, but he did not seem to have the strength to find the words. Then one foot was hurting so sharply that it roused him and broke the habitual film of dull pain, and he realized that somebody had seized his foot and was kissing it. He kicked feebly to get it free, and then he heard Brother Bernard saying, "The man meant no harm. He is ill with a fever, and he thought if he could kiss your foot, he would be made well. We will see that no one else bothers you."

But in a moment somebody was clutching at the ass so it could not move, and Francis was instantly alert. It was the first clear moment that he had had for hours. He said sharply to Bernard, "Let us stop before we get to Rieti. There will be too many people in the Bishop's palace."

Then he heard an excited voice speaking. "O Holy Francis, do not stop now. There is a guard coming out from Rieti, and one of the confraternities is following with candles, and all Rieti is ready to receive the saint who comes to honor us!"

Francis protested sharply now, for he could see clearly enough that Leo and Bernard were waiting for him to answer.

"There is the vicarage at San Fabiano," said Bernard presently, "but it is only a little house."

"It will be big enough," said Francis eagerly, "and if no one else can come in, so much the better." But he had reckoned without the citizens of Rieti and their guests from Rome. As he tried to sleep that night, it seemed to him that there was a great crowd around the house, shouting and pushing against the thin walls, and when he awoke in the morning, a couple of strangers were kneeling at his bedside. Bernard explained to him that they were chamberlains whom the Pope had sent, but when Francis tried to raise himself to salute them, he did not have the strength. Then they seized his hands and began to kiss them, and Francis was too weak to draw them away and hide them in his sleeves. Then the pain closed in again, and the stillness behind the pain. Now and then he heard people coming and going as if it were a noise afar off, like the sea whispering in the shingle in the dark. Then he heard curses and, horrified at the blasphemy, he roused himself.

"It is the priest of San Fabiano," said Brother Leo.

"He does not sound like a priest."

"The horses are trampling his vineyard, and the crowd have been plucking the half-ripe grapes and eating them."

"He will bless the wine," said Francis sharply; "and how will he dare when he has cursed so those who plucked the grapes?" Now he flung back the pain as if it were a coverlet pinning down his wasted body, and he struggled to sit up, and he told Leo to bring the priest to him. But when he felt the presence of the man at his bedside, he spoke to him with respect, "Reverend Father, cursing will not restore what has been damaged."

"But that is all my income," said the still angry priest.

"How many ass loads does it usually yield you?"

"Fourteen."

"Then," said Francis, "leave off your cursing, and I will supply whatever falls short of that." The priest knelt down and kissed Francis' hand, and then some peasants pressed into the little cottage. When Leo and Bernard tried to turn them back, a voice shouted, "He is my only son. If he can only kiss the saint's hand, you will see."

Francis held up his hand, and somebody kissed it, and he felt moisture on it, and Francis wept. "Their need is so great," he said, "and I can do so little."

Then Leo spoke to Francis, "If we go to the Cardinal, he will at least be able to keep your chamber clear, and you can sleep." So Francis let them put him in a litter. With the motion he fell asleep, but he soon awoke again to feel people pressing around him.

"What God has given, I must share," he said. "But I have so little strength to do it." And he was relieved when they came in out of the heat into the cool palace, and the Cardinal cleared the room.

"I shall put a guard at the door," said Ugolino, "so you can sleep."

But now Francis was conscience-smitten. "I hate to deny the needy anything."

Though he could not see his face, Francis heard Ugolino's snort. "From the tales of miracles that are flying around the city, you have not denied anybody much of anything. Now I bid you forget it all and sleep."

But it was not simply the people who came asking for a miracle who troubled Francis. After a few days' rest, he felt strong enough to thrust aside the curtain of his pain; so he inquired if Brother Pacifico had come with them. When they brought him to his bedside, Francis asked him if he would go to the Bishop's choirmaster and borrow a viol that he might sing to him. "Maybe your music will content my body," he said, "so that it will let go its stranglehold on my spirit."

But Brother Pacifico was shocked. "There are men at the door of your chamber," he said, "and watching outside the windows, and they will hear the music, and they will say, 'Is this a saint who is dying with a fiddler for his chaplain?'"

"I never pretended to be a saint," said Francis indignantly. Then as he felt Brother Pacifico shrink away from his bedside, he sighed, "If we had not thought about what people say, we would not be here."

But when Ugolino came and told him that the Pope was sending his own physician, the Saracen Tabald, over to see him the next day, Francis asked him if he were simply going to look at him, or would he treat him. Ugolino hesitated, and then he sat down on Francis' pallet and said, "Brother Francis, I will not deceive you. He says there is nothing to do but to cauterize."

Brother Leo cried out, and Francis said to Ugolino, "If I whimper even a little, many will be scandalized here; so let me go on to the hermitage where there will be only my own, and what God sends me I will gladly take." Ugolino protested the suggestion and said that he would clear the area around the Bishop's palace so that no one would intrude. But Francis shook his head—"A man's dying is the last worship he gives God, and the last witness to his brethren."

So he was carried out again to the road and taken to the little hermitage of Fonte Colombo on its wooded cliff, high in the hills beyond Rieti. While the Saracen doctor heated his irons, Francis questioned him as to what would happen.

"You may scream as much as you like," said the doctor, "and not be ashamed."

Francis felt Brother Leo shiver at his side, and he heard the other brethren slipping out of the room. Though his eyes were now dim, he could see the fire in the surgeon's brazier, and he held out his hand to it—"Oh, Brother Fire, who have so often warmed me and lighted my way in darkness, and ever been so helpful and cheerful, be gentle with me now." And then he said to the surgeon, "Do your duty quickly." He braced himself as he heard the hiss of the iron against his flesh, but to his astonishment the pain seemed only a little thing compared with the agony that had throbbed now for days in his head. And praying aloud to God, he gave thanks that Brother Fire had been so gentle with his fellow creature.

But in the days that followed, though a succession of doctors shook their heads above his bed, Francis knew that he was no better for all their attention. Yet he sympathized too much with their disappointment to find it in his heart to tell them so. And still less could he bring himself to tell them that it did not matter. For even in the fire of his agony he knew that his prayer had been answered, and he was content, knowing that only thus could the shadows be burned away from the light of God's presence.

It was not until he heard Leo praying that he might be delivered from his suffering that he roused himself to try to find words for what was now the theme of all his days. "It is God's will," he tried to explain to Leo, "and in His will is my fulfillment and my joy, and there is nothing more that I can want save the completing of what He has begun."

Sometimes he lay for hours low under the pain as under a blanket, and then he prayed only a wordless prayer; and, again, when by some miracle of God's grace he managed to rise above the pain, he sang, making both the music and the words of his songs. These were joyous songs, songs of triumph over the fear of pain, and of thanksgiving for the peace that could be won only from pain.

Seeing that he was of such good heart when he came to visit him, Cardinal Ugolino told him that even if the Saracen's iron had quenched the light of his eyes, it had not quenched the light of his spirit. And now it was at Siena that there was a doctor whom the Cardinal of Ostia would have him see. This time Ugolino put a strong guard about Francis' litter so that the people of the countryside might not vex him. But suddenly in the road three poor women appeared together. Though Francis had seen but dimly anything along the way, he saw now that these three women were of a height, and that though they were in poor clothes they bore themselves with great dignity. Francis bade Leo, who had come to his side, give them alms for the love of the Lady Poverty, and the three women blessed him, and one of them said, "God be with you, Lord of Poverty!"

And Francis exclaimed with delight, "They have called me by that name I would rather have than all the world's titles!" And he bade Leo look after them and see where they had gone. But Leo cried out with astonishment that though the road went straight before them, with nothing but low bushes at either side, they were not to be seen anywhere.

Then Francis began to make a new song in French in praise of My Lady Poverty as the fairest of all the world's ladies. And to Leo and Bernard it seemed that he was more like himself than he had been for months and they began to be hopeful once more. But when they came into the city, and the Bishop and his clergy and a great crowd of people came out to meet them, Francis seemed unconscious of their presence. Only when the old Bishop knelt down stiffly and kissed his wounded feet did he shiver as if the pain had grown unbearable. That night he lay unconscious while the doctors came and went in his room, and he grew steadily worse until the day came when he vomited blood. Then Leo and Bernard looked at each other, and they said, "He is dying!" And as Francis lay, pale as one already dead, unmoving on his pallet, all his brethren looked at one another, and Brother Giles cried out, "What will become of us when he who is our father leaves us without protection to the wolves?" And he repeated his question, and he looked defiantly at Leo and Bernard, and he saw the fear in Bernard's face and the bitterness in Leo's, but nobody rebuked him. Brother Leo put his finger to Francis' wrist, and he nodded to Brother Bernard, and the latter said, "Before you leave us for a better world, Brother Francis, will you not say some word that may go back to the Portiuncula and to Rome?"

Rousing himself at last, Francis called Leo to his side and bade him write that he sent his blessing to all of the brethren in the Order and all who would ever come in the years ahead, and, gasping for breath, he tried to put into a word a message that they could not forget: that they must always love one another, and they must not fail in their allegiance to Lady Poverty, and they must be obedient to their mother, the Church. That message Leo had written out again so that copies could be sent both to Ugolino, who had gone back to Rome, and to Elias at the Portiuncula.

When Elias received that message, he called some of the brethren who shared the burden of rule with him, and he read it to them with tears. They all cried out, "He is dying," and they advised Elias to go to Siena and bring him back to Assisi.

Giving orders that word should be sent to the Podestà and to the Bishop, Elias hurried off. But the messenger Leo had sent reached Siena before Elias, and he told the brethren there that Elias had wept at Francis' message, and that he was hastening to his bedside. The brethren looked sullen enough at the news that Elias was coming, and Leo shrugged his shoulders at the story of his tears. But Francis, who had seemed quite oblivious to what was passing, suddenly spoke, "He will take me home to the Portiuncula; like a good son he will bring his father home to die."

At that, Brother Juniper, who had insisted on going to Siena when he heard that Francis was dying, laughed bitterly. "He does not trust these thieving Sienese to give up your body when you are dead, Brother Francis." And though for once Leo and Bernard and the others were so shocked at Brother Juniper that they thought, "It is no wonder that Brother Elias has beaten you for a clown," Francis laughed. It was the thin cackle of a sick man, but it warmed the hearts of all who heard it.

When, a couple of days later, Elias came in and knelt down, weeping, at the foot of Francis' bed, and begged Francis to go at once to the Portiuncula, Francis agreed without argument.

"There is no other place," he whispered to Leo, "where I think the narrow path to paradise is so straight and so sure as there." Then it seemed to Leo and to Bernard that he lost all interest in the proceedings.

But later, when they were on the road, a poor man broke through the company of friars who had grown negligent because they thought Francis was quite unaware of what was going on, and began to tell his story of a dead wife, and children who were crying for bread. To the surprise of his companions, Francis roused himself and bade the man take the cloak that covered his litter. When Elias started toward the intruder, Francis cried out feebly but clearly, "It is too good a cloak for such beggars as you or me. Make these fine gentlemen pay you a price for it." When Elias and one of the brethren he had brought with him tried to seize the mantle, the man looked to Francis to see if he meant what he said. Francis was smiling; so he clung to the mantle until Elias gave him a piece of silver to let it go. It seemed to the watching Leo that Francis closed his eyes in satisfaction then.

Again, for many miles Francis seemed completely unaware of what was going on around him. When Leo and Bernard protested that it would take them longer to get back to the Portiuncula if they went around by Gubbio and Nocera, as Elias commanded, Francis seemed to hear nothing of the altercation above his head. He gave no sign of hearing even when Elias explained that that was the only way they could be sure of avoiding the territory of Perugia, and Brother Leo hissed in his face, "That is all you are thinking of, hanging onto his poor body!"

Francis seemed completely unaware, again, when the soldiers from the Commune of Assisi arrived, and with a great clatter spread out along the road so as to guard the little company of friars, and Leo wept with helpless vexation as Elias disposed his forces as if he were a general in the field. But when a little later they had come into the mountains and the soldiers began to complain of hunger, and when they tried to buy food from the peasants, came back with empty hands, Brother Juniper stooped down laughing by the litter to tell Francis. "Buffoon!" cried Elias. "Have you nothing better to do than wake the dying with your clowning?" Juniper dodged the upraised arm of Elias, and he bent lower and said, "Brother Francis, the poor fools have tried to scatter their dung over the countryside, and even these greedy peasants will have none of it."

Francis aroused himself, and when he understood what had happened, he called a couple of the scowling soldiers to him, and he said, "Charity you cannot buy for all the pebbles in your pouches, but go and ask these good people to give food to the hungry for the love of God, and you will be fed." He laughed thinly when Elias came and told him that the peasants had given the soldiers more even than they had needed, and he seemed to relax like a man who had done what was expected of him, and he slept. Nor did he stir when the bells of Assisi began to come drifting over the fields to them, and fresh horsemen rode out, and then, as the night was falling, some of the Bishop's clerks came with tapers. He seemed quite unaware when Brother Elias, having talked with the commander of the guard of the Commune, bade the little company turn aside from the path to the Portiuncula and take the road to the city. When Leo and Bernard protested against the longer journey for the dying man whose strength was already exhausted, Elias brushed aside their objections, "He will be safer in the Bishop's palace."

"Safer from whom?" asked Leo bitterly.

But Elias answered him in a perfectly matter-of-fact tone, "From the Perugians."

"You would do better," said Leo, "to send word to Sister Clare and her sisters to pray for him."

"That," said Elias as readily as if he had no thought but to oblige even the most sullen of his brethren, "will be done at once." And he called two of the friars who had come out to meet them and told them to take torches and go to San Damiano and beg Sister Clare to pray for Francis. Then he paused, and added slowly, "And for all of us, his children."

6

That day had been such a fire of pain that it seemed to Francis that everything mortal of him must be consumed in its blaze, and then the pain had relaxed its grip a little, and like a fire had sunk into its embers. And now Francis became aware of a whole host of minor discomforts and irritations: the swelling of his legs, the aching of his back so that no position was comfortable, the stifling heat in the room, the stench of the fever, the itching of the bandages above the old wounds. It was at that moment that an old friend of his came in from Arezzo, a doctor. In times past Francis had smiled at the solemnity with which Buongiovanni had spoken of his craft, prefacing every least professional hint with, "According to our science." And in spite of himself Francis admired the way in which he made the caution that would protect him from the suspicion of undue claims seem like modesty, as if he knew a great deal more than he professed. "But at least," said Francis to himself, "he is not one of these flattering doctors of the Pope and the Bishop, who have caught the court habit of saying what the great want to hear. He will tell me the truth."

So Francis asked him what he thought of his prospects. "You have only to look at me," said Francis, trying to catch a little of the day's last light with his fading eyes, "to know that it can make no difference to me whether I stay or go. For a long time now my only prayer has been that God's will be done."

It took the doctor a while to come to the point of his answer, but when he did, it was unmistakable. "So far as our science can tell," he said, with that inimitable suggestion that his modesty did less than justice to its competence, "your state is beyond remedy. You will probably live till"—and Francis could hear the light hiss as he pursed his lips—"the end of September, or the beginning of October."

"That I can do," said Francis softly to himself, but aloud he thanked the doctor for his candor, and then catching the sound of a sob in the company that he knew had come into the little room, he raised his voice, "To a Christian who has tried, however imperfectly, to walk in the ways of God, it can be nothing but good tidings that he will soon see the face of his Master." So he bade Brother Leo and Brother Pacifico sing the song in praise of all the creatures whom God had made. When they came to the end, he made another strophe to be added to it, a praise for Sister Death-of-the-Body, whom no man may escape and whose coming need affright no man who has been faithful to the service of God. And he bade Leo and Pacifico repeat this last strophe until they had it perfect. But now he could hear all over the room the rustle of weeping, and he turned his face away from it.

That night he dreamed for the first time in weeks, and in his dream he was a young man running down the road from Assisi to San Damiano. He was afraid of his father, but as he ran, the fresh mountain air about his freely moving limbs refreshed him, and he felt all the strength of his youth within him. And it seemed to him that the birds were singing in the trees, and the sunlight, sifting through the poplars and the ilex along the way, turned his path to gold. It was with great desolation that he awoke to find himself still bogged in weakness and pain. And he wept to think of all the grace and strength that he had wasted, and he marvelled that when this life which God gives to man is so fair a thing, he spends it to so little good, and comes at last to this wretchedness of regret.

He felt Brother Leo's hand, so light once, now so heavy with anxiety, on his forehead, and it came sharply to him that if no light could lift his darkness, he must not let his darkness put out the light for others. "The sun is still rising," he said to himself, "even if you will never see it again." Aloud, he asked Brother Leo if it was day, and when Brother Leo said that it was, he asked him to bring Brother Pacifico to sing him the Canticle of the Sun, and not to forget Sister Death when they gave thanks to God for the goodness of His creation. And as they sang, it seemed to Francis that the music lifted him above the great abyss of despondency to which he had awakened.

Then he heard a firm step on the tiled floor of the Bishop's room, and the low voice of Elias telling him how glad he was that he felt like singing. There was something doubtful, though, in Elias' low and respectful voice, and as Francis waited for him to say more, Elias explained, "The guard were clustered at the window as I came in, listening."

"Were they scandalized?" asked Francis, and he heard the angry intake of Leo's breath above him, and a groan from where Bernard had been kneeling as they sang.

Elias coughed. "They thought it odd to hear singing coming from a room—"

And then came the mocking voice of Brother Juniper—"In which a saint is dying," he completed the sentence.

But Brother Elias took Francis' hand in his and kissed it, and Francis felt it wet. Then Francis gathered his wits, and slowly he said to Elias, "I have so little strength left, I cannot think of the guards and all the people of this world, but only of my brethren." And so he begged Elias to let him go to the Portiuncula, saying, "God has given me my brethren for my special charge, and for them I must do what little I can do in the hours that remain."

Brother Leo and Brother Bernard and the rest begged Elias to grant Francis this last request. "It will take more soldiers," said Elias at first, "but the Assisians will give us all we ask," he added, as if knocking at the wall of contempt that rose around the bed of the dying man.

But in a wavering voice, as if he were drifting off to sleep, Francis said, "Little Brothers, love one another."

Brother Leo and Brother Bernard were thankful that Francis seemed to be asleep and so quite unaware of the clatter of arms and of the crying of the throng thrusting about them as they came out of the Bishop's palace. And for the first time they were thankful for the strong arms of Elias' guard, for the crowds crying and shouting about them would have torn the dying man's garments to pieces if they could have reached him.

But when they came out on the road, and the clear country air lifted a little the weight of the day's heat, Francis began to ask where they were, and Leo and Bernard named for him the various landmarks they passed. When they came to the turn in the road near the leper hospital, from which across the valley they could look back and see all Assisi like a terraced hillside moving with golden steps up the sides of Monte Subasio, Francis cried out sharply for them to stop. They set his litter down, and he asked them to lift him up, that with unseeing eyes he might gaze across the valley to the city which he would see no more. He remembered how he had stood here with his father when he was a boy, and Peter Bernardone had said that once devils dwelt here; then had come the news of Christ's coming to earth, and they had become Christians. "And though, God knows," Peter Bernardone had said with his robust laugh, "we are not the Christians we should be, as the priests keep reminding us, still we are not the devils we once were." Francis remembered this now with comfort. There was so little any man could do, and yet that little made such a difference that his heart overflowed with love and gratitude, and he blessed the city before him and all who should love it as he had loved it, and he prayed that all who sought the light of God might there find the shadow of it at least, even as he had.

It was evening when they reached the Portiuncula, and all the brethren came out with tapers, and for a moment catching a dim whitening in his darkness, Francis remembered the lights that had gone out to meet the Lady Clare, and he asked Leo to let her know that he had come back where he wanted to be. And that night he lay contented, it seemed to him stretched out on the surface of his pain. He said to himself, "I have nothing to do now but to wait for the light step of my sister, Death, and the summons to my Master's presence." But in the morning the voices of his old companions plucked at his content, and Brother Bernard said with urgency, "You cannot leave the Order in the hands of Brother Elias! Do you name another."

But Francis shook his head. "I am not the Cardinal Ugolino." Then as Leo joined his voice to Bernard's, Francis bade him write, and he dictated his idea of what the Minister of the Order should be like: a man who loved poverty, and who loved the brethren and thought only of helping them on the way to God.

Another day Brother Bernard and Brother Giles were watching at his bedside while Brother Leo went up to San Damiano to see Sister Clare. This time it was Brother Giles who asked Francis to leave some word for the guidance of the Order when he should be gone from them; for there were many voices speaking now, said Brother Giles, and in the discord, the truth would be lost. And so all that day and the next between sleeping and waking and lying exhausted with pain, Francis dictated the things that he thought were essential. Again, it was love for the brethren and for poverty, and obedience to the Church and to the guardians and ministers, but above all love—the love of God, which alone can bind up the distracted hearts of men. And when he had finished, one of the brethren who had been a lawyer in the world asked Francis to let them read it to him that he might sign it and seal it. But Francis cried out sharply, "Do not put your faith in parchments or seals, for they fall to dust, and only what is written in the heart of man will live!"

That night he was so weak that the brethren thought his hour had come, and they crowded around him, asking for his blessing. He put out a hand, and he felt a strong head bowed beneath it, and he said, "Is it Brother Elias?" And he blessed him, and in him all the brethren whom God had given him, or would give him, even to the end of the world. There was a great silence around his bed; then a sharp voice spoke, and it was hard to recognize the voice of Brother Bernard, "Give us a word, Brother Francis, that we may carry in our hearts always!" But Francis shook his head, for he was past speaking.

With a great effort he whispered to Brother Elias, "Strip me naked and lay me on the floor that I may leave this world as a poor friar should, possessing nothing." Francis felt the tears falling on his face as somebody gently took the tunic from his body, and then he heard the voice of Elias, firm and calm, "Brother Francis, I command you in obedience to put on this tunic and this hood and these shoes which I am lending you." And when they pressed Francis to say something more to them, he rebuked them, saying, "I have done my part, do you yours." But when they asked him for a blessing, he blessed them all, beginning with Brother Bernard, "who was the first whom God gave me," he reminded them. And when Brother Leo came in and told him that Sister Clare and all her sisters were in the chapel praying, Francis bade Leo tell Sister Clare that he blessed her, too, and that he bade her keep the low way in which he had set her feet, which was the way of Christ and His Mother on this earth, no matter who should give her other advice.

As the day wore on, he bade the brethren take him out of his bed and lay him on the ground and put ashes on him. When the doctor bent over him and said something in a low voice which he could not understand, Francis cried out cheerfully, "Welcome, little Sister Death!" Then as his voice failed, he began to recite the great Psalm of the penitent, "I have cried unto the Lord with my voice." As his voice fell, the brethren took up the chant, and no one stirred until they had finished the last petition, "Bring my soul out of prison." Then Brother Leo lifted Francis' hand, and finding it quite cold, kissed it and folded it within the sleeve. And all the brethren stood about in silence, looking at the still figure, and it seemed as they looked, that the tautness in the face of the dead man relaxed, and then above the low roof of the Infirmary they heard a great fluttering of wings and a joyous burst of song.

As the hooded larks flew away, they heard the voice of Elias, strangled with weeping, "Let us go at once to Assisi."

Brother Leo, kneeling at Francis' side, seemed not to hear him; but Brother Bernard and Brother Giles rose hotly and dragged Brother Elias to the door of the little hut, and Brother Bernard said, "Leave him here."

"Are you mad?" asked Brother Elias.

"This is where he belongs! Bury him before the altar in the church."

"How long do you think those walls would stand?" asked Brother Elias. But already Brother Bernard knew that the plea was in vain. They could hear the voices of the crowd outside the porter's hut, and presently Elias went out to face them, while Brother Bernard and Brother Giles looked at each other in despair. But all Brother Leo would say when they appealed to him was that they beg Brother Elias to let them stop at San Damiano on their way.

When he returned, Brother Elias looked around the little group of Francis' oldest friends, and he thought, "How can I make them understand even that I loved him?" And when Leo repeated his petition that they stop at San Damiano on the way to Assisi, Elias agreed at once.

And this time it was Sister Clare and the Poor Ladies who were waiting with tapers in the doorway of the little convent of San Damiano. When Elias bade all the guard of soldiers stand back, and the brethren who carried the bier of Francis set it down, Clare fell with outstretched arms across it, and her sisters huddled around.

"Leave him here," said Clare, looking up into the face of Elias. "This is where he began." Elias said nothing but looked helplessly at her. Then she looked back at Francis, looking so extraordinarily fresh and young and serene in the light of their torches, and she drew her veil across her face as the bearers lifted the bier and went up the road, with all the brethren following, chanting. When she looked out again after them, she saw the torches of the funeral procession dancing like fireflies through the night. But when she turned to shut the door of the convent, she heard a low sobbing. It was Brother Leo. She said nothing, but she stood there looking at the figure huddled on the doorstep. The night was quiet now in the moonlight, and presently Brother Leo raised his face. "Brother Elias will build a great church over him, stone upon stone," he said. "He will build the greatest church in the world."

"That will be foolish of him," said Clare, "but you are more foolish if you think that even the greatest church in the world can cage the spirit of Brother Francis."

Without a word Leo turned and took the path down to the Portiuncula, and Sister Clare with trembling fingers made fast the door of her convent.

7

"Did you ever think you could be so happy?" said the little novice, the youngest of the sisters who were that July day helping Sister Clare arrange some red roses on the altar at San Damiano. Sister Clare smiled at the child, her niece Amata, and the little sister went on gaily. "This is what Heaven must be like," she said, stepping back and admiring the roses against the yellowed stone of the old altar.

"They should have been white," said Sister Clare thoughtfully, "but I gave Brother Thomas all the white ones." Her face sobered. It was not two years since Brother Francis had left them, and still that sense of desolation fell like a mist over her mind whenever she thought of it. She tried now to think of the flowers on the old Roman sarcophagus Brother Leo had described so indignantly and Brother Thomas so admiringly. But what she saw were the lilies growing out of the sarcophagus in the courtyard of her father's house, and the young man standing there in the torchlight.

"Are you not happy?" said little Sister Amata, and Sister Clare rebuked herself.

"Of course, child," she said. "I rejoice that the whole world now will know how holy our Brother Francis was." And then she returned briskly to the day's business. "You can get a couple more tapers," she said, "and then we will leave it, until we hear the bells."

"Until we hear the bells," she repeated to herself. And then one of the sisters came to tell her that Brother Sylvester had arrived to sing the Te Deum for them. She went to the door to greet him, and she noticed how empty the road was. All the surrounding country, even the old and the hungry who usually came to their doors, had gone up to Assisi. "And all the brethren at the Portiuncula, too," she said.

Sylvester looked at her sharply, and then he looked at the portress, and when she looked away, he spoke softly, "All except Leo and Giles and Bernard. They will sing the Te Deum in the little church. The rest are—" Sylvester shrugged his shoulders—"Brother Elias and all of them. They said it would not be courteous to the Pope not to be up at San Giorgio with the crowd."

"Elias made no difficulty?" asked Clare.

"No, I think he guessed how they felt."

"You know, he almost always does," said Clare, looking thoughtfully at Sylvester. "That is the thing I can't understand about the man. He does understand most of the time, and yet it makes no difference. But let us not worry about that today," said Sister Clare. "All the sisters are so happy, and the lepers went up to the city wall where they could see."

"Francis would have liked that," said Sylvester. "On the way just now I met some farmers who had come in from a distance, and they were going up. He would have liked that." And then the bells came tumbling down the hillside, and Sister Clare hurried into the chapel to join her sisters. Up at San Giorgio there would be a picture of Brother Francis, painted by a new artist whom the Pope had discovered. He had written to Sister Clare asking her if she would like a picture for San Damiano, too, and she had replied that here of all places in the world there was no need, and he had said no more. When the *Te Deum* had been sung before the sad-eyed old Byzantine crucifix, and all the sisters had given thanks in silence before the altar, and Sister Clare, remembering how long it might seem for some of the older sisters' knees and for the attention of the younger, had at last given the signal and risen, a joyous burst of talk broke out all around her.

"Isn't it wonderful?" said one of the younger sisters. "To have a saint whom one knows in heaven!" The others laughed at her.

But one of the older sisters said, "I knew just as soon as they made the Cardinal Ugolino Pope that the canonization would go through quickly."

"I can't see what difference it makes," said another of the older sisters a little tartly. "We all knew that Brother Francis was a saint anyway."

"Hush," said another of the sisters. "You talk like the Patarins."

But Sister Clare pushed smiling through the little throng and went into her garden. This was where she had last talked with Brother Francis, and she tried, as she so often had all these years, to think what he would say, what he must be saying now in heaven. For although she had always known what the world was making such a marvel of today, it seemed to her now that a veil had descended and had come between that familiar little figure and herself. And quite irrelevantly she thought, "I shall ask him what to do, but he will not have any need to ask me any more." And she knelt down and put her head against the wall of her garden.

For a long time she knelt there, it seemed to her, not thinking anything in particular, not even feeling anything in particular. "I am a barren and unprofitable servant," she said presently, half-aloud. And then she heard laughter, a young man's laughter, and for a moment she wondered if Francis, having put on the garment of immortal youth in the fields of the blessed, were laughing at her. But it was only Brother Thomas from Celano, who was writing the life of Brother Francis, and who had come down to tell the sisters of the great pageant in the square before San Giorgio. Sister Clare heard one of the younger sisters crying out, "Sister Clare will not want to miss any of this. Do wait a moment, Brother Thomas, till we get her." And she let herself be brought into the refectory where all the sisters were gathered happily around Brother Thomas and Brother Sylvester, who was trying not to look curious. To still the excitement, Sister Clare asked Brother Thomas, "Did you put our flowers on the tomb?"

"No," said Brother Thomas. "I could not get near because of the crowd." And at the look of disappointment on Sister Clare's face and the little "Oh" of dismay that ran all around the room, he laughed again. "Somebody must have told the Pope," he said, "because when he came into the square, he looked around, and he sent one of his chaplains up to me, and he said when I came up, 'If you are going to write the story of Brother Francis' life, you must see it all,' and he bade me sit on the step of his throne. Then he saw the flowers, and he asked me what they were, and I told him. And before ever he mounted his throne, with all the great ones of the world waiting there, he went into the church of San Giorgio, with his guards clearing the path, and he himself put them on the tomb, and he said so that everybody could hear, 'Brother Francis, here are Sister Clare's flowers.' "

And as Clare began to weep, Brother Thomas looked surprised, and he said, "Brother Elias, who was the Pope's deacon, he wept, too."

But the younger sisters cried out impatiently, "Tell us all about it, Brother Thomas!"

For a moment Brother Thomas, with his homely face and dancing eyes, waited as if he wanted to be teased for his story. And then his enthusiasm swept him away. "You know how it is," he began, "on a great feast. Only this was greater than any feast that ever was." All the eyes around him shone. "They had hung out tapestries and rugs on the balconies, and they had strung great garlands of laurel and flowers from house to house, and they had carpeted the square before San Giorgio with box, and strewn it with flowers like jewels. And all the balconies and the roofs were filled with ladies in their silks and their jewels, and their golden fillets and shimmering veils."

At the cries of delight from the younger sisters, Sister Clare frowned, and then she remembered the young man she had once seen standing by the Roman sarcophagus in a silk robe as brilliant as any of the flowers in the courtyard. So she said nothing.

"And all the bishops and the abbots in their vestments"—Brother Thomas was now quite lost in his story—"and the standards of all the communes in Umbria, and the ambassadors and their suites. And the sun was shining on all the jewels, and there was a great choir singing. You would have thought the heavenly host had come to earth in Assisi!"

Now some of the older sisters were shaking their heads. Thomas caught the rebuke and hurried on to tell of Pope Gregory's great oration in praise of Brother Francis and the reading of the scroll of the miracles of Francis, of the wondrous cure after cure. "There they were at the foot of the Pope's throne," said Brother Thomas, "where everybody could see them. Some of them held up an arm or showed a leg, and one old fellow pointed to his head, where the great sore had been." Some of the sisters laughed at this. "And from all over the square came cries from people pushing through the crowd and shouting, 'I was cured, too,' until the Pope bade the cardinal who was reading to hurry up with it. Indeed, I saw Brother Juniper pushing his way from the end of the square where some of the brethren from the Portiuncula were standing, those who had refused to go up with the rest to be near the Pope's throne. And Brother Juniper began to shout, 'This is but trumpery. I was a great sinner, and he made me sorry for my sins.' People began to say, 'Peace, fool, that is only what every preacher does.' And the Pope must have heard the tumult, for he said to the cardinal who was reading, 'Hurry up with that.' Then Cardinal Ranieri gave his judgment on the miracles that were proved, and everybody was silent."

"What a clown Brother Juniper is!" said one of the older sisters.

But Sister Clare shook her head. "As usual, I think Juniper has a point. What he said of himself is true of all of us."

"And when they had completed the formalities," said Brother Thomas soberly, "the Pope proclaimed that our Brother Francis was raised to the altar, and they sang the *Te Deum*. Then the Pope and all the great prelates went into San Giorgio and knelt down by the tomb. Then the trumpets blew, and all the bells of Assisi began to ring."

"We heard you," said one of the younger sisters with excitement. "And we went in, and we sang the *Te Deum* here."

But Thomas went on. "And the bells began to ring across the valley, and then the great bells of Perugia began to answer. It seemed as if the whole world were filled with bells."

"And the birds were singing," said one of the older sisters, "those hooded larks whom Brother Francis always called the best friars of all."

Suddenly, all the little company fell silent, and Sister Clare went back to her garden. Before she went, she left word with the portress that if Brother Leo or Brother Bernard or Brother Giles came over from the Portiuncula, they should let her know at once.

As she had thought they would, they came soon after.

"It is a blessed day," said Brother Leo soberly.

"It would be," said Brother Giles, "if the Pope had not laid that cornerstone."

"Cornerstone?" asked Clare.

"Yes, for that church that Elias is always talking about."

"The biggest church in all the world," said Bernard bitterly.

"Let us," said Sister Clare, "come in to his church now that Brother Francis is on the altar, and let us beg him to ask God that His will be done in this."

But Brother Giles held to his point, "Saint or not, he would not want a big church."

"Now that he is canonized," said Brother Bernard, "I do not see how they can deny him his will about poverty."

But Sister Clare said only, "Let us kneel down here in his church and ask him." When they had finished praying, she took them back to the garden. She had charged the portress not to disturb her for anybody else, but they were hardly in the garden when one of the younger sisters came running in, breathless with excitement.

"Two priests are at the door, and the portress says one of them is the Pope!"

Clare had hardly reached the vestibule of the convent when the familiar figure of Ugolino appeared in the doorway. He had taken off all the rich vestments which Thomas of Celano had described with so much enthusiasm, and he had put on a pilgrim's dress almost as simple as the friar's own. Only the emerald ring on the hand he lifted as they sank to their knees betrayed Gregory, the Pope. As Sister Clare rose, still pale with astonishment, Gregory smiled at her. Surely, the protector of Saint Francis' sisters should visit them this day. Then he bade his companion wait outside with the mules that had brought them down.

"Do you wish to come into the chapel?" said Sister Clare.

"We went into the chapel, and we prayed to Saint Francis before we rang your bell. That is where it began," he said.

When they reached the garden, he looked at Sister Clare and the brethren. "You are the oldest, the first ones," he said gently. Then he paused as he saw the tears in Sister Clare's eyes. He looked around the little garden, and out across the valley, and for a moment he listened to the birds singing in the trees below. He shook his head. "It is good, Sister Clare, that you can stay here and keep it so."

At the wistful look on the Pope's face, the hurt in Leo's face blurred. He said almost pleadingly, "He wanted us all to keep it so."

Then Gregory sat down on a little stone seat, and he looked at the friars standing around him. Then he bade them be seated on the flagged pavement at his side. "You know," he said, "I think that Peter would have preferred never to have left those Galilean fields, or the lake where he had fished so often until he caught that miraculous draft of fishes that ended all fishing for him. But you and I would not be sitting here under the protection of Christ's cross if he had had his will. And so with Francis. He would have stayed with the farmers who came up from the fields today, but his message has gone far beyond. Even those rebellious Romans of mine, they sent their ambassadors; so did the Emperor, who gives me no peace; and the doctors from Paris and from Oxford in England were there. Francis is bigger than any of us, and what he is doing today," said Gregory, "is bigger than anything we could have dreamed of."

"Then why," said Leo passionately, "do you let Elias heap up that stone monstrosity above him?"

"It does not matter how many feet of stone it is above the dust of Francis; the poor and the sick will reach him for their healing."

"It is pride," said Bernard. "It is burying him under a mountain of dung."

Sister Clare put out her hand toward Bernard, but Gregory the Pope folded his legs more comfortably. "In the end," he said, "I grant you, when every mountain is brought low, these stones will crumble like everything else man has done. But until then we have man's work to do."

"But Francis said—" began Bernard.

"Oh," said Ugolino, "not a stone of that will belong to the Friars Minor. It is the Pope's palace that is rising there, and it will be a refuge for my successors here in the peace of your Umbrian hills, whether it be the violence of the summer heat or the violence of the unresting Romans which they flee."

"It is a subterfuge," said Bernard.

"I don't think so," said Gregory. "It is a fair exchange. Our little brother will protect the Pope from the Emperor and the Romans and

the rest of the hazards of his position. And the Pope's guards will protect Francis from the relic-hunters, who will I assure you, be more
persistent than even your old neighbors from Perugia. It will be a
symbol, too," said Gregory, as Bernard looked more closely at him. "It
will preach to the world when you and I are silent in the dust. The
foundation of St. Peter's in Rome is the grave of the first Pope, and
the foundation of this church in Assisi is the grave of your founder.
Beggar for fisherman! And for the walls of that church there will be a
painter some day, like the young man who did that picture of Francis
before which we knelt today, and he will paint the story of Francis on
those walls. And those who cannot read Brother Thomas' story which
he has been collecting from all of you—from all of us"—Gregory corrected himself—"who knew him, they will read the story on the walls.
You do well, my brethren," said Gregory the Pope, and he stretched
out his hands in appeal, "to live the life Francis lived here at San
Damiano and down there at the little house at the Portiuncula; but
there are many mansions in God's kingdom, and I, whom God has
made for a few days the doorkeeper, cannot forget them."

The face of Leo had grown gentle as the Pope talked, but something
wary had come into Giles' face as if he were afraid that he might be convinced against his will.

"Oh, my brethren," said Gregory the Pope, "whether it be in the
Lateran Palace or in this palace here, I shall not, I promise you, forget
that Mary has chosen the better part. But in giving me this charge"—
and he lifted his hand so that the emerald ring gleamed in the light—
"Our Lord has given me the part of Martha, and that I must do."

No one spoke, and Brother Bernard, who had never lost his magistrate's habit of listening to what men said of each other, remembered
that all men said that Gregory the Pope lived as plainly as a monk in
the Lateran Palace, even as he had in the palace of the Bishop of Ostia.
And they all looked out into the reddening sunset, and the Lady Clare
watched as she so often had at this time of day how in that light the
grayest of the sea birds that came inland along the Tiber, whitened and
turned to flame. And now it seemed to her that that was the way it
was with Brother Francis. And she watched the bird of fire fly off into
the high heavens until it was beyond her sight, and she wondered what
other eyes were now following its flight. And for the first time it
seemed to her that peace had come into her spirit as softly as the

breeze rippling through the darkening treetops. She turned, and without saying a word, she knelt at the feet of the Pope, and one by one all of the little group of the companions who had first known Saint Francis followed her. And Gregory blessed them, not with the papal blessing but with the blessing of Saint Francis, "May God give you peace!"